THE PERELANDRA ESSENCES

THE PERELANDRA ESSENCES

A Revolution in Our Understanding
and Approach to Illness and Health

MACHAELLE SMALL WRIGHT

PERELANDRA, LTD.
CENTER FOR NATURE RESEARCH
JEFFERSONTON ❀ VIRGINIA

THE PERELANDRA ESSENCES:
A Revolution in Our Understanding
and Approach to Illness and Health
Machaelle Small Wright

FIRST PRINTING 2011
E-Book Edition 2011
Copyright © 2011 by Machaelle Small Wright

For information, write Perelandra, Ltd.

This book is manufactured in the United States of America.
Designed by Machaelle Wright.
Cover design by Machaelle Wright.
Cover tweaking by James F. Brisson, Williamsville, VT 05362.
Formatting, layout and computer wizardry by Machaelle Wright.
Copyediting by Elizabeth McHale, Williamsburg, MA 01096.

Proofreading and GROMs extraordinaire:
Beth Shelton, Jeannette Edwards, Rebecca Colbert and Karla Johnson.
Consultant and cheerleader: Otis Woodard, M.D.
Catering: Connie and the gang at Thyme Market, Culpeper, VA

This book was formatted, laid out and
produced using QuarkXPress software.
Printed on recycled paper.
Published by Perelandra, Ltd., Warrenton, VA 20188

Library of Congress Control Number: 2011930692
Wright, Machaelle Small
THE PERELANDRA ESSENCES:
A Revolution in Our Understanding
and Approach to Illness and Health
ISBN: 0-927978-84-9

2 4 6 8 9 7 5 3 1

TABLE OF CONTENTS

In memory of
Björn E. W. Nordenström, M.D.
With deepest gratitude for his work,
his integrity and his quiet courage.

THE PERELANDRA ESSENCES

Introduction

The Perelandra Essences

The Perelandra Essences are oral solutions
that are taken to balance, stabilize and repair the
body's electric system and its circuits during times of illness,
injury and stress. They also are taken for maintaining
the overall strength and balance in
the electric system.

SOMETIMES THE MOST DRAMATIC and game-changing developments in science, medicine and life have as their foundation simplicity. If you feel that the above description of the Perelandra Essences is perhaps a little too concise and over-simplified, at first glance I might agree with you. What I can tell you is that those two sentences are accurate. The rest of this book explains, describes and demonstrates what those two sentences mean. What follows will introduce you to a revolution in our understanding of health and healing.

Part One

THE ESSENCES AND
THE ELECTRIC SYSTEM

Chapter 1

The Human Electric System

When Magellan's expedition first landed at Tierra del Fuego, the Fuegans, who for centuries had been isolated with their canoe culture, were unable to see the ships anchored in the bay. The big ships were so far beyond their experience that, despite their bulk, the horizon continued unbroken. The ships were invisible. This was learned on later expeditions to the area when the Fuegans described how, according to one account, the shaman had first brought to the villagers' attention that the strangers had arrived in something which although preposterous beyond belief, could actually be seen if one looked carefully. We ask how they could not see the ships...they were so obvious, so real...yet others would ask us how we cannot see things just as obvious.

—John Mattingly
The Cancer Cure That Worked,
Fifty Years of Suppression

The human electric system is a vast network of circuits that runs through and around the body. Every element, every organ, every system in the human body has its electric circuits. Every molecule, every cell, every aspect of the body has its circuits. And every level of being (physical, emotional, mental and soul) has its own electric circuits. The most extensive and complex system in the human body is its electric system. If we could stretch an average adult's electric system out in a straight line, it would be about forty-seven miles long.

There are a relatively few mainstream physicians who are willing to admit even to the possibility of an electric system in the human body. They say things such as, "Maybe…we think…sort of, I think…yeah, well…We'll get data on that and get back to you later." But there is a growing body of researchers who are actually doing serious study into the human electric system and one such person has done a considerable amount of research. His name is Björn E. W. Nordenström, M.D.

I've been talking about Dr. Nordenström since the late 1980s. At the time, he was the head of the Diagnostic Radiology Department at Karolinska Institute in Stockholm, Sweden. The Karolinska Institute is recognized worldwide as one of the premier forward-thinking hospitals for treatment and innovative research. When I hear the name "Karolinska" in a news report, I pay attention. I can't remember how I found out about his research but when I connected Dr. Nordenström's work to my own Essence research, I knew the two of us were on the same track: we were going after the same body of information but in two completely different ways.

One of the things that caught my attention about this man were his credentials. Dr. John Austin, a radiologist at Columbia Presbyterian Medical Center and the editor of Dr. Nordenström's groundbreaking book, *Biologically Closed Electric Circuits (BCEC),* stated in a 1985 interview that Björn Nordenström's credentials "were not just impeccable but extraordinary." For me, they were breathtaking. In the 1950s he developed several notable breakthroughs in diagnostic radiology, including fine needle biopsy and balloon catheterization. Even with his stellar reputation, these ideas were initially met with significant amounts of opposition by his peers. But today they are routinely used throughout the world. In the 1960s he became Chief of Diagnostic Radiology at Karolinska Institute. His colleagues said he was brilliant, a genius. When he published his book, *BCEC,* they added "But maybe a little odd." He was a member of the Nobel Prize Assembly in Medicine and Physics from 1967 through 1986, and served as President of the Assembly in 1985. He also authored or co-authored more than 150 publications in radiology, electrobiology and pharmacology. And he was awarded the International Scientific and Technological Cooperation Award by the People's Republic of China because of his work in their country on tumor regression.

During the 1950s, he noticed streaks, spikes and coronas in X-ray images of lung tumors. In 1965, he began his investigation into these X-ray anomalies. He came to the conclusion that the streaks, spikes and coronas were the result of water movement, movement of ions and restructuring of certain tissues due to the influence of various electrical and electrochemical phenomena.

Nordenström realized that the human body contains electric circuits and that current travels through vessels and tissues as if they were electrical cables. This electric current in the human body travels through blood vessels, through the walls of the capillaries both into and out of surrounding tissues.

His research led him to propose a closed loop, circulatory, self-regulating model for healing that was much more detailed and complete than conventional wound healing models. In other words, he described a circulatory system where continuous energy circulation and circulating electrical currents support healing, metabolism, growth, regulation, immune response, etc.

Using his biologically closed electric circuit (BCEC) theory, Dr. Nordenström then developed electrochemical therapy (EChT), a technique for the treatment of cancer and other tumors. EChT assists the body's normal BCEC electrochemical healing processes by complementing and assisting the naturally occurring internal electric fields and currents that support the process of healing. (This is where you might wish to think back to that first sentence in the introduction: "The Perelandra Essences are...taken to balance, stabilize and repair the body's electric system and its circuits during times of illness, injury and stress.")

Using his EChT technique Dr. Nordenström inserted one platinum needle electrode inside a cancerous tumor and another platinum needle electrode outside the tumor. It was a minimally invasive procedure, and the patient was fully conscious throughout with only local anesthesia. He would then slowly build up the voltage mechanically and increase the electrical charge between the two needles. He found that by doing this he could reconnect and temporarily enhance the electric circuits that had been damaged by the tumor. This electrical reconnection caused the tumor to dramatically reduce in size or disappear altogether. At Karolinska he first tested his theory with a group of twenty cancer patients who had been diagnosed as incurable after all other available treatments had failed. From this group he had a 46 percent response with his EChT technique: that is, a significant reduction in tumor size or complete disappearance for up to three to five years. Don't forget, this group had already been diagnosed as incurable after all other options were exhausted. He repeated his EChT technique with more groups with equal, if not better, results.

In 1983 he published his book, *Biologically Closed Electric Circuits*. And this is when the medical community started going a bit nuts. Never mind his stellar reputation. Never mind his many years of meticulously recorded research and proven innovative developments. Never mind his astounding success rate with his "incurable" patients.

Björn E. W. Nordenström, M.D. committed a cardinal sin in the eyes of the medical community. What was that terrible sin, you ask? Instead of publishing his ideas on biologically closed electric circuits in a five- to ten-page article that could be published in a recognized scientific journal and then reviewed by his peers, he published a 357-page book. Are you trying to figure out where the "sin" is in this? Well, the medical community is used to reading short articles. This is what they are comfortable with. They would not read a 357-page book. There were too many pages.*

In his concluding remarks in *BCEC,* Dr. Nordenström wrote:

> The author has attempted several times to prepare the information of this book as a series of separate articles. These attempts have, to a large extent, been discouraging. One reason is that working nowadays across established specialities is extremely difficult, not to say dangerous. Each section is in itself probably of limited interest. Only when the different pieces of information are put together do the contours of an important biologic mechanism become evident.
>
> …It is the hope of the author that the material presented will encourage scientists of different specialities to continue this work. The various aspects of BCEC systems will require interdisciplinary cooperation if improved and truly deep understanding of its manifold possibilities is to be attained.

The editor of Dr. Nordenström's book, Dr. John Austin, stated in an interview that he agreed with Dr. Nordenström's unusual decision to publish a book rather than short articles saying that Nordenström's theory was "too big for a paper."

Shortly after the book was published, Dr. Morton Glickman, a radiologist at the Yale New Haven Hospital, was asked to write a scientific review of *BCEC*. It took him one year to complete the review. In a 1985 television interview Dr. Glickman said, "I really looked for holes because it was so off the wall. I couldn't find any holes. By the end of the book, I was persuaded. I started out skeptical like everyone else does, but it was just very careful, very thorough, complete and immanently persuasive."

In an interview, Dr. Nordenström was asked how he thought history might judge his work. He said, "The knowledge about this [BCEC] will come. You cannot stop it because it's right. But it's revolutionary because it has so many implications and, therefore, many people in a very reasonable way are reluctant."

This soft-spoken, modest, brilliant man died on December 31, 2006.

His research and work have continued. In 1993 the International Association for Biologically Closed Electric Circuits in Medicine and Biology (IABC) was officially formed by Dr. Nordenström who served as its first president. According to the Association's website, the membership consists of medical doctors, biologists, biophysicists, engineers, educators and business professionals. IABC members are involved in the development of electrotherapeutic, thermotherapeutic and magnetotherapeutic techniques, in combination with conventional therapies, for the treatment of a wide variety of health problems, including cancer, diseases of the visual system, connective tissue disease and neurological disorders. Approximately 300 members are actively engaged in related research and clinical studies in a wide variety of locations, including Australia, Brazil, China, Cuba, Denmark, Germany, Great Britain, Greece, Hungary, Indonesia, Japan, Korea, Sweden and the U.S.

Enter stage left: The Perelandra Essences.

P.S. IN THE PERELANDRA DVD, *The Human Electric System and the Perelandra Essences,* I spoke about Dr. Nordenström's research. What I said and the details that I presented back then were based on the early information I could find about his work. You will find some of the details that I've included in this book different from those in the DVD. For example, in the DVD I say that he had a 70 percent response with the first group of patients. In this book I write that he had a 46 percent response. In the DVD I say that the first group comprised breast cancer patients. In this book I point out that the first group had lung cancer. Another early group had "incurable" breast cancer. When I gave the workshop that is recorded on DVD, I presented the best "facts" I could find back then. It's now many years later and we have the advantage of time, Google and YouTube. What a difference time and technology make. The details as presented in this book are current. Although some of the Nordenström "facts" I presented in the workshop are not completely accurate, the intent and context in which they were used are still valid.

Chapter 2

The Road Map to Illness and Why the Perelandra Essences Are So Effective

LIKE HEALING LIKE. This is one of the most important principles in healing. It's actually a universal natural law called the "Horizontal Healing Principle." And it boils down to those three words: like healing like. For the most efficient, most effective, most complete and thorough healing, we need to respond to a health problem with the tools, techniques and "medicines" that comprise the elements that are horizontally compatible with (similar to) the makeup and characteristics of the problem.

> The Horizontal Healing Principle is reflected fully in the Perelandra Essences: electrical patterns balancing, stabilizing and repairing the body's electric system and its circuits.

The Perelandra Essences are water-based solutions holding electrical patterns derived from the different kingdoms and elements of nature. Each electrical Essence pattern balances, stabilizes and repairs the body's electric circuits in two ways: (1) They address weakened or damaged circuits in targeted areas of the body that have been hit by illness or injury, and (2) they also provide the needed balancing for specific mechanical functions and properties that are contained in and are part of biological electric circuits no matter where the circuits are located in the body. In this case the condition of a circuit and its ability to function are the primary focus for the Essence pattern and not the specific circuits that are directly causing injury or illness due to circuit damage. An example to clarify: In #1, the focus would be similar to a heart that has been damaged by illness or disease. In #2, I'm talking about a damaged artery that needs to be repaired for optimum function of the circulation, whatever the condition of the heart. In this case, we have a mechanical malfunction.

And why, you ask, do we need to focus so much attention on the body's electric system? Surely something this massive and complex ought to be able to take care of itself? Well, we focus on our electric system because it is the key to healing. *The underlying foundation for the body's healing process is its electric system. The healing process is activated and driven by the electric system.* If circuits are damaged, the healing-process foundation weakens and the process itself is compromised and weakened. If damaged circuits are repaired, the healing-process foundation strengthens and the body's healing process becomes fully functional. I don't just mean healing little things like sore muscles or the common cold when I refer to injury or illness. I mean healing the full range of conditions we categorize as injury, from minor to critical. And I mean the full range of conditions we categorize as illness, from sniffles to chronic and life threatening. It's *everything.* No matter what health problem we might experience, it includes electric circuits in need of repair and balancing. We cannot experience an illness or injury without also experiencing corresponding problems in the electric circuits connected with that illness or injury. The *underlying cause* of a health issue can be found in the body's electric system. In short, every health issue we experience includes an underlying electric-circuit problem.

It helps to picture the relationship between the body's electric system and a specific health issue as a straight line:

THE BODY'S ELECTRIC SYSTEM   ILLNESS: FLU AND ITS SYMPTOMS

●——●

At one end of the line you see the body's electric system. At the other end we have the illness. In this case it's seasonal flu with all its annoying symptoms. When we think about illness, we make the mistake of focusing on the wrong end of the line—that is, the illness end. After all, it's the exhaustion, headache, coughing, stuffy nose, chills, fever and nausea that catch our attention and make this end of the line easy to notice. But the illness and all of its symptoms are the *end manifestation* of a problem that began with our electric circuits. When flu viruses enter the body, the very first thing that responds to this intrusion is our electric system. Everything we experience, everything that impacts our body internally and externally, positively or negatively, is detected, identified and processed by our electric system *first.* The body reacts and adjusts according to how our electric system sorts and processes the intrusion. It is our electric system that determines and drives all our body's responses as well as its healing process.

When flu viruses overwhelm the electric system causing damage to circuits, or if circuits are already damaged or weakened, the electric system cannot set up the needed immune system response. Electric circuits function properly when they are closed and balanced. Once circuits are damaged we are dealing with "wild wiring"* that weakens and interferes with the function of the electric system and its immune response throughout those areas of the body that are normally supported by the now-damaged circuits. The body receives "faulty" information and a weakened, unbalanced immune response takes place in all the body's cells and systems that have been affected by the viruses. What we end up with are viruses that now have the upper hand and have fully seated in the body in a major bout of seasonal flu with a large assortment of uncomfortable symptoms. The body is now tasked with the job of repairing the damaged circuits and initiating the appropriate healing process for moving the flu viruses out of the body. *The electric system must balance, stabilize and repair first before the immune response can be initiated and properly set up.* Now we are lying in bed suffering the indignities of seasonal flu while our body focuses its attention and efforts on repairing its electric system so that the necessary immune response and healing process can commence.

If the flu viruses do not overwhelm or damage our circuits, then the electric system remains strong and the body can correctly set up the appropriate response. The body is able to either incorporate, process or eliminate the virus, depending on what is appropriate in light of the type of virus and scope of intrusion and in light of what is needed to maintain the body's overall balance. The ability to incorporate, process and eliminate is a critical part of the body's immune response and healing process, and is activated and supported by a balanced electrical foundation. In the case of our flu example, with a balanced and strong electrical foundation we can experience a mild, short-lived bout of seasonal flu accompanied by a couple of equally mild symptoms. Or sometimes the electric system and body can function together so efficiently that we experience no symptoms at all, and after a good night's sleep we feel fine.

Like healing like. Electrical Essence patterns balancing, stabilizing and repairing electric circuits. When we apply the Perelandra Essences to a health problem, we work with that horizontal line differently. Instead of addressing the symptoms, we address the electric system and its damaged circuits. If left unattended, we force

* WILD WIRING: Electric currents can surge, arc, fire erratically and weaken.

the electric system to balance, stabilize and repair itself. And this can be time and energy consuming.

Now, to be honest, the body and its electric system are designed to self-repair. It would make no sense to think that something this extensive and this important to the balance and function of a human being would have no mechanism built in for self-repair. After all, the partnership between the body and its electric system are constantly functioning, 24/7. The electric system isn't just identifying, sorting and processing "stuff" that negatively impacts our body. It is registering every minute element that comes in contact with our body on all its levels, in any way, and from any direction. That includes the things that make us smile and feel good as well as the things that annoy us or make us sick.

Under normal conditions the body and its electric system work in a smooth, seamless partnership. But in today's world we are being "pounded" in unprecedented ways. Life's increasingly fast and stressful pace; the increasing amount of information pouring into us due to new technology; the rapid deterioration of our land, water and air; the compromised quality of our food supply . . . all of these things adversely affect our electric system, making its ability to maintain strength and balance more difficult. Sometimes the system can repair quickly on its own and, when a health issue pops up, we hardly experience any symptoms. And there are times when we will not notice a problem at all. In these cases our electric system and our body are functioning together well and are doing the job the two were designed to do. An intrusion can be immediately eliminated. But if we are sitting there feeling sick, that's an indication that the electric system's self-repair is going to take some time and could use some help.

Unlike illness where the problem has often been initiated by pathogens entering the body, an injury is a damaging event that occurs *to* the body, such as a cut, a hit, a fall or a car accident. An injury is not a pathogen that the body's immune system can battle. It is literally body damage. Consequently it includes corresponding damage to the electric system. As with illness, an injury will not begin to heal until the electric system is first repaired. In short, the body and its electric system respond to illness and injury in the same ways. For both situations, the electric system must be balanced and fully functioning in order for the healing process to be activated and the body to recover efficiently and well.

Whether for illness or injury, the electrical patterns from the correct Perelandra Essences, when administered orally, immediately shift to the electric system and are drawn to and fuse with the damaged circuits, thus providing the balancing elements needed for their repair. (Like healing like.) Now you have a strong electrical foundation again and the body's healing process is no longer compromised. That allows the electric system and the body to focus directly on the illness or injury and to set up the appropriate immune system and healing responses. At the illness/injury end of the horizontal line (p. 12), you have symptoms or injuries that are being fully addressed and processed. In short, you have a fully functioning healing process going on, and you will experience a quick recovery that defies all expectation. We tend to grossly underestimate how powerful our body's natural healing process is. Mostly this is because we have no need to pay attention to it until we get in trouble and we're hurting or not feeling well. When uncompromised and fully functioning, it is remarkably powerful and efficient.

It's surprising how quickly the electric system can repair and the body can recover when we use the Essences to repair damaged circuits. Over the past thirty years I've come down with full-blown seasonal flu about three times. By testing* myself for Essences every two to three hours, I was able to move through the flu and eliminate all the symptoms in twenty-four to forty-eight hours. By testing every two to three hours, I made sure my circuits maintained balance during the healing process and remained fully operational. At other times, I was able to pick up the first signs of flu or some other bug coming on and use the Essences to shore up my electric system so that my body could properly identify, sort and eliminate the problem right away and I, in turn, could avoid getting sick.

* More on testing and determining the correct Essences in chapter 4.

What is that first sign of trouble that I notice? When circuits are damaged, it isn't just one small area of the body that is affected. The entire electric system suddenly weakens a bit. After all, this is a massive, interconnected collection of biologically closed electric circuits that now have been damaged in one or more areas, causing "wild wiring." When that occurs, the body has a sudden drop in its electrical support and you suddenly feel exhausted. I'm not talking about feeling mildly tired because you didn't get enough sleep the night before. I'm talking about a different feeling of exhaustion. You're going along with your day just fine and then suddenly you feel the rug pulled out from under you. You were fine five minutes ago, and now you can barely hold up your head or speak a coherent sentence. Normally we stoically force ourselves to ignore that exhaustion, pump in something with a high sugar or caffeine content for some fast fake energy and just push on. I've discovered that if I don't ignore the exhaustion and test myself for Essences right away, I can repair the circuits, restore my energy level, and prevent myself from getting sick. It's an effective form of early detection and my electric system and body can get on with addressing the problem and doing the job they were designed to do.

I've been talking a lot about flu viruses. But what other kinds of health issues can the Perelandra Essences address? Here's a short list just to get you thinking:

> If you get a cold or the flu, test for Essences.
>
> If you have an earache or eye strain, test for Essences.
>
> If you get a burn or cut, test for Essences.
>
> If you have sore muscles or a sprained muscle, test for Essences.
>
> If you get sunburned, test for Essences.
>
> If you have a headache or migraine, test for Essences.
>
> If you have muscular dystrophy or multiple sclerosis, cystic fibrosis, or some other chronic illness, test for Essences.
>
> If you have a different neurological disorder, test for Essences.
>
> If you are depressed, test for Essences.
>
> If you feel detached from life, test for Essences.
>
> If you notice you can't formulate a clear thought or sentence, test for Essences.
>
> If you are unusually confused or panicked, test for Essences.
>
> If you have a broken bone, *go to the hospital and get the bone set.* Then test for Essences.
>
> If you are constipated, test for Essences.
>
> If you have diarrhea, test for Essences....

Those last two, constipation and diarrhea, may seem like they are two opposing situations and, quite frankly, they are. However, they are each caused by some electric circuits being in need of repair. But the circuits that are the underlying cause of the constipation are different from the circuits that are the underlying cause of the diarrhea.

What the Perelandra Essences won't do:

> They will not set broken bones, but they will greatly speed up the recovery process once the bones are set.
>
> They will not provide needed surgery, but they will greatly speed up the recovery process once we get out of surgery.

They do not take the place of stitches, but they will greatly speed up the recovery process once we get the stitches.

In short, doctors and hospitals still have a place in the health regimen that includes the Perelandra Essences. We just need them a lot less often. But when we do need conventional medicine, we don't stop using the Essences. Instead, we combine them. By monitoring our electric system and providing the repair it needs throughout the healing process, we greatly enhance the effectiveness of conventional treatment and medication, and shorten the time we need to use them.

Years ago I received a letter from a woman who had talked to me during one of our early open houses. She wrote:

> I came to Perelandra to see your beautiful gardens and speak to you about my four-year-old daughter Jessica. Jessica had broken both her fibula and tibia only two days before. I spoke with you and you prompted me to buy the Essences. You said when you break both bones, you break the electric system in the body and that the Essences would repair the electric system and that the leg would heal twice as fast. Well, I followed your sound advice. And the doctors ended up looking at me strangely and saying, "What have you done to this leg?" Instead of healing in the ten to twelve weeks they had predicted, Jessica was in a walking cast in just five days and the doctors removed the cast altogether after four weeks.

Jessica was able to move so quickly through the healing process because her body didn't have to take the time or provide the additional energy it takes to repair her electric system once she was given the Essences. Little to no repair is going to happen in the body until the electric system is first repaired. Once we take the responsibility for repairing that system, the body can then get on with the business of healing.

At this point, it may seem like what I'm describing is impossible to imagine or "too far out there." Or just too good to be true. You even might be experiencing one of those Fuegan moments! But I stated in chapter 1 that not long after first reading about Björn Nordenström's work with biologically closed electric circuits I realized that he and I were going after the same body of information, but in two completely different ways and from two different directions. Using his electrochemical therapy (EChT), he was able to achieve successful results in patients with "incurable" cancer by using two electrodes to stabilize and close the circuits around tumors. Using the correct electrical Essence pattern, we are able to achieve successful results for our many health issues by repairing, stabilizing and closing the damaged circuits. One result is achieved by inserting two electrodes in and around a tumor and mechanically closing an electric current. The other result is achieved by administering pattern-infused Essences orally to repair, balance and stabilize the damaged circuits, thus closing the circuits.

Chapter 3

A Human Being's
Four PEMS Levels

THERE'S MORE TO CONSIDER when we think about our electric system and what it supports. The human being comprises four levels: physical, emotions, mental and soul (PEMS). Who a person is, his characteristics, and how he functions depends on coordinated interaction between these four levels. The bridge that connects the four levels is the body's electric system. And the underlying foundation for each level providing what it needs to function on its own is the body's electric system. When we are talking about human health and the electric system, we must take into consideration the circuits that support and connect all four of these levels.

● PHYSICAL LEVEL. So far we have focused our attention on health issues that show up on the physical level—injury and illness. These types of issues are usually the most obvious to notice and the easiest to recognize. But when considering the physical level and its electric circuits, it's important to understand that our attention should not be limited to illness and injury. Everything on the physical level is supported by the body's electric system: every physical movement, every voluntary action, every involuntary action, every cell function, every muscle movement, every organ function. The activities of all the body's different systems are activated, driven and supported by the circuits connected to each physical element. Every element in our body includes electric circuits as part of its makeup. There is nothing in the body that does not have its own circuit or collection of circuits. And while we are thinking about all these circuits, also remember that these electric circuits running through every element of our physical body are all connected and, when balanced and undamaged, they are closed. No wild wires flapping about.

To make things a little clearer, let's try something here. I'm assuming you are sitting. (If you are reading this book while clocking in your daily miles on a treadmill, you are going to have to get off the treadmill and sit down for this!) Imagine that you have moved your electric circuits from your body to a spot in space about six feet in front of you. They have formed a four-foot-in-diameter circle with a billion circuits crisscrossing inside the circle. Don't imagine a three-dimensional ball. Instead see a flattened, one-dimensional circle suspended in space. This way none of the circuits are hidden and they're all visible to you. It looks like a jumbled mess, but it's actually all connected and organized. Now, get ready to raise your right arm. Don't actually move it, but just *decide* you are going to move it. Notice some of the circuits lighting up. Next, slowly — *very slowly* — raise your arm toward the ceiling. As you move the arm, notice that different circuits light up and the pattern of lighted circuits keeps changing as you raise your arm. When you have it raised, stop the movement and slowly wiggle one finger back and forth. Notice that the pattern changes again with each finger movement. Now slowly lower your arm and return it to an at-rest position. All the while, notice how the lighted circuit patterns keep shifting.

This little exercise illustrates how your body's electric circuits support a simple movement. If you keep the movement slow enough, you may even see that the circuits light up a fraction of a second before the arm changes position. The arm movement doesn't activate the circuits. It's the activated circuits that initiate, drive and support the movement. Without the proper activated circuits supporting the movement, the arm is paralyzed. If in this exercise we start out with a paralyzed arm, our first focus will need to be on the arm's electric circuits, and we will need to repair those circuits. We can't make the arm move without the needed circuit repair occurring first.

⊙⊙⊙

● EMOTIONS LEVEL. We humans can be an emotional lot. We can be happy, sad, scared, proud, confident, goofy, in love, out of love, mean, hateful, kind, caring… The list could go on. Every one of our emotions is part of who we are as humans. They are part of what makes up our human body. And guess what? Each emotion includes its own collection of electric circuits. We cannot express ourselves in an emotionally balanced way unless the circuits supporting an emotion are fully functional.

Balanced, stabilized and repaired circuits support balanced and stabilized emotions. If we experience a deep, all-consuming sadness that we cannot pull out of, it's because the circuits that support our *balanced* feelings of sadness could be overstimulated and need stabilizing. Our normal balanced range for experiencing sadness is now being impacted by wild wires and we are feeling and expressing sadness with an over-the-top intensity that we can't handle or process. Essences don't eliminate our emotions. They don't stop us from hurting or grieving or feeling happy or being joyful. They ensure that our electric circuits are functioning properly so that we experience our emotions within the balanced range that is unique to us as individuals. They help us feel and express emotions cleanly. They address any circuit issues connected with an emotion so that we can experience that emotion without feeling that it is holding us captive.

I've received a number of letters over the years from people who describe being with a loved one in the hospital while the loved one was dying. Throughout the hospital time, the writers remembered to take Essences daily. In their letters they describe how they were able to continue functioning and thinking and making decisions while everyone else around them (the non-Essence users) fell apart. They talked about feeling grief without the grief swamping them and being amazed that they were able to get through this intensely difficult time so well.

Have you ever wondered why negative emotions can make us physically sick and positive emotions can keep us healthy and even move us through a health crisis? It's not magic. We just need to look to our electric system for the answers. All our circuits are linked and connected, creating one closed-circuit system. The emotions level is connected with the physical level through its electric system. And because we are talking about a biologically closed electric system, the impact of emotions-level activity isn't just confined to its own circuits. The dynamics of our emotions are transferred to our physical body through the connected circuitry. If there is a negative-emotion transfer, the physical circuits' balance and strength are impacted negatively, which can be so severe that it can lead to a health problem that is directly related to the negative emotion. And a damaged or out-of-balance physical body transfers its dynamics electrically to circuits supporting the emotions level. This is why we can become depressed when we are sick or injured. A positive-emotion transfer to circuits that support the physical body can further strengthen and support the body and add needed stabilizing to circuits that are stressed or damaged because of illness or injury. The two levels are connected and interacting, making the experience of being sick or injured more than just a physical experience.

21

● MENTAL LEVEL. We think, consider, communicate, read, write, memorize, plan and organize, learn, teach, understand, take tests, give speeches and presentations, invent, design, build, follow instructions, make the decision to not follow instructions, debate, mount coherent arguments... All of these are mental-level activities. And you guessed it: Everything we do that falls under the classification "mental" is fully supported by its own collection of electric circuits. These circuits support, function and interact on the mental level exactly as the circuits support, function and interact on the physical and emotions levels. When the mental-level circuits are in need of balancing, stabilizing and repair, different parts of our mental activity go off-kilter. Try as hard as we might, we can't think straight. When we speak, our words come out all jumbled. We get lost in the middle of our thoughts and forget what we were just talking about. We become easily distracted. You know what I'm talking about. We've all been there, and somehow we manage to survive those moments when we suddenly (and uncharacteristically) sound and act like idiots.

I consider myself a relatively intelligent person. But when my mental-level circuits get some wild wiring, my I.Q. can drop about fifty points in a nanosecond. Case in point: About thirty-five years ago, I went to a flower essences workshop given by a chiropractor. At one point about half-way through the day, he said something that I didn't understand at all. It was like he suddenly started speaking in tongues. So I asked him to repeat it. And he did. I still didn't understand what he was talking about. Everyone else seemed to be getting it, but his words were just bouncing off my head. So I asked him to say it one more time. Again, nothing. I was prepared to thank him for his patience, sit down and accept that this was information that apparently was beyond me. Instead, he asked me to come up and he tested me for flower essences right then and there. He gave me one drop of one Bach flower essence. In less than five seconds, I understood what had up to that point been a mystery. I said, "Okay, now I get it," and sat down. The concept he was talking about had been simple. Where the words had bounced off my head when I didn't understand, now those mental-level circuits were repaired and the meaning of the words gently enveloped me. I can say to you that it was this experience—personally experiencing a state of total confusion cleared up with one drop—that pulled me headlong into the world of flower essences. About six years later, I began researching and expanding on the concept of flower essences, which resulted in the development of the Perelandra Essences.

ᘯᘯᘯ

● SOUL LEVEL. Now this is an interesting level. The essence of our soul is electric. Its dynamics are electrical. Its activity is electrical. And the underlying foundation for supporting all the parts and pieces that make up the soul level is electrical. All this electrical activity combined with an extensive grid of circuits enable the soul to interface effortlessly with the circuits that support the other three levels, providing a direct, immediate and interactive connection.

And what does our soul level give us? Our soul "holds" all the elements of who we are. But it doesn't just hold our conscious experience of who we are. The soul also holds the patterns and information that are beyond what we currently and consciously know. It holds the patterns and dynamics of our potential selves—who and what we can be. Someone once said something like this: "Who are we? Are we who we think we are? Or are we who others think we are?" Well, I can modify this quote a bit and apply it to the soul. The soul holds the patterns and dynamics of all that we think we are. But it also holds the patterns and dynamics of all those characteristics, abilities and activities that are currently beyond our conscious awareness and imagination of who we think we are. If "anyone" is going to know who we truly are, it's our soul. The collection of all those patterns, both currently obvious and unimaginably expanded, are electrical and together make up the dynamic level we call "soul."

The wonderful thing about the soul is that it holds who we are now and who we are capable of being (our "POTENTIALS"*) *in balance*. On our soul level we are a balanced microcosm that embodies all that we currently and consciously know about ourselves and a balanced macrocosm that includes the expanded potential of all that we can be but don't realize yet.

At this point, you're probably thinking about yourself and wondering what happened. When we look at the mess we've become, it's hard to see all that soul-level balance. So what happened? Well, free will is what happened. What makes humans different from the nature kingdoms (besides our general lack of cloven hooves) is our ability and enthusiasm to exercise free will. This means that at any moment of the day we can choose to experience something or do something that falls within the guidelines of our personal soul-level balance or we can choose to operate outside those guidelines. With free will we can consciously override what our soul knows. And we tend to do this quite often. Life becomes an exercise of identifying decisions and activities that pull us outside our range of soul-level balance and then doing what we need to do to return to functioning within that range. The more we

* POTENTIALS: The soul "houses" many different elements that can be defined as potential. Humans of course possess "potential" in the general sense—but what I am referring to here are the individual "elements" of the human's larger general "potential." Because there are many, I refer to them here as "POTENTIALS."

function within our range of soul-level balance and the more we consciously reflect that balance, the healthier we are physically, emotionally and mentally.

So, here we are with a soul level that holds the dynamics of who we are and who we can be. The who-we-are-now circuits support each of our characteristics, traits and abilities throughout the other three levels. But then there are all those POTENTIALS that we currently know nothing about. These soul-level dynamics are automatically "downloaded" to the other three levels only when the physical, mental and emotions levels can support the information and activity of a new expanded function. It's the appropriate development of our physical, emotions and mental levels that triggers the download of a soul-level POTENTIAL to the other three levels, thus changing the soul dynamic from "POTENTIAL" to "current"—or unconscious to conscious.

The downloading of our POTENTIALS from the soul level is a natural and automatic process. We don't have to do anything special to access POTENTIALS. The soul automatically sets up a download first in the brain and central nervous system when the physical, emotions and mental levels and their electric circuits have been developed and are ready for the new, expanded activity. Because the range and scope of a POTENTIAL'S information and activity can be vast, it's rare that we experience a download of a full POTENTIAL with its complete range of ramifications. This would shatter our electric system and cause serious problems on each of our four levels. When we are ready for a download, only that portion of the POTENTIAL that our electric system, brain and central nervous system can readily support will be shifted. This allows us to incorporate a new dynamic comfortably and safely and gives us a sense of moving forward, one manageable step at a time. The four PEMS levels then function together to integrate the new expanded dynamic so that we can consciously work with it in practical and useful ways.

> IMPORTANT: Because the soul functions in balance, it will not go rogue and activate a POTENTIAL or any portion of a POTENTIAL that is beyond the capability of the electric system, brain and central nervous system to support or beyond the ability of the PEMS levels to successfully integrate.

But I'm sure you'll agree that if there is a way we humans can mess up a balanced, natural process, we'll find it. On its own, the soul level won't operate as a rogue dynamic. But we can consciously decide to go rogue. This is that free will "thing" working again. We can decide to take what is automatic, natural and balanced "in hand" and willfully override it in order to show the world how it's really supposed to be done. (It's okay to take a moment to reflect on our unique talents in this area and just sigh a few times before reading on!) I find that people who try to force an expanded soul-level activation are often motivated by a desire to be perceived as "spiritually cool." Actually, when we try to force a POTENTIAL from the soul level we are not spiritually cool; we're spiritually dumb. It's fascinating how we humans can decide that what we consciously know about ourselves trumps what our soul "knows" about who we are. Then there are those equally dopey times when we get into a misguided competition with someone. ("My neighbor/spouse/friend can do X, so I'm going to figure out how to do X. And just for good measure, I'll show up my neighbor/spouse/friend and figure out how to do Y, too.") Both of these situations — the need to be perceived as spiritually cool and the equally misguided sense of competition — can drive our desire to force an expanded POTENTIAL dynamic from the soul level.

Can we succeed with our stubborn determination? Can we suddenly do some amazing thing that we had no clue how to do just five minutes before? Well, the short answer is no. Usually we just manage to throw a large monkey wrench into our electric system and create a bunch of wild wiring that leads to internal chaos. On the soul level we are overriding a natural process that is already in place and working. On the other three levels, we have not developed properly and are not prepared or able to support the download of an expanded POTENTIAL. So the forced dynamic literally overloads and/or breaks a bunch of circuits, and our ability to understand or function with our new forced POTENTIAL fails — usually in disastrous and embarrassing ways that can lead to serious delusions, discomfort and health problems.

What I've written describes how the soul-level circuits operate in coordination with the rest of our electric system. But to get this concept across, I may have left the impression that the soul-level circuits that support our POTENTIALS are static. They are just sitting around our soul level waiting for us to develop ourselves physically, mentally and emotionally so that these static circuits can safely activate and move through a downloading process. *Nothing that makes up who we are as human beings is static.* It's all active. When a POTENTIAL is ready for downloading, its already-active circuits just activate *differently* involving the soul-level POTENTIAL's circuits, the rest of the body's electric system, the brain and the central nervous system. The POTENTIAL shifts from our unconscious to our conscious, thus changing its status from "POTENTIAL" to "who we know we are." *In short, the downloading process is that shift of already-active soul-level circuits from unconscious to conscious.* That's when we become aware that we can operate in a more expanded way and we have the full-body support to continue working with this expansion in useful ways.

25

There is one other thing I'd like to add about the soul level. When a POTENTIAL shifts from unconscious to conscious, it feels new to us because we have only just now become consciously aware of it. But a soul-level POTENTIAL is active and is as much a functioning part of who we are as writing or walking or singing. Who we are as human beings includes all that we are consciously aware of about ourselves plus all those POTENTIALS that we are not consciously aware of. But each one of those attributes and dynamics is active.

So what am I getting at? Well, because all the soul-level circuits are active, there's a whole bunch of POTENTIALS activity that we are already participating in on a regular basis. It's just that we're not aware of this activity. Reality is much larger than we've been led to believe and our participation in that reality is much greater than we think. People become frustrated and impatient because they think there are levels of life that some people can participate in but, for whatever reasons, are being denied to them. Not only is reality not withheld from us, we are actively and regularly participating in the larger reality according to who we are as individuals and how we are defined as full human beings.

Our soul level provides the electrical foundation for our POTENTIALS activity. And because the activity is supported by these soul-level circuits, it does not require that we be consciously aware of it. As we develop who we know ourselves to be and expand the stabilizing support of our circuits on each of our PEMS levels, the activities we are not currently aware of will shift and become part of our conscious activity and abilities.

Our soul-level POTENTIALS are only potential because we are not conscious of them. Not being conscious of them doesn't render them inactive. It just means we don't consciously know all that we are doing. And since this expanded activity originates from the soul level, its electrical foundation supports the activity *in balance.* We are not off somewhere robbing banks or mugging little old ladies. We are participating in activity and reality in ways that are consistent with our soul dynamics and balance. And by "activity," I don't mean to imply that we always have to be physically doing something somewhere. Activity also includes mental and emotional experience and growth.

All that we experience and learn from our expanded unconscious activity becomes a part of who we are. We don't lose it just because we aren't conscious of it. Rather, it broadens and deepens the scope of our POTENTIALS. So we are actively developing our potential even while we are unaware of those POTENTIALS. When it comes time for us to shift a POTENTIAL from unconscious status to conscious, as much breadth and depth that our PEMS circuits can support is included in the shift. So reality is not excluded from us, thanks to our soul level. And we are not losing time in our development when it comes to those activities around which we are unconscious. We have an impressive development program going on whether we are aware of it or not. All we have to do is stay out of its way and let it go on. Our focus needs to be on developing those things we are aware of and learning how to make them fully functional in useful ways. This is how we prepare ourselves for our soul-level's new information and expanded activity. Pay attention to the mundane in life and the fantastic will take care of itself. The long view is to shift from unconscious to conscious all that our soul knows us to be. At that point we will be one conscious, integrated human being capable of functioning at our full capacity. In the meantime, we can relax. Really. This is going to take awhile. But for now, when you wake up after a full night's sleep feeling like you've been dragged behind a runaway stage coach for eight hours, you'll know you've probably had a pretty active and expanded time on that soul level of yours. Someday you'll become aware of what you were doing. It probably didn't involve a runaway stage coach.

A FINAL POINT ABOUT THOSE PEMS LEVELS BEFORE MOVING ON

In order to explain the human system's four levels and how they interrelate, I've represented them as if they are four separate and distinct levels that are suspended in space with a few "bridging" circuits connecting them. A more accurate way of understanding these four levels is to visualize them as a single unit with their circuits intertwined, connected and acting in concert with one another.

> Physical: My arm moves.

> Emotions: I notice my arm is flabby and that makes me sad/mad/ indifferent/fascinated at my own aging process.

> Mental: I think about what I'm doing with this movement and come to the conclusion that I could move my arm differently and experience greater ease and efficiency in that movement.

> Soul: My arm movement is fully in sync with the parameters my soul has set for who I am and what range of movement I am able to experience.

Chapter 4

The Perelandra Kinesiology Testing Technique:
Our Electric System's GPS

So HERE WE ARE, faced with forty-seven miles of multilevel, interconnected and intertwined electrical wiring, and the key to restoring and maintaining our health lies in the balance and strength of all these different circuits. When we are faced with a health issue, we have to be able to identify quickly which circuits are in need of balancing, stabilizing and/or repair. To do this, we need a way to access our electric system for testing. Well, we're in luck. Not only do we have a quick, convenient, effective, accurate and low-cost tool for testing biologically closed electric circuits, this tool also happens to be horizontally compatible with our electric system and the Perelandra Essences, as well. It's called "The Perelandra Kinesiology Testing Technique" (PKTT*).

* We at Perelandra have taken to pronouncing "PKTT" as "pik-it."

Kinesiology testing or muscle testing has been around for centuries and has been used as a diagnostic health tool in a number of ways. I've modified the traditional kinesiology method so that we can use it to self-test and accurately access our electric system any time we need to address a physical-, emotions-, mental- or soul-level problem. Another advantage of PKTT: Besides identifying circuits in need of repair, we also have to identify which Perelandra Essences can repair those circuits. The five sets of Perelandra Essences contain a total of fifty-one bottles, each holding a different electrical pattern that balances, stabilizes and repairs specific areas and imbalances in our electric system. PKTT enables us to identify quickly the precise circuit or group of circuits in need of help and, at the same time, it pairs that information with the Perelandra Essence bottle(s) that provide the needed balancing, stabilizing and repair. PKTT eliminates confusion and guesswork when it comes to working with our forty-seven miles of electric circuits and the fifty-one bottles of Perelandra Essences.

PKTT is horizontally compatible because it is used to directly access the electric system and assess the condition of circuits by reading the strength or weakness of our muscles. Our muscle condition is determined by and corresponds to the strength and weakness in our electric system. If the electric system is stressed or damaged, the muscle(s) weakens. Conversely, if the electric system is balanced and strong, the muscle(s) remains strong. So for full horizontal compatibility, we use an electric-circuit testing tool to monitor an electric system in order to treat a circuit weakness with an electrical pattern contained in the Perelandra Essences. Electric > electric > electric. Perfect horizontal compatibility.

THE PKTT PEP TALK

PKTT requires that you learn a process. It's like learning a new dance step or how to drive or a new football play or a new computer program/game… We learn things all the time and don't think too much about it. PKTT is like all these other things: We learn the steps and then we practice it in order to become more proficient. It's much easier to learn PKTT than it is to program your DVR. Maybe I should say that another way: More people have success learning PKTT than they do programming their DVR. Really, PKTT is simple to learn and to do. Anybody can do it because it uses your electric system and your muscles. If you are alive, you already have these two things. You don't have to purchase any gizmos to do PKTT. Unfortunately people refuse to believe that anything can be so simple. So they create a mental block—only "sensitive types" can do this, or only women can do this. It's not true. PKTT happens to be one of those simple things in life just waiting around to be learned and used by everyone.

What makes me a little crazy is when I hear someone talk about how hard it is to learn PKTT. I'm convinced that these folks have never taken the time to learn PKTT, and most likely the reason is they hate learning curves. They hate going through the process of learning. Or they are insecure about themselves and believe they aren't capable of learning anything. Well, there's no way I can remove this learning curve. PKTT has a learning curve and that's that. But it's not like you're learning to build a nuclear reactor. As learning curves go, this one is pretty gentle. So learn to love your curve! After all, anything worth learning has a learning curve.

I don't mean to intimidate you (actually, I do mean to intimidate you), but small children can learn to do PKTT in about five minutes because it never occurs to them that they can't do it. And they're still into that "learning thing." Life is a big learning adventure to them. If I tell them they have an electric system, they don't argue with me about it—they just say, "Cool," and get on with the business of learning how to do the testing.

Your first big hurdle will be whether or not you believe you have a viable electric system that is capable of being tested. Here's a good test: Place a hand mirror under your nose. If you see breath marks, you have a strong electric system. (If you don't see breath marks, you're in trouble.) Now you can get on with learning PKTT!

PKTT SELF-TESTING STEPS

1. THE CIRCUIT FINGERS. If you are right-handed: Place your left hand palm up. Connect the tip of your left thumb with the tip of the left little finger (finger #4). *Not your index finger.* I'm talking about your thumb and little finger. If you are left-handed: Place your right hand palm up. Connect the tip of your right thumb with the tip of your right little finger. By connecting your thumb and little finger, you have just temporarily created and closed a new electric circuit in your hand that is external and easily accessible for testing.

*Fig. A: Circuit Fingers—
tip to tip.*

Before going on, look at the position you have just formed with your hand. If your thumb is touching the tip of your index or finger #1, laugh at yourself for not being able to follow directions, and change the position so you touch the tip of the thumb with the tip of the little finger (finger #4). Most likely this will not feel comfortable to you. That is because you normally don't put your fingers in this position and they might feel a little stiff. If this feels awkward, you've got the first step of the test position! In time, the hand and circuit fingers will adjust to being put in this position and they will feel more comfortable.

*Fig. B: Circuit Fingers—
pad to pad.*

Circuit fingers can touch tip to tip *(Fig. A)*, finger pad to finger pad *(Fig. B)*, or thumb resting on top of the little finger's nail *(Fig. C)*. I rest my thumb on top of

Fig. C: Circuit Fingers—thumb on little finger.

Fig. D: The test fingers.

Fig. E: The testing position.

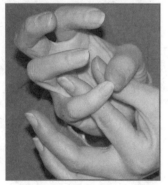

Fig. E: The testing position—left-handed.

my little finger. I suggest this position for anyone with long nails. You're not required to impale yourselves for this.

When you have the circuit fingers in position, they form a circle. If you straighten fingers 1, 2 and 3 a bit, you'll get them out of the way and you'll see the circle.

2. THE TEST FINGERS AND TESTING POSITION. To test the new circuit (the means by which you will apply pressure), place the test fingers, thumb and index finger (finger #1) of your other hand *(Fig. D)*, inside the circle you have created by connecting your circuit thumb and little finger. The test fingers (thumb/index finger) should be right under the circuit fingers (thumb/little finger), touching them, with your test thumb resting against the underside of your circuit thumb and your test index finger resting against the underside of your circuit little finger *(Fig. E)*. Don't try to make a circle with your test fingers. They are just placed inside the circuit fingers that do form a circle. It will look like you have two "sticks" inserted inside a circle.

3. POSITIVE RESPONSE. Keeping this position, ask yourself a simple question in which you already know the answer to be "yes." (Ex: "Is my name _____?" Insert your real name.) Once you've asked the question, press your circuit fingers together, keeping them in the circular position. *Using the same amount of pressure,* try to press apart or separate the circuit fingers with your test fingers. Press the lower thumb against the upper thumb, and the lower index finger against the upper little finger.

The action of your test fingers will look like scissors separating as you apply pressure to your circuit fingers. Your testing fingers (the fingers inserted in the circuit circle) will remain in position within the circle *(Fig. F)*. All you are doing is using these two testing fingers to apply pressure to the outer two circuit fingers. *Don't try to pull your test fingers vertically up through your circuit fingers.*

If you have ever been kinesiology tested by a physician using the conventional steps, the PKTT circuit position in step 1 corresponds to the position you take when you stick your arm out for the physician. The testing position in step 2 is in place of the physician. After you ask the yes/no question and you press your circuit fingers tip-to-tip, that is equal to the physician saying, "Resist my pressure." Your circuit fingers now correspond to your outstretched, stiffened arm. Trying to push apart those fingers with your testing fingers is equal to the physician pressing down on your arm.

If the answer to the question is positive (if your name is what you think it is!), you will not be able to push apart the circuit fingers. The electric circuit will hold, your muscles will maintain their strength, and your circuit fingers will not separate. You will feel the strength in that circuit.

> IMPORTANT: Be sure the amount of pressure holding the circuit fingers together is equal to the amount of your testing fingers pressing against them. Also, do not use a pumping action (pressing against your circuit fingers several times in rapid succession) when applying pressure to your circuit fingers. Use an equal and continuous pressure. Play with this a bit. Ask a few more yes/no questions that have positive answers.

Now, I know it is going to seem that if you already know the answer to be "yes," you are probably "throwing" the test. Well, you are. What can be a little tricky with PKTT is learning to equalize the pressure between all four fingers and these questions are your tool for calibrating that pressure for feeling the strong positive. You are asking yourself a question that has a positive answer. (Ex: "Is my name _____?" Insert your real name.) The obvious answer to this question is yes. A positive, even in the form of a correct answer to a question, will not have an adverse or weakening impact on electric circuits, and the related muscles to those circuits will remain strong. If your circuit fingers are separating when you know you should be getting a positive response, you are applying too much pressure with your test fingers. Or you are not putting enough pressure into holding your circuit fingers together. You need to keep asking the question and playing with the testing until you feel pressure in *all four fingers* and the pressure in your test fingers is not separating your circuit fingers. You don't have to break or strain your fingers for this; just use enough pressure to make them feel alive and connected. When this happens, you now have a clear positive PKTT response.

4. NEGATIVE RESPONSE. Once you have a good sense of the positive response, ask yourself a question that has a negative answer. (Ex: "Is my name _____?" Insert a completely bogus name and not a nickname or a name you wish you had.) Again press your circuit fingers together and, *using equal pressure,* press against the circuit fingers with the test fingers. This time, if the test-fingers' pressure is equal to the circuit-fingers' pressure, the electric circuit will break, and the circuit fingers will weaken and separate. Because the electric circuit is broken, the muscles in the circuit fingers do not have the strength to hold the fingers together. In a positive state the electric circuit holds, and the muscles have the strength to keep the two fingers together.

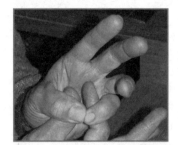

Fig. F: Positive response with the circuit fingers still closed.

Fig. F: Another view of the positive response.

Fig. F: A third view of the positive response.

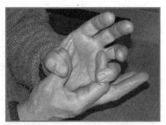

Fig. G: Negative response— a lot of separation.

Fig. H: Negative response— a little separation.

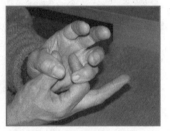

Fig. I: Negative response— medium separation.

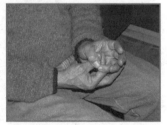

Fig. J: Forearms resting in a person's lap while testing.

DIFFERENT STYLES IN HOW THE FINGERS SEPARATE. How much your circuit fingers separate depends on your personal style. Some people's fingers separate a lot—like two or three inches *(Fig. G)*. Other's barely separate *(Fig. H)*. Mine separate about a quarter of an inch *(Fig. I)*. Some people's fingers won't separate at all, but they'll definitely feel the fingers weaken when pressure is applied during a "no" or incorrect answer. Some say all they feel is a little "pop" when the circuit breaks. Let your personal style develop naturally.

RESTING YOUR FOREARMS. If you are having trouble feeling anything, do your testing with your forearms resting in your lap *(Fig. J)*. This way you won't be using your muscles to hold your arms up while you are trying to test.

TO CALIBRATE AND EQUALIZE THE PRESSURE used by the circuit fingers and the testing fingers for negative responses, play with questions that have obvious negative answers. Continue adjusting the pressure between your circuit and test fingers until you get a clear negative response.

When you're feeling a solid separation, return to positive questions. Once again, get a good feeling for the strength between your circuit fingers when the electric circuit is in a positive state. Then ask a negative question and feel the weakness when the circuit breaks and is in a negative state. Practice your testing by alternating the questions. It's perfectly fine to keep asking the same question with the known negative answer over and over. You don't have to give yourself a headache trying to come up with different questions. Your electric system isn't grading you on creativity. The same is true when testing the positive response. Just use the same question with the known positive answer.

In the beginning, you may feel only a slight difference between the two. With practice, that difference will become more pronounced. For now, it is just a matter of trusting what you have learned and what you feel—and practicing.

The PKTT Calibration

Especially in the beginning, and even sometimes after you have been doing PKTT successfully for awhile, you may lose the strong feeling of the positive response and the weakness of the negative. In short, you've lost the equal pressure between your circuit and test fingers and one set is overpowering the other. As soon as your testing feels a little off or funny to you, do a PKTT Calibration so that you won't waste time doing a bunch of testing and not being sure of the accuracy of those answers.

If you want accurate results, you will have to retest those steps where you felt your testing to be suspect. So do a PKTT Calibration sooner rather than later. It'll save time in the long run. Here are the steps:

1. Ask yourself a question that you know has a positive or true answer and test for the response. Adjust the pressure between your testing and circuit fingers until the pressure is equalized and you feel a strong, positive response. Play with this a bit and get a good feel for the strength of the positive response.

2. Then switch to a question that has a negative or false answer and equalize the pressure until you clearly feel the circuit break and/or see the fingers separate.

3. Alternate your questions between positive and negative a few times to get the feel of holding the equalized pressure no matter what the question. In no time, you will have the "PKTT feel" back and you can resume testing where you left off.

Another Method of PKTT

There is a method of PKTT that creates an external closed electric circuit by placing the pointing finger of your test hand on your thigh. The electric circuit that you are using runs down the center of the leg, and you are creating and closing a new and accessible external circuit by connecting it with the circuit in your finger. If you have a physical impairment and working with the regular testing position is difficult, this may be easier for you to use.

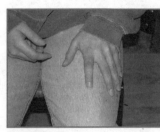

Alternative Method:
Step 1.

1. Place the pointing finger (finger #1) of your test hand palm-down on top of the center of your thigh. This finger should lay flat on the leg. Your other test-hand fingers may be in whatever position is comfortable.

2. Place the pointing finger (finger #1) of the other hand in a palm-up position under the first knuckle of the test finger. Make sure the knuckle on each pointing finger is in contact, not just the tip of the finger.

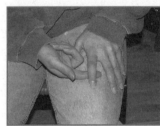

Alternative Method:
Step 2.

3. Ask a positive question, press your test finger down on the leg, then try to lift up the finger of the test hand with the same amount of pressure that you use to hold the finger down on your leg. Your test finger will feel strong and you will have difficulty lifting it up from the thigh. That's your positive response.

4. Now ask an obvious negative question, press your test finger down on the leg, then try to lift up the finger of the test hand with the same amount of pressure that

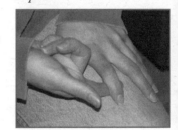

Alternative Method:
Step 3—positive response.

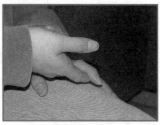

Alternative Method:
Step 4—negative response.

you use to hold the finger down on your leg. The circuit will break, your circuit finger will weaken and it will lift up from your leg. This is your negative response.

5. Alternate your questions between positive and negative a few times and test the answers.

Whenever your testing feels mushy or weird and you need to get that old PKTT feeling back, do a PKTT Calibration using this alternate testing method.

PKTT TIPS

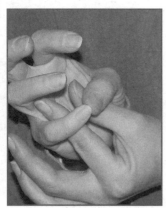

The testing position—
left-handed.

● If you are having trouble feeling a positive and negative response in the circuit fingers, try switching hands—the circuit fingers become the test fingers and vice versa. Most people who are right-handed have the particular electric circuitry that is used in PKTT in their left hand. Left-handers generally have the circuitry in their right hand. But sometimes a right-hander has the circuitry in the right hand and a left-hander has it in the left hand. You may be one of those people. If you are ambidextrous, choose the circuit hand that gives you the clearest responses. Before deciding which to use, give yourself a couple of weeks of testing using one hand as the circuit hand to get a good feel for its responses before trying the other hand.

● If you have an injury such as a muscle sprain in either hand or arm, don't try to use PKTT until you have healed. PKTT involves your muscles, and a muscle injury will interfere with the testing—and the testing will interfere with the healing of the muscle injury.

● If your hands are sore from all the PKTT testing, consider two things: (1) You may have equal pressure among your four fingers and you are getting good results but you are working too hard. Dial back the amount of pressure you are using for pressing your circuit fingers together and for working your testing fingers. You may need to calibrate your four fingers until you get used to the feel of the new equalized pressure level. (2) Your hands and fingers are not used to being in the PKTT position. For most people the PKTT position will feel awkward in the beginning because they don't normally hold their hands and fingers like this and their muscles don't quite know what to do. If you are feeling strain and soreness, you may need to work with PKTT a little more gradually in order to give your hand and finger muscles time to "train" and adjust to the new position and movement. It doesn't take long for the muscles to train properly and for the soreness to disappear. The important thing is to keep working with PKTT so that your muscles will get used to the testing.

● Also, when first learning PKTT, do yourself a favor and set aside some quiet time to go through the instructions and play with the testing in order to build confidence in your testing. Trying to learn this while riding the New York subway during evening rush hour isn't going to give you the break you need. But once you have learned it, you will be able to test all kinds of things while riding the subway.

● Sometimes I meet people who are trying to learn PKTT and are not having much luck. They have gotten frustrated, decided this wasn't for them, and have gone on to try to learn another means of testing or they try to substitute something they already know like pendulum testing and dowsing. Well, I'll listen to them explain what they did, and before they know it, I've verbally tricked them with a couple of suggestions about their testing, which they try, and they begin feeling the PKTT responses for the first time—a strong "yes" and a clear "no." The problem wasn't PKTT. Everyone, as I have said, has an electric system. The problem was that they wanted to learn it so much that they became overly anxious and tense—they blocked.

So since you won't have me around to trick you, I suggest that if you suspect you're blocking, turn your focus for several days, even a couple of weeks, to something completely different. Then trick yourself. When you care the least about whether or not you learn PKTT, start playing with it again. Approach it as if it were a game. Then you'll feel the strength and weakness in the fingers.

> HELP: If you're confused or still not getting a satisfactory "yes" and "no"
> after several weeks of trying, don't feel shy about calling our Question
> Hot Line for help. (1-540-937-3679—Answered Wednesdays from
> 10 A.M. to 8 P.M., Eastern Time.)

TROUBLESHOOTING PKTT

Suppose the testing has been working fine and then suddenly you can't get a clear result (what I call a "definite maybe") or get no result at all. When using PKTT to test the Perelandra Essences, check the following:

● SLOPPY TESTING. You press apart the fingers *before* applying pressure between the circuit fingers. This happens most often when we have been testing for awhile and become over-confident or do the testing too quickly. I think it happens to all of us from time to time and serves to remind us to keep our attention on the matter at hand. (Excuse the pun.)

Especially in the beginning, start a PKTT session by "warming up"—that is, by calibrating your fingers and pressure. Ask yourself some of those obvious questions. Feel a few positive and negative responses. This warm-up allows you to equalize your finger pressure and reminds you what positive and negative responses feel like before you start.

● EXTERNAL DISTRACTIONS. Trying to test in a noisy or active area can cause you to lose concentration. The testing will feel unclear or mushy. Often, simply moving to a quiet, calm spot and concentrating on what you are doing will be just what's needed for successful testing.

● FOCUS OR CONCENTRATION. Even in a quiet spot, one's mind may wander and the testing will feel fuzzy or weak. It is important to concentrate throughout the process. Check how you are feeling. If you're tired, I suggest you not try to test until you have rested a bit. And if you have to go to the bathroom, do it. That little situation is a sure concentration-destroyer.

● YOUR BATTERY FLUIDS ARE LOW. If we are dehydrated, our electrical responses can be weakened or unreliable. Drink water! If you're in the middle of testing and you feel thirsty, stop the testing and drink water. If you are thirsty before you start testing, drink water before you begin. If you have a tendency towards dehydration because you don't drink enough water throughout the day, have a glass of water next to you during the testing and drink up when you feel thirsty.

FINAL COMMENTS ON PKTT

PKTT is like any tool: The more you practice, the better you become at using it. Practice helps you get over the initial "this-is-weird-and-the-damned-testing-isn't-working" stage. *The only way I know to get over this hump is to practice testing.* It is impossible to *reason* yourself over the hump. (Many have tried and have failed miserably.) Through practice you will develop clarity in your testing, you'll learn your personal pitfalls and you will fine-tune your technique. The good news: Because you'll be testing the Perelandra Essences frequently, you have a built-in opportunity for lots of practice. And you'll be multitasking: You'll be improving your health by using the Perelandra Essences to address a circuit problem while practicing PKTT. In no time, you'll move through the beginner's learning curve and become comfortable with both PKTT and the Essences. Oh yes, and you'll end up feeling healthier as well.

In teaching PKTT, I have found that something interesting happens to many people when they are learning it. Every block, doubt, question, concern and personal challenge they have, when faced head-on with something perceived as unconventional, comes right to the surface. It is as if the physical tool of PKTT itself forces all those hurdles to show up. So they learn PKTT right away and are using it well. Then, all of a sudden it is not working for them and they are tormented with self-doubt. When they tell me about it, I realize that the thing they do differently now that they didn't do at first is double-checking their answers—and rechecking, and rechecking, and doing it again, and again... Each time the answers vary or the fingers get mushy and they get a definite maybe. Self-doubt is driving both the double-checking and the answers.

Well, again the issue is not PKTT. The real issue is why they are suddenly doing all this rechecking business. What has surfaced for them are questions around their ability to do PKTT and their belief that such unconventional things really do happen—and are happening to them. They are now facing a wall of self-doubt and a major lack of self-confidence.

This happens to most of us to one degree or another as we learn PKTT and how to work with the Perelandra Essences. It's important not to be hard on yourself when you realize it's happening to you. The only way I know to get over this hurdle is to defy it—keep testing the Essences and *stop all double-checking*. Take whatever Essences test positive in the first test and observe your health improvements. That's your verification that the testing is accurate. The successful results eliminate self-doubt and give you back your confidence. The alternative is to succumb to fear and stop working with PKTT and the Essences. But that doesn't accomplish anything. So take the plunge and stop the double-checking.

Here's the good part: If you make a mistake in your testing and take an Essence that you don't need, your electric system "reads" that the Essence isn't needed and it will reject that Essence and move its pattern right out of your body. You don't need it because the circuits that are related to this Essence are balanced, strong and do not need repair. Consequently, the Essence pattern isn't doing anything and the electric system sees it as a benign presence or excess baggage. Getting rid of an unneeded pattern is an act of your electric system's strength and a natural response when it is dealing with anything that does not add to the body's health and balance. In short, as far as PKTT and the Perelandra Essences are concerned, you and your electric system experience no adverse effects from a mistake. The only thing you'll notice is that the health problem you are trying to address will only partially improve or go unchanged because you're not working with the correct Essences.

ONE LAST SUGGESTION: Give yourself about a year to develop a strong confidence with PKTT. You'll be able to use it right away and test Essences right away. But over time and with practice you'll feel a PKTT gracefulness set in. The testing will feel natural and will move quickly and smoothly for you.

PKTT vs DEFINITIONS

The Perelandra Essences no longer include a definition for each bottle's pattern. I originally included these definitions because, in the world of flower essences, it's a tradition to include them. But the Perelandra Essences have been developed to be used differently than flower essences and the definitions are a distraction that hold you back from using them well. I still provide the basic description of what each set as a unit addresses, but I've tossed out the definitions for the individual bottles.

With this book we are taking a quantum leap in understanding the Perelandra Essences and how to use them to their fullest. Because of PKTT, definitions have always been a minor part when working with the Essences. But over the years I've seen how some just can't help themselves and rely on the definitions to self-diagnose. I can't even begin to describe to you what a limitation this puts on identifying the correct Essence for a specific health issue. The human electric system is far too complex for this. When someone tries working solely with definitions, they are just guessing and wasting time—and trying to avoid learning PKTT. When a flower essence practitioner tries to select a Perelandra Essence for you using the definitions method, they are wasting your money. The most efficient and accurate tool for addressing the electric system and all its circuits is PKTT.

Chapter 5

The Setup
for Getting Started

THIS IS WHAT YOU WILL NEED TO START
WORKING WITH THE PERELANDRA ESSENCES.

YOUR CIRCUIT AND TESTING FINGERS

If you are missing a critical PKTT digit or a hand, or if you are paralyzed or otherwise impaired, call our Question Hot Line and we'll work with you to try to set up a good PKTT system that gives you accurate test results and addresses your physical issues as well. We may not be able to overcome this kind of hurdle, but we'd sure like to have the chance to work together with you so that you can benefit from the Perelandra Essences as well.

THE PERELANDRA ESSENCES

There are five different sets of Perelandra Essences that work in combination with one another and cover the full range of what's needed to balance, stabilize and repair an electric system: Rose, Garden, Rose II, Soul Ray and Nature Program. Each set is produced from electrical patterns derived from the Perelandra garden and the nature kingdoms that are part of Perelandra's seventy-seven acres. The electrical patterns contained in each bottle are set in a water-based solution that is preserved with brandy or white vinegar for safety and longevity. The pattern held in each bottle addresses different circuitry in your electric system and different kinds of circuit damage. The Essences are bottled in *concentrate form* in pharmaceutical dropper bottles that make it easy for you to place one drop of a needed Essence on your tongue or several drops of the Essence in a glass of water to be sipped throughout the day. Because they are used one drop at a time and because they are well-preserved, each bottle has an indefinite shelf-life. You'll be keeping and using these sets for many years.

A Brief Description of the Five Perelandra Essence Sets

● THE ROSE ESSENCES (SET 1) are a set of eight Essences that function with one another to repair and balance the electric circuits that support us as we proceed through our normal evolutionary process. As we move forward and address new situations, learning curves, challenges and ideas, there are mechanisms within us that are set in motion to facilitate our periods of growth. The Perelandra Rose Essences balance, stabilize and repair the circuits that support us and our process mechanisms.

● THE PERELANDRA GARDEN ESSENCES are a set of eighteen Essences that balance and restore the electric circuits that are needed to address physical, emotional, mental and soul issues that we face in our day-to-day life in today's world.

● THE ROSE ESSENCES II are another set of eight Essences that address the body's electric system as a whole and the specific circuits that are connected with our central nervous system (CNS). They also address the electric system's and circuits' support of the functions within the CNS that are activated and/or impacted during a deep expansion experience or soul-level shift of potential from unconscious to conscious. Here, one is not simply processing ordinary, everyday changes and challenges. When faced with this kind of expansion, the CNS is required to function in new ways, and with patterns and rhythms yet to be experienced. The Rose Essences II set addresses that phenomenon by balancing, stabilizing and repairing the electric system and its circuits that support all deep-expansion activity.

● THE NATURE PROGRAM ESSENCES are a set of nine Essences that address and reestablish an electric system's balance in two ways: (1) They strengthen the system so that the body can address a viral, fungal or bacterial imbalance and reestablish its proper microbial balance. (2) Sobopla, Moon and Bowl Essences address the electric system's and body's balance in light of its relationship to the larger environmental picture.

● THE SOUL RAY ESSENCES have been developed to balance, stabilize and repair the body's electric system and circuits that are connected with and support an individual's soul-level activity. They also address the circuits that support an individual's development towards conscious awareness of this activity, as well as the circuits that support the integration of the soul-level activity with the physical, emotions and mental levels. Without balanced electrical support, the electric circuits can become overloaded and overwhelmed. This will result in discomfort, disorientation, pain and disorder on the physical, emotions and mental levels. What I have found surprising

about the Soul Ray Essences is how many times they are needed for common illness and injury (simple and severe) and for mental and emotional issues. We may not understand just why we need these Essences but, after using them for a short time, we will definitely understand how much they help us recover our balance when we experience problems on any PEMS levels.

If you feel strongly about the Essences and you want to make the leap to include them in your health regimen, I suggest that you get the Perelandra All Essences Set. It includes each of the five sets and it's the most cost-effective way to go. If you'd like to take advantage of the All Essences Set savings but the idea of working with all those bottles in the beginning overwhelms you, all you have to do is choose just one set to start and put the other four sets aside. As you feel more confident, add each of the other four sets to your testing, one set at a time. It won't take long for you to be testing all five sets.

I do not recommend that you purchase one bottle at a time. It's the least economical way to go and you won't have what you need on hand to effectively monitor your electric system when needed. But you can purchase one of the five sets at a time. However, to ensure that you provide complete coverage for your electric system, your goal will be to have all five sets available eventually. If you can't purchase the five sets up front, the best way for you to get started right away may be to purchase one set at a time. Working with one set now is much better than waiting to buy the five sets later.

Unfortunately I can't recommend the best "starter set" for you. Based on the condition of each person's electric system, different people will need to start with different sets. One way to determine your starter set is to notice which one you are most drawn to as you read the list of the five sets.* Or you can set up a PKTT by asking the question (aloud):

> Which Perelandra Essences set would be my best starter set?

Then ask,

> Is the Rose Essences set my starter set? (Test the question.)

* You're not blindly guessing with this. You are literally picking up on all four PEMS levels how your electric system is responding as you focus on each set, one at a time. If one or more bottles in a set provides the balance your system needs right away, your system will respond to that improvement, you will feel a strong pull and you will be drawn to that particular set.

If you get a positive response, this is your starter set. But don't stop there. Ask the same question for each of the other four sets. Be sure your testing includes all five sets. You may need more than one starter set and the test results will indicate what else is needed. If you still want to begin with just one set, pick the one that attracts you most out of the group that tested positive. Just keep in mind the eventual and ultimate goal: The most comprehensive way to monitor and repair electric circuits is to work with all five sets.

ANOTHER POINT ABOUT THE FIVE SETS: Once you start using the Essences and experience what they can do, you will want to test your family members and the people close to you. Actually, once people around you see your changes, they'll be asking you to test them. The issues they want to address and the Essences they need may be quite different from the ones you need. This is another instance where working with all five sets is important.

● When purchasing the Perelandra Essences you will need to make two additional decisions.

1. Do you want your Essences preserved in brandy or distilled white vinegar?

There is no quality difference between these two preservatives. It's a matter of personal taste—literally. Some people love the brandy-preserved drops and other people love that Italian salad taste. Besides giving your Essences a long shelf-life, the preservative protects the Essence pattern from damage caused by temperature extremes and eliminates the need for refrigerating them. This means you can take your Essences along when you go on a winter hike across the Himalayas or leave them in the car when you drive across the Gobi Desert. The patterns will be unharmed. And since you'll be taking the Essences one drop at a time, the preservative extends their shelf-life indefinitely.

2. When purchasing multiple sets, what size bottles do you want to get? Half-ounce or dram ($^1/_8$ ounce)?

We offer several combinations of sets, including the Perelandra All Essences in two bottle sizes: half-ounce and dram ($^1/_8$ ounce). By offering the smaller bottles when purchasing multiple sets, we're able to extend lower prices to you. (The dram size is not available when purchasing just one set alone.) Here are the pros and cons of each size:

Dram bottles

Pros: They are smaller; more portable; fit in a drawer, gym bag or briefcase more easily; and they're less expensive.

Cons: The smaller bottle means there's a smaller volume of Essence. You'll need to refill them more often. Some people feel their hands are too big and make for clumsy bottle handling.

Half-ounce bottles

Pros: Some people prefer working with the larger bottles. The larger Essence volume per bottle lasts longer and, over the long run, is more cost-effective. There is less refilling: a half-ounce bottle holds four times more volume than a dram bottle.

CONS: Although portable, they are bulkier when fitting into different nooks and crannies at home or at the office. The initial cost is greater than the dram combination sets.

A Personal Note

I've always been a little uncomfortable suggesting that people purchase all five sets of the Perelandra Essences right away. I'm sensitive to the fact that I'm talking about money, and as the developer, producer and distributor of the Perelandra Essences, there is an obvious conflict of interest. But I feel urged to take a firm stand about this suggestion for three reasons:

1. The five Perelandra Essence sets work in combination with one another and cover a full range of an individual's electric circuit needs.

2. I've noticed over the years that most people who initially ordered a single set eventually end up ordering all five sets. They came to the conclusion on their own that to get the full range of support and effectiveness, they need to have on hand the full range provided by the five sets.

3. Because of this, we decided to help out and put together the All Essences Set as well as the other set combinations with discounts so that as many people as possible could take the full leap right away.

PEN, PAPER, CALENDAR & THE ESSENCE RECORD CHART

Essence Record Chart.

You'll need to keep a list of the Essences that test positive and the dosage information for reference. The simplest thing to do is record this information on a sheet of paper. We also have an Essence Record Chart that lists all of the Perelandra Essences. All you have to do is place a check next to each Essence name that tests positive, thus eliminating the need to write the names over and over and over and over... The Essence Record Chart is available online to download and print at no charge. If you prefer to purchase a pre-printed pack of fifty charts, we have this for you as well. But remember, the chart is a convenience and not a requirement. And finally, when Essence testing be sure you have on hand a calendar for figuring out dosage dates.

MAKING ESSENCE DOSAGES

Have on hand a half-dozen or more empty half-ounce dropper bottles (glass droppers only) and blank labels for when you are to take the same combination of Essences over several days. You may purchase these supplies from Perelandra. You'll also need to add a preservative to this solution: brandy or distilled white vinegar. *(Use only distilled white vinegar. For brandy, use only plain brandy and not fruit or flavored brandy.)* We don't supply the preservatives, so you'll need to pick up a small bottle of whichever one you prefer.

NOTE: While you're out shopping for vinegar or brandy, you might want to stop by an office supplies store and pick up a box of Avery labels, 1"x 2⅝" size. This is the size that works well for labeling bottles and you can get 3000 to a box. You need to label each dosage bottle you make. All brown-glass dosage bottles look alike and you may have more than one dosage period going on at the same time, each requiring its own labeled bottle.

PERELANDRA ESSENCE TELEGRAPH TEST CHECKLIST

You do not need this chart in the beginning when learning how to do a Basic Essence Test. However, this chart is important when working with the Basic Telegraph Test, and when telegraph testing chronic or serious illness and injury. You may download the chart from our website at no cost, or you may purchase pre-printed packs of fifty charts directly from us. Or, you may use the two sample charts included in this book (pp. 89 and 138) as templates for testing. For this you'll need to record what tests positive on a separate sheet of paper.

Essence Telegraph Test Checklist.

NOW YOU ARE READY TO START
TESTING THE PERELANDRA ESSENCES.

Part Two

THE PRIMARY ELECTRIC SYSTEM REPAIR PACKAGE

Chapter 6

The Basic Essence Test

HERE'S WHERE IT ALL COMES TOGETHER: what you've learned about your electric system, PKTT and the Perelandra Essences.

We begin with the Basic Essence Test. As the name implies, this is your basic test. But "basic" has two meanings: (1) Start here. It's where you begin when learning how to work with the Perelandra Essences. (2) This test is your base. It is the core or nucleus of all Essence testing and provides the foundation for the other processes presented in this book. You will use the Basic Essence Test often and for as long as you are working with the Perelandra Essences. In the beginning, this is the only test you will be using.

The Basic Essence Test focuses on your electric system and its circuits as one large, complex, multicircuited, intricately interconnected unit. It checks the system for any weakened circuits that are impeding how the system is functioning as a coordinated unit and identifies the Essences that are needed to repair and rebalance those circuits, thus strengthening the electric system as a unit.

The process for finding the Essences that are needed is based on a simple electric-system concept. If I place anything within three feet of my body, my electric system immediately identifies the thing and knows if its inclusion strengthens or weakens my system. If I place an Essence bottle in my lap, it is sitting well within that three-foot range. Even though the Essence pattern is contained in a closed bottle, it is still part of that bottle as a unit. The electric system isn't responding to an empty bottle. It is "reading" a dropper bottle plus its contents.

If the Essence pattern in the bottle doesn't stabilize or strengthen the system, it is seen as unhelpful and superfluous. The electric system, including the closed circuit you created with your two circuit fingers, temporarily weakens and you will test negative for that bottle. Once you remove the bottle from your lap and outside the three-foot range you will remove its weakening effect and your electric system will immediately return to its original state. This is similar to the concept that kicks into action when you make a mistake and take an Essence that isn't needed: The electric system rejects the pattern (it's superfluous and doesn't provide any help) and removes it from the system.

If the system has a weakness that this Essence would repair, the proximity of the pattern that's contained in the bottle literally and temporarily strengthens the system, including the closed circuit you've created with your fingers, and you will test positive for that bottle. Once you remove the bottle outside the three-foot space, your system will adjust back to its original state. You need to take a drop of an Essence orally for it to actually repair the circuits and have a lasting effect.

> TO SUMMARIZE: If an Essence tests positive (your circuit fingers remain connected), that's a yes and you need it. If an Essence tests negative (your circuit fingers separate), that's a no and you don't need it.

It's important with any Essence testing that you maintain focus on what you are doing and don't let your mind wander. You'd be surprised how easy it is for unwanted and unnecessary thoughts to amble through the mind and distract you from the test. It's also important to coordinate your intent and actions while testing. The accuracy of the PKTT results will suffer if you think about what you're going to do after the test (have a beer!) while you are in the midst of testing step 2. I've provided you with some help: You'll notice in the Basic Essence Test steps that you are to state certain intents and questions. They are designed to keep your mind, thoughts and actions corralled and moving in concert throughout the test. Never skip over these key sentences whenever doing a Basic Test—not now or twenty years down the road. And especially during the first six months of your learning curve, I urge you to say them *out loud*. This helps you maintain focus on what you are doing. If you want more help, say everything out loud—the steps, the questions and statements, the names of the Essences as you test them, the result of each test…You don't have to shout. Just speak in a normal volume. If someone is around who could hear you and you find this embarrassing, whisper the questions. You need to be able to literally hear your own words. But you don't have to entertain the neighbors.*

FINAL NOTE ABOUT FOCUS. I have said that the energy field of an Essence extends out three feet. But in the Essence testing steps I'm also telling you that you can do a

* This is a useful trick to remember. Once you've gotten through the beginner's stage and you've learned how to maintain your focus on the test, you will still have challenges from time to time and find it difficult to keep your mind from wandering. For example, when you need to test Essences but you are tired, sick, excited, agitated or in pain, say all the steps out loud. If you engage your hearing, you will find it's much easier to keep your attention on what you are doing even during these kinds of challenges.

clean and accurate Essence test with a whole box of Essences in your lap. Now you have eight or more Essences within the three-foot range. In case you are wondering how this testing is possible, the answer is focus.

When testing the Perelandra Essences, focus, among other things, functions as the bar bouncer: "You can go in." "You have to wait." "You stand over there." So you can put all fifty-one bottles of Essences in your lap and, if your intent and focus is to test them all, your "focus bouncer" has just given all the Essences a pass and the electric system will activate for testing them all. If your intent and focus is on testing just one bottle among the fifty-one that are laying in your lap, your focus bouncer will only let one bottle in through the door and only the circuits connected with that one bottle will be activated. The trick is the quality of focus a person can hold while testing. We live in an age of multitasking, iPads and iPhones. People are well trained to allow their attention to bounce around and to split their focus. So, in the Essence testing steps I don't have you dump all fifty-one bottles in your lap and then direct you to focus on one bottle at a time. Unless you are exceptionally disciplined and trained in focus, that would lead to something looking like mental chaos. Instead, you put one bottle at a time in your lap. (Unless it's to test a combination with several bottles, and then you put that one combination in your lap.) The focus on the one bottle neutralizes the impact of the other bottles on the electric system. When I direct you to set an entire box of Essences in your lap, your focus and intent is on determining if any of the individual bottles in that box are needed. If you get a positive, then you take the bottles out of the box, one at a time, to find out which one(s) in that box are needed. In short, your focus is being directed in specific ways within the steps and your electric system is moving right along with that focus. And this makes your "focus bouncer" very happy.

* To reuse solution bottles, wash the bottles and droppers in hot, soapy water *two times,* rinsing them well, and air dry on a clean paper towel. Do not touch the glass dropper with your fingers (or anything else). But it's okay if the glass dropper lightly touches the clean paper towel during the drying process. Always handle the dropper by the rubber bulb.

BASIC ESSENCE TEST STEPS

SUPPLIES:

- the Perelandra Essences
- pen, paper and calendar
- option: a blank Perelandra Essence Record Chart
- one clean solution bottle*
- brandy or distilled white vinegar preservative
- a blank label

Fig. A

Fig. B

Fig. C

Fig. D

* There is no shortcut for checking a step 4 Essence combination. The bottles that test positive must be taken out of the box(es) and placed in your lap in order to test them properly as a combination.

PREPARE FOR TESTING: Drink some water. Go to the bathroom, if needed. Find a quiet spot and sit comfortably. Place the boxes of Essences and the other supplies within easy reach.

1. State your intent to do a Basic Essence Test:

> I want to do a Basic Essence Test.

2. Place each box of Essences, one at a time, in your lap *(Fig. A)*. Ask:

> Do I need any Essences from this box? (Test.)

If you get a negative, you don't have to test the bottles from that box because none are needed.

If you test positive, move the box off to one side and test each bottle from that box individually by placing the bottle in your lap to determine which ones are needed *(Fig. B)*. Ask:

> Do I need _____ Essence? (Test.)

3. Check your results by placing in your lap just the bottles that tested positive *(Fig. C)*. Ask:

> Are these the only Essences I need? (Test.)

If the response is positive, that's a "yes." Go to step 4. If only one Essence is needed, skip step 4 and go to step 5.

If you get a negative, retest the other Essences. A negative means you missed an Essence and need to find what was missed. After retesting, ask the question once more:

> Are these the only Essences I need? (Test.)

If the response is still negative, keep testing the Essences to find what you missed and you get a positive response to the question. This will verify that you have all the needed Essences.

4. If you have more than one Essence, check them as a combination by placing all of them in your lap *(Fig. C)* and asking:

> Is this the combination I need? (Test.)*

If you get a negative but the Essences tested positive when tested individually, you need to adjust the combination.

Place each of the combination bottles separately in your lap *(Fig. D)* and ask:

> Do I remove this bottle from the combination? (Test.)

Whatever tests positive gets removed. This means that when the individual Essences that tested positive were put together, a combination was created that made one or more of those Essences unnecessary. The whole was stronger and more effective than the sum of its parts.

Put the remaining combination bottles in your lap *(Fig. E)* and ask:

Is this combination now correct? (Test.)

You should get a positive. If you don't, test the *original* combination again (the combination before you removed any bottles), and keep working at it until they test positive as a unit.

5. Take these Essences orally, one drop each. Record the Essences on the sheet of paper or on your Essence Record Chart.

Fig. E

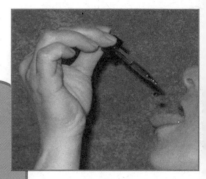

Careful: Pay Attention to "Dropper Hygiene"!

• Rinse the dropper off with warm, soapy water before putting it back into the bottle if you accidentally touch the dropper with your mouth or tongue. This keeps your saliva from affecting the Essence pattern.

• Don't touch the glass part of the dropper while you're washing it. (Use clean latex or non-latex gloves.)

• Always hold an Essence dropper by the rubber bulb.

• If you have difficulty taking an Essence directly from the dropper without it hitting your mouth, put one drop of each needed Essence in a clean spoon. It doesn't matter if the spoon touches your mouth since you won't be trying to stuff it back in your Essence bottle.

• Wash the dropper anytime you drop it or touch your clothes with it or the dog licks it or…

• *The general rule: Don't put a dirty dropper back in the bottle.*

CROSS-CONTAMINATION. If you need more than one Essence, open each bottle one at a time, take a drop of that Essence, put the dropper back into the bottle and close the bottle. Don't try to form an assembly line by opening all the needed bottles at one time in order to administer each drop more quickly. With this setup it is too easy to put a dropper in the wrong bottle. Working with each bottle one at a time ensures that you are not making a dropper/bottle mistake. If you manage to cross-contaminate or even suspect you've cross-contaminated, you'll need to throw out the bottles in question and order replacements.

The Beginner's Break: Daily Essence Testing

Steps 1 through 5 make up the first half of the Basic Essence Test. The full test includes testing for dosage which determines how many days and how many times a day you are to take the needed Essences. However, over the years I've recommended daily testing when getting started. Here's how it goes:

AFTER COMPLETING STEP 5 and taking each Essence that tested positive, record the results. Put your Essences away and get on with the rest of your day.

THE NEXT DAY, do another Basic Test, completing steps 1 through 5. Take those Essences, record the results, put the Essences away and get on with your day.

THE NEXT DAY, do another Basic Test, steps 1 through 5. Take those Essences, record the results, put the Essences away and get on with your day. And so on.

In short, you will be testing Essences daily. There are a number of advantages to daily testing:

> • You work with a simplified Basic Essence Test while you go through your learning curve.

> • You don't have to learn about dosages or how to make a solution bottle should you need a combination of Essences for more than one day. By testing daily, the combination you get today will show up in tomorrow's test, if needed again.

> • With daily testing you start repairing and balancing your electric system right away and you support that progression on a daily basis. Should something happen in your life that challenges your electric system in a new way and threatens to require additional repair, it is quickly addressed in the daily

testing. This allows your system to move through the early repair process more efficiently.

● By testing daily you give yourself the golden opportunity (as they say) to practice PKTT. I recommend daily testing for the first four to six months. It gets you through the initial balancing and repair your electric system has needed for a long time and it definitely gets you through that awkward early stage when learning PKTT.

Daily Testing Beyond the Beginner

● Testing Essences daily is an excellent approach while you are sick. It provides that in-the-moment support that helps move you through the illness very quickly. As a matter of fact, if you get sick you can do a Basic Essence Test every two or three hours. This moves things along even more quickly.

BUT I WARN YOU: The faster you move through some illnesses, the less "gentle" the process can become. You are trading relative comfort for speed. Sometimes things will come out of orifices you didn't know you had. This more intense journey doesn't last very long (usually twenty-four to forty-eight hours), but you definitely notice that you and your body are working very hard and at a quick pace. In short, testing every two to three hours (waking hours only) isn't for the faint-hearted. You may wish to opt for the more gentle route by testing two to three times *daily* and take an extra few days to come through the illness.

● While recuperating, continue with the daily Basic Essence Test. Recuperation periods last a lot longer than we think. By testing once daily, you accomplish two things: (1) You move through the recuperation period more quickly and efficiently. (2) You ensure that your recuperation time is not cut short. How do you know you are through it? You start to test clear, no Essences needed. *When you test clear for seven days straight, you are officially out of the recuperation period and can stop the daily testing, if you wish.* Moving completely through recuperation is vital if we want to restore ourselves to full health. If we cut it short, we resume our daily routine in a weakened condition that leaves us vulnerable to a return of the illness or for catching something else that might be swirling around.

● Take the same approach as dealing with illness when moving through an injury. But because of the nature of an injury when compared to an illness, a once-daily Basic Essence Test is generally all that's needed. You'll test positive for some Essences in the first test of each day but test clear (no Essences needed) for the other tests later that day. If this continues for four or five days in a row, you'll know that one daily test is enough. If something happens during your recovery that complicates the healing or you feel you've hit a snag and have stopped moving forward, check again to see if you need to do a Basic Essence Test more than one time daily. (For the next four or five days, test several times each day. If you test clear after the first test of the day, you still need only one daily test.)

Remember not to short-change the injury recuperation period. When doing daily testing, you need to test clear for seven days straight before assuming you have moved completely through your recuperation and can stop the daily testing.

● THE BASIC ESSENCE TEST OPTION FOR SERIOUS ILLNESS. Daily testing is also helpful when you are dealing with a long-term illness or condition.* These are situations that demand special attention. For example, if you are dealing with cancer or you have heart disease or you're facing any other serious illness or condition, it is important to monitor your electric system daily. The Perelandra Essences are safe to use in combination with needed conventional treatments. In fact, a daily test supports those treatments, makes them more effective and helps keep your body moving forward more efficiently. If your treatments are intense, stressful, depressing and/or painful, you may need to do a Basic Essence Test more than once a day. Don't hesitate to add the extra daily tests.

* For a more comprehensive Essence approach to long-term issues, see chapter 9, *Telegraph Testing Chronic Illness*. The steps and guidelines apply equally to chronic illness and chronic injury.

If you have successfully moved through a serious illness and its recuperation period, I strongly recommend that you continue doing the Basic Essence Test as a regular part of your daily regimen. The last thing you want is to step away from monitoring your electric system's balance and risk falling back into that illness or condition. In this situation, I feel you need to take your body's hint and accept that, for your own health and well-being for the many years ahead, you need to remain vigilant and give yourself (and your electric system) extra help on a daily basis.

What's the "Normal" Number of Essences That Can Test Positive in One Test?

Another way of saying this: "Oh no! I just tested for ___ Essences! Yikes, am I crazy? Am I messing up the testing? Can you take too many Essences at once? Help me... *HELP ME! I. THINK. I'M. DYING!*"... A good number of people who have moved through the Essence learning curve can relate to this.

● Here's the good thing about using PKTT: You test positive for whatever you need. It removes all the guessing. So whatever Essences test positive, you take. That can be anywhere from one Essence to all fifty-one Essences. Whatever you test for is your "normal." If you test positive for one Essence today, that's today's "normal." If you test positive for twenty-five bottles tomorrow, that's tomorrow's "normal." You just need to take one drop of whichever Essences test positive each day. In the beginning your electric system can move through a rather complex initial repair and balancing. So let your test results lead the way and don't draw any conclusions about the number of Essences that you need each day. Needing a single Essence doesn't mean you are any more or any less special than the person who needs all fifty-one Essences. Just don't read anything into this. Take the needed drops and allow yourself to move forward according to your unique needs.

● For the first month, you could test for one or two Essences each day. Then you get into the second month and suddenly forty bottles test positive. You are not failing or slipping backwards. It's just the unique rhythm of balancing, stabilizing and repair that your electric system is going through.

● Let's say that from the minute you start daily testing, all fifty-one Essences test positive. The next day fifty-one Essences test positive again. The next day it happens again. And after two or three weeks, it's still happening. Keep breathing. You're not dying and you're not alone. I don't know what percentage of new Essence users test positive for everything for a string of days or weeks, but it's not a rare situation. You may think that needing fifty-one bottles is nuts, but that's not the crazy part. We tell whoever finds themselves in this situation to just keep taking whatever tests positive and, if they continue to need all fifty-one Essences week after week, to expect that *at the end of three months* they will begin testing positive for fewer and fewer bottles. The crazy part is that like clockwork the testing changes at the end of three months. I have no idea why this particular timing occurs or why it's the same for so many different people in so many different situations. We've had people contact us and say that, much to their amazement, the testing changed right at the end of the three months just as we said it would. If you find yourself in this situation, I urge you not to panic and to take whatever you need for as long as you need it.

By the way, don't get goofy and decide on your own that you are going to take all fifty-one Essences for three months rather than bother with the daily testing. You may be one of those people who need only one or two Essences. If so, you waste your Essences by taking all those unneeded drops. You also require your electric system to go to the additional trouble of releasing the unneeded patterns out from the system each day. I repeat: *Take only what you need for as long as you need it.*

TESTING FOR DOSAGE

Once you are comfortable working with the first five steps of the Basic Essence Test and you've completed the four- to six-month period of daily testing, include dosage testing every time you do a Basic Test. (But remember, there is no need to test for dosage any time you go back to daily testing.) Dosage testing adds two important pieces of information for fine tuning your Essence use: (1) You find out how many days you are to take those Essences. Whether you test positive for just one Essence or several in combination, it's important to take them over the full period of time they are needed and to know when to do any follow-up testing. (2) You find out how many times a day you are to take an Essence or combination. Sometimes you will need to take them more than once daily in order to receive full benefit.

Number of Days

Once you've completed the Basic Essence Test steps 1 through 5 (pp. 54–55), continue with steps 6 through 10.

Fig. G

6. Hold in your lap all the bottles that tested positive as a combination or unit *(Fig. G).* If only one bottle tested positive, hold that bottle in your lap.

7. Ask:

> Do I need the Essence(s) more than one time? (Test.)

If negative, that means you have already completed the dosage (in step 5) and you have completed the Basic Essence Test. You can put away your Essences and get on with the rest of your day.

NOTE: If you are addressing something like an illness or condition that you feel should logically require Essences for more than one day, yet you tested negative for step 7, assume that rather than taking the same combination day after day, you need to do daily testing. In order to move successfully through the problem, you need different Essences each day. You've already taken the Essence(s) you need today in step 5 and you need to do a new Basic Essence Test tomorrow. Continue testing daily until you test clear for *seven days straight.**

8. If you got a positive PKTT response in step 7, find out how many days you are to take the Essence(s). Do a sequential test. With all the needed Essence(s) still in your lap, ask:

* When completing a daily testing regimen, you need to test clear for *seven days straight.*

When completing a Basic Essence Test that included dosage and follow-up testing, you only need to test clear for *three days straight.*

Do I need these one day? (Test.)

Two days? (Test.)

Three days? (Test.)

Do a count until you get a negative response. For example: If you need to take these Essences for three days, you will test positive when you ask, "One day?", "Two days?", "Three days?" When you ask, "Four days?" you will test negative. That tells you that your electric system will be assisted and strengthened by taking those Essences for three days. However, on the fourth day they no longer strengthen or repair your electric system and they are considered superfluous, so you'll get a negative response.

HINT: If you test positive for seven days, you can save yourself some PKTT wear and tear if you switch from testing dosage one day at a time to one week at a time. With the first seven days that tested positive you already know you are to take these Essences for seven days. That's one week. Now ask:

Two weeks? (Test.)

Three weeks? (Test.) And so on.

If you test positive for three weeks but negative for four weeks, find out how many days between the third and fourth weeks you are to take the Essences. Ask:

Three weeks and one day? (Test.)

Three weeks and two days? (Test.) And so on.

Since you already tested negative for four weeks, you know that you won't have to test beyond three weeks and six days.

Times per Day

9. To receive maximum benefit, find out if you need to take the Essences more than once daily. Do another sequential test. (If you are testing a combination of Essences, treat them as a unit. Don't break up the combination and test each bottle separately.) While still holding the Essence combination in your lap, ask:

Do I take the Essences once daily? (Test.)

Two times daily? (Test.) And so on.

Your last positive response tells you how many times per day the Essences are needed. Generally, Essences are to be administered one to three times daily: in the morning and/or in the evening and/or in mid-afternoon.

MANAGING DOSAGE
INFORMATION.
Be sure you make a note of
the dosage information with
the list of needed Essences
and that you don't rely on
memory. Also include the
dates the solution begins
and ends. Here's what it
can look like:

2 weeks/3days, 2x daily:
A.M. & P.M.
5/1/11 to 5/17/11

You will include this
information on the solution
bottle label, as well.

See p. 67 for an example of a
Basic Essence Test including
dosage and follow-up testing.

10. If you are to take these Essences once or twice daily, test to see if it is best to take them in the morning, afternoon or evening, or any combination of the three. For example, you may need to take an Essence combination just once daily. By testing you find out if you should take that combination in the morning or in the afternoon or in the evening. Ask:

Do I take these Essences in the morning? (Test.)
In the afternoon? (Test.)
In the evening? (Test.)

You'll get one positive test result indicating that this is when you should take the Essence(s) each day to receive maximum benefit. If you are to take Essences twice daily, you'll get two positive results. If you are to take them three times a day, assume you are to take one dose in the morning, another in the afternoon and a third dose in the evening.

To Eat or Not to Eat, That Is the Question

You don't have to take the Perelandra Essences on an empty stomach—or a full stomach, for that matter. Just take the Essences you need, wait *ten seconds* and then eat or drink whatever you want. Or wait *ten minutes* after eating or drinking and then take your Essences. And as far as the Perelandra Essences are concerned, there are no dietary restrictions you need to follow. (Chocolate for everyone!)

Also, the Perelandra Essences don't interfere with medicines—and medicines don't interfere with the Perelandra Essences. Again, take the Essences you need and wait *ten seconds* before taking any medication. The ten seconds give the Essences ample time to move into your electric system and to start the balancing, stabilizing and repair of the circuits in need.

MAKING A SOLUTION BOTTLE

Make a solution bottle if an Essence combination is to be taken more than a couple of days (and untwisting all those bottle caps each day will be annoying), or if you need to take it several times throughout the day and must carry the solution around. To make a solution bottle you will need *(Fig. H)*:

Fig. H

- A clean, brown-glass, half-ounce dropper bottle. The bottle must have a glass dropper. Do not use a plastic dropper.

- Your preservative of choice: brandy or distilled white vinegar. Do not use anything else as a preservative when working with the Perelandra Essences.

- A clean solution label for recording your name and dosage information on the bottle. This is essential because all brown dropper bottles look alike, and if you have more than one active solution bottle with different Essences and different dosages, you're in trouble if you didn't label them.

- Spring or untreated water. If this is unavailable, tap water will do.

1. Add five drops of each Essence needed to the empty dropper bottle *(Fig. I)*.

If you wish to economize on the number of drops you use, test for how many drops of each Essence are to be added to your half-ounce solution. Do a sequential test for each bottle one at a time. Ask:

Do I need one drop of _____ Essence for this half-ounce solution? (Test.) Two drops? (Test.) And so on.

Fig. I

Do a count until you get a negative response. You may find that some of the Essences require fewer than five drops and you will save on the number of drops used for those Essences. (Or you can give yourself a testing break and just add five drops of each needed Essence to the half-ounce bottle!)

2. Then add one teaspoon of brandy or distilled white vinegar if you want to preserve the solution *(Fig. J)*, and fill with water. You can also refrigerate the solution, thus eliminating the need for preserving it in brandy or vinegar.

3. Take one dropperful (about ten to twelve drops) for each dosage. Once you make a solution bottle, the Essence drops have been diluted and are no longer concentrated. This is why you need to take one dropperful for each dosage. *Don't forget to label your solution bottle.* (See sample labels on p. 67.)

Fig. J

Solution in a Glass

Fig. K

If you wish to make a solution in a glass rather than a dropper bottle:

1. Add nine drops of each needed Essence concentrate to *four ounces* of water *(Fig. K)*.

2. Add three teaspoons of brandy or distilled white vinegar if you want to preserve this solution. Refrigerate it if no preservative is added.

3. Drink one good sip for each dosage needed.

> NOTE: If you have an allergy or a problem with brandy or distilled white vinegar, you can still use the Perelandra Essences by always making a preservative-free solution. If you need to take the solution throughout the day, you can still carry the preservative-free solution in the dropper bottle with you. Add five drops of each needed Essence to a half-ounce dropper bottle and fill with water. Just remember to put the bottle in the refrigerator each night. If you don't need to carry the solution around, add nine drops of each Essence to four ounces of water in a glass. Then refrigerate. The amount of brandy or vinegar contained in each drop of concentrate is negligible when diluted this way.

FOLLOW-UP TESTING, NEW TESTING AND PREVENTIVE/SMART TESTING

* TO SET YOUR FOCUS. Example: For your Basic Essence Test, Broccoli Essence tested positive. You are to take it once daily for four days. Each time you take a dose of Broccoli Essence say "Basic Essence Test." Then put a drop of Broccoli Essence on your tongue. If you are taking a drop of three Essences directly from their bottles, you need to say "Basic Essence Test" three times. However, if you make a solution bottle with those three Essences combined, you only need to say "Basic Essence Test" once just before putting a dropperful of the solution in your mouth.

● FOLLOW-UP TESTING. Let's say you are to take Essences for a certain number of days. Once you complete that dosage period, do a new Basic Essence Test *within forty-eight hours* as a follow up to find out if any additional Essences might be needed. When Essences are needed one time only, the follow-up test is done within forty-eight hours after taking that one dose. Continue doing follow-up testing at the end of each dosage period until you test clear. When you test clear for *three straight days,* you know that you have completed the series of follow-up testing and no additional Essences are needed at that time for that issue.

● ADMINISTERING DOSAGES. Each time you take the Essence solution during the prescribed dosage period, prepare yourself first by activating the circuits the solution is addressing. Do this by reading aloud the focus/intent that is written on the bottle label.*

IMPORTANT: Once you make a solution bottle, the Essence drops have been diluted and are no longer concentrated. For each dosage, you will need to take ten to twelve drops (one dropperful).

● DO A BASIC ESSENCE TEST ANY TIME. Really. *Don't wait to get sick.* If you are not addressing a specific health issue, I suggest you regularly monitor the state of your electric system so that any needed balancing, stabilizing and repair can be caught right away before it becomes a health problem. Consider doing a Basic Essence Test for general monitoring weekly or every two weeks.

● IF YOU ARE GOING THROUGH A STRESSFUL TIME, do daily testing so that the stress doesn't make you sick and you can continue functioning.

● YOU START TO FEEL UNDER THE WEATHER. You can feel something "coming on." Do a Basic Essence Test as soon as possible. If I start to feel bad, I do several tests that day and/or evening just to make sure my electric system has everything it needs to take care of the problem. You'll probably only need to do this for one day. But if you still feel under the weather the next day, continue the same routine until you no longer feel a sickness hovering or lurking over your shoulder.

● COMMUNAL SICKNESS. The people around you at home, work or school are getting sick and are sneezing and coughing all over you. But you're not sick—yet. Do a Basic Essence Test as soon as possible and test again several times a day until you test clear; no further Essences are needed. Then do a Basic Essence Test once a day until everyone stops sneezing, coughing, wheezing or whatever.

● TEACH your family members and co-workers about Essences and how to test them so that they can stop catching every little thing that waltzes by them and you don't have to go into full Essence battle mode every time they get sick. If given the option, they might prefer not getting sick! It's such a drag on everyone.

● REMEMBER TO TAKE THE NEEDED DOSAGES (one dropperful per dose) for the full period of time prescribed. Also, record the end date for the solution on a calendar or computer so that you'll know when to do the follow-up testing.

● PERSISTENT SYMPTOMS OR INJURIES. Should a Basic Essence Test and the follow-ups not take care of all the symptoms or injuries, set up for a Basic Telegraph Test. (See chapter 7, *The Basic Telegraph Test.*)

PKTT AND THE ESSENCE TESTING REFINEMENT

In the beginning and while you are getting used to holding your focus on a bottle while testing it, place the box off to one side and test each bottle from that box individually by placing the bottle in your lap and asking, "Is _____ Essence needed?" After *lots* of Essence testing and when you feel confident that you can keep your focus on *one bottle at a time* and not let your eye wander to the next bottle, you can eliminate the single-bottle lap routine. Keep the box in your lap while you focus on one bottle at a time and test it. The key is to do whatever you need to ensure that you are getting accurate test results. Don't try to hot dog your testing. For good Essence testing, you need to proceed with care, so only advance to this refinement when you know you can hold your focus on one bottle at a time when they are sitting side by side in the box. Also, even after working successfully with this refinement, don't be afraid to revert back to the single-bottle lap routine anytime you're not sure you can control your focus.

Stop Here: Learning Curve Alert!

Give yourself a break and learn to work with the things you've read about up to this point: PKTT, the Perelandra Essences, the Basic Essence Test and daily testing. The operative words here are "comfort" and "confidence." When you feel comfortable and a little confident with what you've learned so far, it's a safe bet that you can take on new information without feeling overwhelmed. You don't have to wait for the end of your four- to six-month daily testing period before learning more. I wish I could say that you'll start feeling comfort and confidence in exactly two months, sixteen days, four hours, ten minutes and eight seconds. But the truth is, we all have different timing when it comes to such things. Some will plunge ahead right away and others will need six months before feeling they're ready to take on more. I urge you to pay attention to and respect your comfort and confidence levels.

Focus: Basic Essence Test

6/10/11
Orange Ruffles, Ambassador, Tiffany, #6, F-2
4 days, 1x daily: A.M.
6/10 to 6/13

Sample Labels

> Basic Essence Test
> 4 days (6/10 to 6/13)
> 1x daily: A.M.

6/14/11
Cucumber, Corn, Summer Squash, #5, #6
2 weeks/2 days, 1x daily: A.M.
6/14 to 6/29

> Basic Essence Test
> 2 wks/2 days (6/14 to 6/29)
> 1x daily: A.M.

6/30/11
Moon, Oregold, Zucchini
3 days, 2x daily: A.M. & P.M.
6/30 to 7/2

7/3/11
Clear

> Basic Essence Test
> 3 days (6/30 to 7/2)
> 2x daily: A.M. & P.M.

7/4/11
Clear

7/5/11
Clear

7/6/11
Clear

The Essence names listed in all the examples throughout the book are from the five sets of Perelandra Essences. They were chosen randomly for demonstration purposes only and do not reflect actual testing results.

Chapter 7

The Basic Telegraph Test

IF YOU ONLY WORK WITH two Essence processes, make it the Basic Essence Test and the Basic Telegraph Test. With these two processes you have about 95 percent of your lifetime Essence health needs covered. The Basic Essence Test addresses your electric system as one massive, intricately interconnected unit. As you work with the Basic Essence Test, you'll see that it takes care of a large percentage of your health issues. However, sometimes the situation calls for you to do more—especially when you are dealing with persistent symptoms* or something more complex such as serious disease or injury. That's where the Basic Telegraph Test comes in.

* I use the word "symptom" broadly to include problems and issues you might wish to address that are beyond commonly recognized physical symptoms.

Telegraph testing allows you to use the Perelandra Essences with pinpoint accuracy. Instead of addressing the full electric system as a unit, you now turn your attention to individual symptoms and focus only on the circuits that are connected with those specific problems. For example, you arrive home from work feeling like you're coming down with a cold. Being the wise person that you are, you immediately sit down and do a Basic Essence Test. You take those Essences and then get on with your usual end-of-the-day home tasks. About an hour later you notice that you're feeling pretty good—except for that headache you still have. The other symptoms have disappeared. Your energy level has picked up, you no longer feel congested, your throat doesn't feel scratchy, you don't feel like you have a temperature and your eyes don't feel heavy. The Basic Essence Test with its focus on your full electric system balanced, stabilized and repaired the circuits as a single, interconnected unit that, in turn, automatically eliminated the symptoms that made you feel like you were getting a cold—except for the circuits causing the headache. For this, you need to do more. These circuits are operating differently and need to be identified, isolated, tested and treated separately if you wish to get rid of the headache. How do you know you need to do more? It's simple. Despite the fact that you already did a Basic Essence Test and took those Essences, you still have a headache.

Here's how it works: The electric system operates as one massive unified unit *and* as a countless collection of smaller units of localized, interrelated, interconnected circuits, each supporting a specific PEMS function. See it as a fifty-thousand-piece jigsaw puzzle. You have all these pieces, each with their own colors and shapes. They would be the electric circuits. You put the pieces together and you have one big mosaic—the electric system. In order to deal with the headache, you need to isolate the damaged circuits causing the headache—that is, find the one or more related pieces of the puzzle causing the problem. That collection of circuits normally supports a specific activity. But right now, these circuits are malfunctioning and, instead of experiencing the activity they normally support, you are experiencing the results of all the misfiring—the headache.

To find the right pieces, do a Basic Telegraph Test. Putting it simply but bluntly, a Telegraph Test is a Basic Essence Test on steroids. The secret ingredient of the Telegraph Test and the thing that gives it its brilliance and "magic" is a little thing called "focus." This is another one of those moments when we stand back and say, "Nah. It can't be that simple." Well, it really is that simple. If we combine PKTT and focus, we can isolate and access any circuit or combination of circuits in our electric system. Not only can we access them, we can test them, determine exactly which Essences are needed for repair and treat them. We can do all of this just by combining PKTT and focus.

When I use the word "focus," I'm not talking about the level of focus needed to keep your mind from wandering during a Basic Essence Test. I call that focus gentle or mild. No, the focus I'm now talking about is the kind of attention it takes to listen to someone tell you something important at 2:30 in the afternoon on the floor of the New York Stock Exchange. If you are following every word this person is saying, you are focused on that person and fully hearing and understanding what is being said to you. If you hear that person but at the same time you are aware of the commotion going on around you, you're not fully focused. At best, you're half-listening. In a Telegraph Test, the focus on a specific symptom or issue is laser-beamed. When you are this focused, all the circuits that support whatever it is you are focused on are activated. And now you can test them for needed Essences.

You might feel that this kind of focus is impossible to achieve. Not only is it possible, but we do it a lot in our day-to-day lives. If you've ever experienced reading a particularly good book or working on an art project or listening to a child tell you a delightful story or winning a hotly contested athletic competition or creating a special meal... If at these moments time disappeared and the room or world fell away, then you have experienced the kind of high-level focus you need for a Basic Telegraph Test.

And how does focus pull off this little feat of magic? Think "PEMS levels" (physical, emotions, mental, soul). Every action that makes up who we are as human beings has its own collection of electric circuits that activate, support and hold that activity on each of its PEMS levels. *Focus is a natural mental-level activity that runs throughout the larger electric system and is included in all the countless smaller units of circuits that support each human function.* In chapter 3, I wrote:

> In order to explain the human system's four levels and how they interrelate, I've represented them as if they are four distinct levels that are suspended in space with a few "bridging" circuits connecting them. In reality, the only thing that separates or defines these four levels from one another is the differing nature of their activity. *Physical:* My arm moves. *Emotions:* I notice my arm is flabby and that makes me sad/mad/indifferent/fascinated at my own aging process. *Mental:* I think about what I'm doing with this movement and come to the conclusion that I could move my arm differently and experience greater ease and efficiency in that movement. *Soul:* My arm movement is fully in sync with the parameters my soul has set for who I am and what range of activity I am able to experience. *A more accurate way of seeing these four levels is to visualize them as a single unit with their circuits intertwined, connected and acting in concert with one another.*

The circuits that are connected with that lingering physical headache are part of a package that includes related circuits on the other three PEMS levels: emotions, mental and soul. You activate the entire package of PEMS circuits by engaging in one of the mental-level activities that is already included in the package: focus. In this case, you are focused on the headache. You can't isolate or disconnect any of the related PEMS levels from one another. By activating one level, you automatically activate them all. It's a package deal. Focus on the headache, and now you have activated all the circuits on each of the PEMS levels that are connected with the headache. (Yep. It really is this simple.)

When you focus on the headache, you are directing the action of your focus to a particular target—the headache. When you add to this your intent to telegraph test that target, you have now combined purpose with the targeted focus. Purpose provides two important pieces to a Telegraph Test: (1) It sets up the targeted circuit package for the testing. (2) It also connects that package with the extra closed circuit you create with your testing fingers. You can't do a Telegraph Test without PKTT. This is part of what defines a Telegraph Test. If your intent is to do a Telegraph Test, the setup for PKTT and its connection to your circuit fingers must be automatically included. When you state that you want to set up a Telegraph Test for the headache, your electric system immediately adjusts and includes a circuit-finger connection to the headache package.* When you put it all together, you end up with a well-directed, laser-beamed focus that activates all the PEMS circuits connected with just the headache for the purpose of a Telegraph Test that includes PKTT.

* In step 1 of the Telegraph Test, you state your intent and set the purpose. Don't skip this step. Ever.

I know this may seem a little wiggy to you. Like I'm telling you to work with invisible puffs of pure fantasy and somehow you can get amazing testing results. But what you are really doing is working with your electric system in a deliberate and highly organized manner, using elements of its natural operation to highlight a specific area of circuits through the use of well-defined focus.

One reason this is so effective is that you are maintaining horizontal compatibility by combining focus with PKTT as the testing tool. Focus is an electrical function that is supported by its own electric circuits within the human body. Now you've added an electrical function (focus) to an electrical testing tool (PKTT) for the purpose of testing the body's electric circuits—perfect horizontal compatibility.

The PEMS package concept is important because often the problem we experience on one PEMS level is actually the result of a circuitry issue on a different but related PEMS level. So you can experience a bad headache and all the obvious signs point to this being a physical-level problem. However, the underlying cause of the headache may be in the circuits that are part of the emotions level. In a Telegraph Test, you automatically connect with and test the full package of circuits—always. So if the physical problem is actually caused by wild wiring on the emotions level, the Essences that test positive while you're focused on the headache pain will balance, stabilize and repair the emotions-level wild wiring. Or you may have a headache and the wild wiring isn't just on the emotions level. Circuits may need repair on two or three or all four of the levels. In this case, the wild wiring on each of these levels is connected and functioning together in a mutually supportive but off-balanced manner that results in your headache. Your wild wiring has organized itself. The Essences that test positive repair all the wild wiring and restore the circuits to balance, thus removing the underlying problem causing the headache.

TELEGRAPH TESTING POINTS TO REMEMBER

● THE TELEGRAPH TEST "STARTING GATE." The very first Telegraph Test you do for each issue you wish to address is your "starting gate." This is the only time you will be testing everything that is included on your Basic Telegraph Test (BTT) checklist* at the same time. If you are dealing with five symptoms/injuries, you will do a Basic Essence Test for each one of them in this first Telegraph Test. Picture each symptom/injury in a starting gate. After you complete this first Telegraph Test that addresses each one, get the dosage information and make all of the needed solution bottles: the starting gate opens. Now each symptom/injury will move forward according to its own timing and rhythm. Unless you have some amazingly coordinated symptoms/injuries all moving through their healing process in lock-step with one another causing their dosage periods to end on exactly the same day, you will never have to do follow-up testing for more than one (maybe two) at a time. The bulk of the telegraph testing that takes the most amount of time and effort occurs at the starting gate. And like a race, these symptoms/injuries will not cross the finish line (test clear) at the same time.

* The BTT checklist explanation begins on p. 75.

● "ODD" TESTING RESULTS. When telegraph testing, you are testing one targeted thing *on its own,* in relationship to nothing else. Consequently, if you find the need for the same Essence you just took when you did the Basic Essence Test (you always start a Telegraph Test—step 1—by doing a Basic Essence Test to clear the full electric system**), it is because the isolated circuits underlying that targeted symptom require a direct infusion of the same Essence. You'll need to take that Essence again.

Let's say you do a Basic Essence Test to clear the full electric system first and find that it needs no Essences. Then you focus on the symptom, do a Telegraph Test on those targeted circuits and discover they need ten Essences. How in the world is this possible when the whole system just tested clear? Well, the circuits connected with the symptom and in need of repair are part of a defined PEMS unit*** and their

** CLEARING: This means you have checked your electric system for Essences and taken whatever Essences test positive. If an electric system is "clear," no further Essences are needed.

*** PEMS UNIT: A collection of electric circuitry supporting an activity or function on all its levels.

73

* TO SET YOUR FOCUS. You test for respiratory congestion and Chives Essence tested positive. You are to take it once daily for four days. Each time you take a dose of Chives Essence say "respiratory congestion." *Then* put a drop of Chives Essence on your tongue. If you are taking a drop of three Essences directly from the bottle for respiratory congestion, you need to say "Respiratory congestion" three times. However, if you make a solution bottle with those three Essences combined, you only need to say "respiratory congestion" once just before putting a dropperful of the solution in your mouth.

** If you are dealing with a chronic illness, you will be working with telegraph testing as outlined in chapter 9: *Telegraph Testing Chronic Illness.* But read all of chapter 7 first in order to build a solid foundation on telegraph testing. Once you are familiar with Basic Telegraph Testing, then set up for testing a chronic illness.

imbalance may be enough to cause the symptom you are experiencing but not enough to adversely impact the balance and strength of your full electric system. Although these PEMS units are not isolated from the system, they can sometimes act as if they are isolated and independent.

● ADMINISTERING ESSENCES. Finding what Essences are needed for a specific symptom is only half of the telegraphing procedure. *It is equally important that you focus on the symptom while taking each needed Essence.* This sets up the connections that move the Essence patterns directly into the circuits you have targeted. In this case, you are using focus as the tool to direct the movement of an Essence pattern once it is taken orally and enters the body's electric system.*

● DEALING WITH MULTIPLE SYMPTOMS. Every symptom tells us something. At the very least, it's saying, "Hey. Over here. These electric circuits are not balanced and you have some wild wiring going on over here." That's the good thing about symptoms. They are usually obvious and easy to recognize. Each symptom is a door-way to the problem and we use focus to open all the doors.**

As with the example of the cold that I used earlier, some symptoms arise from imbalances in the electric system itself and are eliminated when we do a Basic Essence Test. If, after about an hour, you still have one or more symptoms remaining, you now need to work with smaller PEMS units and do a Telegraph Test for each remaining symptom. Let's say you need to test three remaining symptoms.

● First, set up the Telegraph Test by doing a Basic Essence Test to clear your full electric system. The Basic Essence Test you did an hour ago does not count. If you don't clear the full electric system first, any Essences the full system needs can taint the results of the targeted circuit tests and the telegraph testing won't be accurate.

● Focus on the first symptom and test Essences for that symptom. Take those Essences and test for dosage.

● Then turn your focus to the second symptom and test Essences for this one. Take those Essences and test for dosage.

● Finally, focus on the third symptom and test Essences. Take those Essences and test for dosage.

You start telegraph testing multiple symptoms that are connected with the same issue by doing one Basic Essence Test for clearing the electric system. Then use your focus to target and activate the circuits connected with each symptom, one at a time. *It is vital that you keep your focus on one symptom at a time and that you don't let your mind wander to any of the other symptoms during the testing.* When you finish with the testing, you have taken care of all of the symptoms connected with the problem you are addressing and, once you've completed any needed dosage period, you've repaired all the wild wiring.

If you have a bunch of symptoms and you get tired or run out of time before testing all of them, just stop after testing as many symptoms as possible and pick it up again *within twenty-four hours.* When you resume the testing, you are opening a new Telegraph Test and will need to clear your electric system first with a Basic Essence Test. Then continue telegraph testing the remaining symptoms—and any new symptoms that may have popped up in the last twenty-four hours.

If you don't have the energy to face telegraph testing while you're sick, concentrate on doing just the Basic Essence Test. Don't bother testing for dosage (number of days and times per day). Instead, do the Basic Essence Test *every two to three waking hours* and take one drop of concentrate directly from the bottle for each Essence needed. Or put nine drops of each Essence concentrate in a glass with four ounces of water and sip it during the next two to three hours as part of your liquid intake. But be sure to do the Basic Essence Test every two to three hours. Your illness will be moving through its stages rapidly, and you will probably need different Essences to support each new stage. If you don't need Essences for one stage, that's great— but test again in two to three hours at the start of the next stage.

Making a BTT Checklist

In the beginning, recognizing all the symptoms that are part of a common illness or injury is a little harder to do than one might imagine. We tend to think in terms of the whole rather than the collection of the parts. Often we have no conscious awareness of the various symptoms that comprise an illness, issue or injury. To keep from sounding like hypochondriacs, we deal with such things as one unit. ("I have a cold.") So when first learning to put together a BTT checklist, we find it will take a bit of effort and focused attention to see, feel and separate the targeted issue into its symptoms.

1. Write down the symptoms you are aware of.

2. Then add the symptoms you noticed and felt were unimportant but are there anyway. They may be part of the problem and you don't realize it. If those symptoms have nothing to do with the targeted issue, they will not test for any needed Essences and you'll need to deal with them in a different Telegraph Test.

* The Perelandra Essence Telegraph Test Checklist is available for downloading free on our website.

3. THE PERELANDRA ESSENCE TELEGRAPH TEST CHECKLIST.* This is a chart that lists all the body's systems and what is included in each system. (It is not the same as the BTT checklist.) By PKTT testing this chart, you discover what areas and parts of your body are involved in your illness or injury. At the top of the chart describe your illness/injury in a few words. Then do a Basic Essence Test to clear your electric system for telegraph testing. Ask:

> Which systems and areas of my body are included in the [insert the name of your illness/injury] and need telegraph testing?

** For an example of the Essence Telegraph Test Checklist and how it's used, see p. 89.

Test the list and place a check beside anything that tests positive. Then add whatever tested positive and isn't already included to the BTT checklist.**

4. THE MAGICAL BTT CHECKLIST INGREDIENT. Here's where I add the magical ingredient for BTT checklists. Read aloud the list you've made, then ask the following:

> Is there a symptom or injury that is part of the [insert the name of the targeted problem] that I don't know about? (Test.)

If the result is negative, you have all of the symptoms/injuries written down on your BTT checklist and you are ready to telegraph test that list. However, if you get a positive response to the question, something else needs to be included on the BTT checklist and you're not picking up what it is. It's either a "hidden" injury or symptom that you can't see or feel or it's something that is beyond your current range of knowledge.

To fully address the targeted area, you need a complete BTT checklist. With your focus on this first mystery symptom/injury, state:

> I name this symptom/injury "Factor-X."

Write "Factor-X" on your BTT checklist. In order for you to get a positive response to your question ("Is there a symptom or injury that is part of the targeted problem that I don't know about?"), a mystery symptom/injury was activated. You assigned an identifying name to it when you stated, "I name this symptom/injury 'Factor-X.'"

Now "Factor-X" identifies the underlying circuits that are the electrical foundation of this mystery symptom/injury.

But don't stop here. You may have more than one mystery symptom/injury. Ask again:

> Is there another symptom or injury that is part of the targeted problem that I don't know about? (Test.)

If you get a positive response, state:

> I name this symptom/injury "Factor-Y."

Continue asking the question and assigning names (just keep assigning letters) until you get a negative to the question and all the mystery symptoms/injuries have been identified and included in your BTT checklist. Because of your willingness to work with the mystery symptoms/injuries, your telegraph testing will be exceptionally effective. Maybe someday you'll find out what those mystery symptoms really were, but for now what's important is balancing, stabilizing and repairing all the circuits connected with the primary issue you want to address.

5. ADD "FOCUS AIDS" to the symptoms/injuries on your BTT checklist. To telegraph test properly, you will need to hold a focus for each symptom/injury you have listed. For most symptoms/injuries all you'll need to do is read the wording you used on the BTT checklist and keep that in mind as you test. Or look at the injury from time to time during the test. For a mystery item, just keep "Factor-X" in mind during the test. However, some symptoms may be difficult to see or feel, or even imagine—such as lymphatic system issues. For each of these you will need a focus aid. Choose a visual symbol or code word that for you relates to the symptom/injury in some manner. Draw the symbol or write the code word next to that symptom/injury on your BTT checklist. Then "officially" link your symbol or code with the symptom/injury by stating out loud:

> I assign this [symbol/code] to [the name of the symptom/injury as described on the BTT checklist].

If it's a symbol, be sure to keep the symbol in your mind as you state this assignment sentence aloud and name the symptom it represents. If it's a code word, insert the word and the symptom/injury as it's written on your BTT checklist as you read the assignment sentence out loud.

When you are telegraph testing a symptom/injury with a code word or symbol, keep the word or symbol in mind as you do the testing *and* as you take the Essences. This [your name] _____   [date started] 2/20/11

BTT Checklist focus: dust mite allergy

Symptoms:

1. Runny nose
        2/20/11: Chives, Tomato, Blaze Imp., #1, V-2
                Dosage: 2 weeks/3 days (2/20 to 3/8), 1x daily: A.M.
        Clear 3/9/11 through 3/16: ✔✔✔✔✔✔ *

2. Watery eyes
        2/20/11: Sonia, V-2, Moon, Zucchini
                Dosage: 6 days (2/20 to 2/25), 3x daily: A.M., noon & P.M.
        Clear 2/26/11 through 3/5: ✔✔✔✔✔✔

3. Itchy throat
        2/20/11: Salvia, Zucchini, Mr. Lincoln, Peace, Eclipse
                Dosage: 1 week/2 days (2/20 to 2/28), 1x daily: P.M.
        3/1/11: Blaze, Maybelle Stearns, Mr. Lincoln, Sonia
                Dosage: 6 days (3/1 to 3/6), 1x daily: P.M.
        Clear 3/7/11 through 3/14: ✔✔✔✔✔✔

4. Cough
        2/20/11: B-2, V-1, F-1
                Dosage: 3 weeks/4 days (2/20 to 3/16), 2x daily: A.M., noon
        Clear 3/17/11 through 3/24: ✔✔✔✔✔✔

5. Immune System (symbol: ★)
        2/20/11: Blaze, Maybelle Stearns, Mr. Lincoln
                Dosage: 2 weeks/6 days (2/20 to 3/11), 1x daily: P.M.
        3/12/11: Nymphenburg, Zucchini, #4 & #7
                Dosage: 4 weeks/2 days (3/12 to 4/10), 1x daily: P.M.
        Clear 4/11/11 through 4/18: ✔✔✔✔✔✔

6. Factor-X
        2/20/11: Okra, Cucumber, Tomato
                Dosage: 3 weeks/1 day (2/20 to 3/13), 2x daily: A.M. & P.M.
        Clear 3/14/11 through 3/21: ✔✔✔✔✔✔

focuses your mind and activates the circuits on one thing (the symptom/injury) to the exclusion of all else. Keep the word or symbol in mind when you take the Essences so that the Essence patterns shift to the circuits connected with the symptom/injury. The focus on the symbol or word has set up all the needed pathways and connections for shifting the Essence patterns.

● ADD THE ORGANIZATION AID. Add a number in front of everything that is listed on the BTT checklist (ex.: 1. headache, 2. chills, 3. exhaustion). The numbers allow for easy reference when working with the Essence Record Chart and writing down all the dosage and follow-up information on separate sheets of paper. For example, all the dosage information for the headache will have "1" in front of it. CAUTION: You can include the number on the solution bottle label, but when taking a dose from that bottle you will need to state the symptom and not just its number.

Your BTT checklist is your "record" for each Telegraph Test that you do. The easiest way to keep a record of all the needed Essences is to use the Perelandra Essence Record Chart. Just attach this and any other pages that hold testing information to your BTT checklist to keep your "record file" complete. You'll be referring to the BTT checklist for any follow-up testing or if you need to refill any solution bottles.

● MULTIPLE INJURIES. When injured in more than one location on the body, treat the injury in each location independently. For example, if you've been in an accident, you may have an injury to your left arm, swelling in your right foot, bruising in your lower back, etc. You've had one accident resulting in a collection of injuries that need to be tested and treated independently as separate symptoms. On your BTT checklist, list the injuries and test each injury, one by one. If your left arm and lower back have the same injury—they're both bruised—don't try to combine them and test both of those areas at once. The circuits connected with the left arm bruise are different from the circuits connected with the lower back bruise. They are two separate pieces of the circuit puzzle and need to be treated separately.

Also, if you have more than one kind of injury in a single location (a cut, bruising and swelling on your left wrist), you need to telegraph test each of those injuries in that location, one injury at a time. Then focus on the injuries in the second location and test each injury one at a time.* I know this sounds like a lot of testing, but the first time you're brave enough to deal with multiple injuries this way and see how quickly your body recovers when all the electric circuits are repaired, you'll be both amazed and inspired—amazed at the speedy recovery and inspired to keep up the testing because you see the benefits. All that testing is worth it.

* On your BTT checklist, record each location that is injured and include all the different injuries present at each location.

79

HINT: Make it a point to test small accidents with just a couple of minor injuries. Even though you're working on a small scale, you'll still see the difference in how the body heals when all the circuits are repaired. You'll also get over your hesitations about working with multiple injuries in multiple locations. Should you have an accident with more extensive injuries, you'll know what to do and feel confident about doing all the testing.

If you have a bunch of injuries and you get tired or run out of time before telegraph testing them all, just stop after testing as many injuries as you can. Then pick up the testing again *within twenty-four hours.* When you resume testing, you are opening a new Telegraph Test and will need to clear your electric system first with a Basic Essence Test. Then continue telegraph testing the remaining injuries.

● A FOCUSING TRICK. If you are having difficulty holding your focus with a specific injury, just touch it or lightly poke it. Even allow yourself to make it hurt *a little.* By doing this, you are activating that injury's circuits and adding a sensory stimulus to your focus. For a short period of time (about fifteen minutes), your ability to hold the focus is much easier. The main thing to remember is that the touch must be enough to create some physical sensation. It can't be one of those feather-light, I-can't-feel-it touches. It's a fine cheap trick and similar to the one I told you to use when you're tired and need to pay attention to the testing: Say the steps out loud. Only now you are involving your sense of touch rather than your sense of hearing. To "deactivate" a touched spot in order to move on and test the next injury, just touch the next spot. You and your electric system will immediately shift focus. Trust me.

Telegraph Test for Focus

To get quality results when telegraph testing, you must maintain a good focus. But let's face it. Sometimes it's hard to hold a focus, even if our life depends on it. You've tried reading the steps out loud. You've done all kinds of poking. And your mind is still wandering aimlessly around the room. If solving this problem involves more than just getting a good night's sleep or you feel you never properly learned how to focus, you may need to telegraph test the circuits that support your focus! You could have some wild wiring in there, and the symptom you're experiencing is the inability to focus. At first blush, telegraph testing focus sounds impossible. If you can't focus, how are you going to hold a focus while testing your focus circuits? Here's what you do:

Telegraph Testing Steps for Focus

1. Set up a Telegraph Test by doing a Basic Essence Test first. Take any needed Essences one time. Do not test for dosage.

2. State:

> I want to test the circuits that are connected with and support my ability to focus. I need for these circuits to remain activated throughout the entire test, even if I am unable to properly hold the focus.

Based on what you've just stated, you have set the intent and purpose of this Telegraph Test. In short, you have defined the scope and parameters of the test up front and the targeted focus circuits will remain activated throughout the entire test.

3. Test the Essences. Take any needed Essences and test for dosage. Wait twenty to twenty-five minutes for your focus circuits to balance, stabilize and repair before doing any other Essence testing.

Test your focus circuits whenever needed. And remember to do any needed follow-up testing once a dosage period for focus ends.

BASIC TELEGRAPH TEST STEPS

SUPPLIES:

- the five sets of Perelandra Essences
- pen, paper and calendar
- option: a blank Perelandra Essence Record Chart
- a blank Perelandra Essence Telegraph Test Checklist
- a watch or clock with a second hand
- a clean spoon
- clean solution bottles (one bottle for each symptom on the BTT checklist)*
- brandy or distilled white vinegar preservative
- blank labels

NOTE: Let's go back to when you came home feeling lousy and did a Basic Essence Test. That's when you found out that you needed to do a Basic Telegraph Test for your lingering (stubborn?) headache. If you tested that you need to take the Essences in the original Basic Essence Test for

* To reuse solution bottles, wash the bottles and droppers in hot, soapy water *two times*, rinsing them well, and air dry on a clean paper towel. Do not touch the glass dropper with your fingers (or anything else). But it's okay if the glass dropper lightly touches the clean paper towel during the drying process. Always handle the dropper by the rubber bulb.

several days, continue taking them through that *full dosage period* and do all the follow-up testing. The Essences for the Basic Essence Test *are not superceded* by the Essences that test positive for the Basic Telegraph Test. Each group of Essences weaves and supports one another.

PREPARE FOR TESTING: Drink some water. Go to the bathroom, if needed. Find a quiet spot and sit comfortably. Place the boxes of Essences and the other supplies within easy reach.

1. State your intent:

> I want to set up for a Telegraph Test.

2. Clear your electric system: Do a Basic Essence Test (steps 2–5, pp. 54–55). Take any needed Essences. Do not test for dosage.

You do not need to test for dosage because this Basic Essence Test is clearing your electric system and preparing it for the Telegraph Test that you will be doing now.

If you test clear and you need no Essences, proceed with the telegraph testing. Not needing Essences for clearing the electric system but needing them when telegraph testing the symptoms is not unusual.

3. Make a BTT checklist of all the symptoms or injuries connected with the issue you are addressing. Include any symptoms or injuries that you are experiencing but may have eliminated from consideration because you feel they are not connected. Include the list of any mystery symptoms/injuries. Also, when dealing with an accident, separate the injuries according to their different locations. (NOTE: You may put the BTT checklist together prior to beginning a Basic Telegraph Test.)

4. Focus on the first symptom or injury on your BTT checklist and ask:

> What Essences are needed for the circuits connected with [insert symptom/injury]? (Test.)

Keep your focus on the symptom or injury while following the Basic Essence Test steps 2–5. Touch or poke the spot if you need help focusing on it.

5. Take the needed Essences for this first symptom/injury. Record the Essences alongside the symptom listed on the BTT checklist.

6. Test for dosage (Basic Essence Test, steps 6–10, pp. 60–62): Find out how many days and times per day you are to take the Essences for this symptom/injury.

If you are to take the Essences just one time, you don't need to do any further dosage testing and you can go on to BTT step 7.

If you are to take these Essences more than one time, complete the dosage testing now. On the BTT checklist next to the symptom, record the dosage information: the beginning and end date of the dosage and how many times per day you are to take it. Also include the times of day you are to take it (morning, afternoon, evening).

If you want to make a solution bottle, wait until after all the telegraph testing is complete and make all the needed solution bottles at one time.

7. Repeat Telegraph Test steps 4, 5 and 6 for every symptom or injury listed on the BTT checklist.

8. When you've finished testing every symptom/injury on your BTT checklist, complete the Telegraph Test for this issue by doing another Basic Essence Test for your full electric system. The focus for this test: Provide a final balancing and stabilizing for your system as a unit after doing all the circuit repair. *Do not check for dosage. These Essences are to be taken one time only.*

9. Make any needed solution bottles (Basic Essence Test: Solution Bottles, steps 1–3, p. 63). To avoid mistakes and confusion, label each bottle right after making a solution. Include the beginning and end date of the dosage and how many times a day you are to take it. Also include the times of day you are to take it (morning, afternoon, evening).

Pat yourself on the back. Put your Essences away and store your BTT checklist. (Consider getting a binder notebook for your BTT checklists and charts.) Take a well-deserved coffee/tea/beer/chocolate break. Now you're free to get on with the rest of your day.

Dosage and Follow-up Testing

● REMEMBER TO TAKE THE NEEDED DOSAGES (one dropperful per dose) for the full period of time prescribed. It'll help you to remember if you set your solution bottles in an obvious place such as in the kitchen or bathroom. Also, record the end date for each solution on a calendar or computer so that you'll know when to do the follow-up testing. If you run out of a solution before the end of the dosage period, just refill the bottle.

● ADMINISTERING DOSAGES. Each time you take an Essence solution during the prescribed dosage period, prepare yourself first by activating the circuits the solution is addressing. To do this, read what symptom/injury is written on the label and keep it in your mind while taking a dropperful (ten to twelve drops) of the Essence solution. That will automatically activate the targeted area and set up the connections for shifting the Essence patterns to those circuits.

> IMPORTANT: Once you make a solution bottle, the Essence drops have been diluted and are no longer concentrated. For each dosage, you will now need to take ten to twelve drops (one dropperful).

● COMPLETING A DOSAGE PERIOD. Once you complete a dosage period for a symptom/injury, do a new Basic Telegraph Test *within forty-eight hours* as a follow up to find out if any additional Essences might be needed. Continue doing follow-up testing at the end of each dosage period until you test clear.*

* This includes symptoms that require Essences one time only. The follow-up test is done within forty-eight hours after taking that one required dose.

● AFTER TESTING CLEAR, do a new Basic Telegraph Test for that symptom/injury for the next seven days. When you test clear for seven days straight, you know that you have completed the series of follow-up testing for this particular symptom and no additional Essences are needed at that time. Cross the symptom/injury off your BTT checklist. If you tested for Essences on any one of the seven days, assume the follow-up series is not complete and continue with the follow-up testing as usual until the symptom tests clear for seven days straight.

● RETURNING AND NEW SYMPTOMS OR INJURIES. Should a symptom or injury that tested clear return, just list it again on the BTT checklist and do a new Basic Telegraph Test for this one symptom, starting with step 1 and testing through step 8. Move it completely through its dosage periods and follow-up testing. Continue this until it tests clear again for seven days straight.

If the returning symptom/injury exhibits any changes or anomalies that differentiate it from the old one in any way, consider this a new symptom/injury that needs to be added to the BTT checklist. Do a new Telegraph Test for that one symptom and move it completely through all dosage periods and follow-up testing. Continue this until it tests clear for seven days straight. If you used a code or symbol on the BTT checklist for the old symptom/injury, do not use that same one for the new symptom/injury. It will need its own code or symbol that you "officially" assign (step 5, p.77).

A symptom that has returned or a new symptom that suddenly pops up while moving a health issue through a telegraph testing regimen means that (1) the circuits that tested clear for a symptom were unable to maintain their balance and now need to be addressed again, and (2) while moving through the healing process for this issue, new circuits that are related to the issue were strained and need attention.

THE HEALTH OVERHAUL SUGGESTION

I've presented the Basic Essence Test and the Basic Telegraph Test primarily from the perspective of an in-the-moment health response. But after working with these processes a few times, you'll realize that working with the Perelandra Essences properly puts a powerful health tool in your hands. (Pardon the pun.) You can expand your Essence work beyond the in-the-moment response to address current health issues that you've been dealing with for awhile: high blood pressure, muscle weakness, back pain, allergies, high cholesterol, weight issues, PMS, a difficult menopause, all the things for which you are taking medication and those things your doctor is constantly warning you about. Take a moment to think about the areas in your health that need to be shored up and strengthened. Make a list. Then start with just one thing, one issue. Set up a Telegraph Test with a good BTT checklist and move it through all the dosage periods and follow-up testing to the end when you test clear. Then take the next thing on the list and do the same. I suggest working with your Health Overhaul list *one issue at a time* so you won't overwhelm yourself. It may take you two or three years to get through the list. But by the time you finish, you will have turned around a whole level of health from weak, questionable and problematic to strong and balanced. I think if you look at it this way, two or three years seems like a reasonable period of time.

85

There may be some health issues on the Health Overhaul list that actually qualify as "chronic" and would be better dealt with by setting up a Telegraph Test for chronic illness (see chapter 9). If you have any questions about which Telegraph Test to use for a specific issue, just PKTT the following question:

Which Telegraph Test do I work with for [insert name of issue]?
The Basic Telegraph Test? (Test.)
The Telegraph Test for chronic illness? (Test)

If you test negative for both options, ask if the issue is best addressed by the Basic Essence Test. In this case, the health problem is the result of a situation in your electric system as a unit and not with individual circuits.

If you test that you should work with the Telegraph Test for Chronic Illness, yet you don't feel the issue you want to address merits the "chronic illness" label, it most likely means that this particular issue would best be addressed with the chronic-illness setup that includes a special focus on the electric system as a unit. Don't get nervous. In this case it's the setup that is important when successfully addressing that issue, and it is not implying that you have some serious chronic illness.

THE DAILY SYMPTOM SWEEP

This process is an amazing little gem. In order to understand the help and relief it provides, you're just going to have to try it. But I don't think the Daily Symptom Sweep is for beginners. It's designed to be an effortless, quick, daily check and, to work with it well, you need to be proficient with PKTT and telegraph testing. The key phrase here is "effortless and quick."

Here's how it works. Each evening sit down with your Essences and think about how you felt throughout the day. Did you have any muscle pain/strain, stiffness, eye strain, ringing ears, more-than-normal sneezing or coughing, more-than-normal impatience or crankiness, nervous ticks, worry, exhaustion...? These are the things you experience that are small and usually ignored. Make a list.

● Do a Basic Essence Test to clear your electric system. Take any needed Essences *one time only.* No dosage test needed.

● Then do a Basic Telegraph Test for each symptom. Take the needed Essences before moving on to the next symptom. Don't test for dosage. The Essences are to be taken *one time only.*

● End with another Basic Essence Test to stabilize and balance your electric system as a unit after all the circuit repair. Take these Essences *one time only.*

● The next evening do it again. Think about how you felt that day and include any lingering symptoms from the previous day. Make another list.

● If you have a symptom or issue that lingers for more than four days in a row, assume that it needs a Basic Telegraph Test including dosage and follow-up testing. Continue addressing it in the Daily Symptom Sweep until you have time to switch over and do a complete Basic Telegraph Test for this symptom. Once you begin the Basic Telegraph Test, discontinue including this symptom in the Daily Symptom Sweep.

It's eye-opening how much our sense of general health and well-being is dominated by the accumulation of "paper cuts" we gather each day. The Daily Symptom Sweep stops these paper cuts from collecting and piling on top of one another day after day. At some point they're going to cause us to say "ouch." That's when we have full-blown symptoms requiring Basic Telegraph Tests that include dosage and follow-up testing. By paying attention to and addressing these little cuts each day, we can monitor the state of our electric system with precision (the "paper cuts" tell us what circuits need attention) and maintain a high quality of electrical functioning throughout all the circuits. I think you're going to be surprised at how much your quality of life improves by doing the Daily Symptom Sweep.

The BTT Checklist & the Starting Gate Tests

Date: 6/1/11

for myself

Focus: Urinary tract infection

Symptoms:

1. Burning sensation when urinating
    Nymphenburg, Celery, Tomato
    1 week/4 days, 1x daily: P.M.
    6/1 to 6/11

2. Urine appears cloudy
    Tomato, F-1
    6 days, 2x daily: A.M. & P.M.
    6/1 to 6/6

3. Passing frequent, small amounts of urine
    Blaze Imp., Maybelle Stearns, Sobopla
    2 weeks/1 day, 1x daily: A.M.
    6/1 to 6/15

4. Lower abdomen discomfort
    #3, #5, #6, Chives
    1 week/5 days, 2x daily: A.M. & P.M.
    6/1 to 6/12

Essence Telegraph Test Checklist:

5. Lymphatic System as a unit ✣
    V-2, B-1, B-2, Tomato
    3 weeks/4 days, 1x daily: P.M.
    6/1 to 6/25

6. Urinary System as a unit ★
    Blaze, Sonia, Tiffany, Peace, Eclipse
    2 weeks/6 days, 2x daily: A.M. & P.M.
    6/1 to 6/20

7. Kidneys, Abdominal Cavity Vessels ✢
    Gruss, Okra, Zinnia, Sobopla
    3 weeks, 1x daily: A.M.
    6/1 to 6/21

8. Factor-X ☺
    Nymphenburg, Celery, Tomato, Okra,
    Summer Squash, Yellow Yarrow, B-1,
    B-2, V-1, V-2, #2, #3, #6, #7,
    Mr. Lincoln, Betty Prior, Sonia,
    Chicago Peace
    6 weeks/4 days, 2x daily: A.M. & P.M.
    6/1 to 7/16

NOTE: The Essence names listed in all the examples throughout the book are from the five sets of Perelandra Essences. They were chosen randomly and do not reflect actual testing results.

Perelandra Essence Telegraph Test Checklist

Name: _for myself_

Intent: _Urinary tract infection_

Date: 6/1/11

First, do a Basic Essence Test to clear yourself. Then focus on the intent and ask, "Which electric circuits need telegraph testing for [read intent]?" Test the list.

___ ___ Cell division/mitosis
___ ___ Tissues: Epithelium
___ ___ Tissues: Connective Tissue
___ ___ Tissues: Muscle Tissue
___ ___ **SKELETAL SYSTEM: unit**
___ ___ Bones of the Skull
___ ___ Vertebrae and Vertebral Column
___ ___ Thorax
___ ___ Upper Limbs: Pectoral Girdles and Arms
    ___ ___ Forearms
    ___ ___ Bones of the Hands
___ ___ Lower Limbs: Pelvis and Pelvic Girdle
    ___ ___ Thighs and Legs
    ___ ___ Bones of the Feet
___ ___ Joints: unit
___ ___ **MUSCULAR SYSTEM: unit**
___ ___ Head (including face and mastication)
___ ___ Neck
___ ___ Torso
___ ___ Upper Limbs (shoulders, forearms, wrists, hands, fingers)
___ ___ Lower Limbs (gluteal region, thighs, legs, feet)
___ ___ **CARDIOVASCULAR SYSTEM: unit**
___ ___ Blood and Blood Cells
___ ___ Mediastinum
___ ___ Heart
___ ✔ **LYMPHATIC SYSTEM: unit**
___ ___ Thoracic Duct and Tributaries
___ ___ Lymph Nodes
___ ___ **RESPIRATORY SYSTEM: unit**
___ ___ External Nose, Nasal Septum, Nasal Cavity
___ ___ Paranasal Air Sinuses
___ ___ Pharynx and Larynx
___ ___ Lungs and Bronchial Tree
___ ___ Mediastinal Surface of the Lungs
___ ___ **INTEGUMENTARY SYSTEM: unit**
___ ___ Skin
___ ___ Sensory Receptors of the Skin
___ ___ **DIGESTIVE SYSTEM: unit**
___ ___ Mouth and Tongue
___ ___ Teeth
___ ___ Pharynx and Esophagus
___ ___ Peritoneum
___ ___ Stomach
___ ___ Small Intestine: Duodenum, Jejunum, Ileum
___ ___ Large Intestine
___ ___ Liver
___ ___ Gall Bladder, Pancreas, Spleen

___ ✔ **URINARY SYSTEM: unit**
___ ✔ Kidneys, Abdominal Cavity Vessels
___ ___ Kidney, Coronal Section
___ ___ Uriniferous Tubule
___ ___ **REPRODUCTIVE SYSTEM**
___ ___ Male: unit
    ___ ___ Testes
    ___ ___ Urethra, Penis, Urogenital Region
___ ___ Female: unit
    ___ ___ Ovaries
    ___ ___ Uterus and Uterine Tubes
___ ___ Breasts
___ ___ Embryo/Fetus, Fetal/Maternal Coverings, Placenta
___ ___ **ENDOCRINE SYSTEM: unit**
___ ___ Pituitary Gland and Hypothalamus
___ ___ Thyroid Gland and Parathyroid Glands
___ ___ Adrenal Glands
___ ___ Gastrointestinal Hormones and Pancreatic Secretions
___ ___ **NERVOUS SYSTEM: unit**
___ ___ Neurons, Nerve Endings
___ ___ Reflex Arcs
___ ___ Central Nervous System: unit
___ ___ Ventricles
___ ___ Meninges of the Brain and Spinal Cord
___ ___ CSF (cerebrospinal fluid)
___ ___ Cerebral Hemispheres
___ ___ Diencephalon
___ ___ Brainstem/Cerebellum
___ ___ Spinal Cord
___ ___ Ascending (Sensory) Tracts
___ ___ Descending (Motor) Tracts
___ ___ Spinal Nerves
___ ___ Nerves to Upper Limbs
___ ___ Nerves to Lower Limbs
___ ___ Dermatomes
___ ___ Cranial Nerves
___ ___ Autonomic Nervous System (ANS)
___ ___ Visual System
___ ___ Auditory System
___ ___ Taste and Olfaction
___ ___ **IMMUNE SYSTEM: unit**
___ ___ Thymus and Red Marrow
___ ___ Spleen
___ ___ Lymph Node
___ ___ Mucosal Associated Lymphoid Tissue (M.A.L.T.)
___ ✔ **FACTOR-X**
___ ___ Factor-Y
___ ___ Factor-Z

Follow-up Testing: Urinary Tract Infection

1. Burning sensation when urinating
   Comfrey, Chives
   1 week, 1x daily: P.M.
   6/12 to 6/18

   B-2, Comfrey, Chicago Peace, #6
   4 days, 1x daily: P.M.
   6/19 to 6/22

   Ambassador, Broccoli, Royal Highness
   6 days, 2x daily: A.M. & P.M.
   6/23 to 6/28

   Cauliflower, #7
   2 weeks/2 days, 2x daily: A.M. & P.M.
   6/29 to 7/14

   Tomato
   1 week/4 days, 1x daily: P.M.
   7/15 to 7/25

   Clear 7/26 ✔✔✔✔✔✔

2. Urine appears cloudy
   Royal Highness
   2 weeks, 1x daily: A.M.
   6/7 to 6/20

   Clear 6/21 ✔✔✔✔✔✔

3. Passing frequent, small amounts
   of urine
   Nasturtium, #7
   2 weeks, 2x daily: A.M. & P.M.
   6/16 to 6/29

   F-1, F-2, Cauliflower
   6 days, 1x daily: A.M.
   6/30 to 7/5

   Nasturtium, Maybelle S., Tomato
   1 week/1 day, 1x daily: A.M.
   7/6 to 7/13

   Clear 7/14 ✔✔✔✔✔✔

4. Lower abdomen discomfort
   F-1
   5 days, 2x daily: A.M. & P.M.
   6/13 to 6/17

   Nasturtium
   3 days, 1x daily: P.M.
   6/18 to 6/20

   Clear 6/21 ✔✔✔✔✔✔

Follow-up Testing: Urinary Tract Infection

5. Lymphatic System as a unit ✠
   Tomato, #3, Cucumber, Zinnia
   3 weeks, 1x daily: P.M.
   6/26 to 7/16

   Sobopla
   4 days, 3x daily: A.M., noon & P.M.
   7/17 to 7/20

   #6
   2 weeks, 1x daily: A.M.
   7/21 to 8/3

   Clear 8/4 ✓✓✓✓✓✓

6. Urinary System as a unit ★
   Eclipse
   3 weeks, 2x daily: A.M. & P.M.
   6/21 to 7/11

   #6, Sobopla
   6 days, 2x daily: A.M. & P.M.
   7/12 to 7/17

   #4, Yellow Yarrow, Oregold
   1 week, 1x daily: A.M.
   7/18 to 7/24

   Clear 7/25 ✓✓✓✓✓✓

7. Kidneys, Abdominal Cavity Vessels ✠
   White Lightnin', #2
   4 weeks/3 days, 1x daily: A.M.
   6/22 to 7/22

   Blaze
   6 days, 2x daily: A.M. & P.M.
   7/23 to 7/28

   Maybelle S., #1, #4, #2
   6 days, 1x daily: P.M.
   7/29 to 8/3

   Clear 8/4 ✓✓✓ (damn)

   Nymphenburg, Yellow Yarrow
   4 days, 3x daily: A.M., noon & P.M.
   8/7 to 8/10

   Clear 8/11 ✓✓✓✓✓✓

8. Factor-X ☹
   Salvia, Chives, Ambassador,
   Nymphenburg, Sobopla, #3
   4 days, 2x daily: A.M. & P.M.
   7/17 to 7/20

   Clear 7/21 ✓✓✓✓✓✓

Chapter 8

Trauma and ETS Plus
(Perelandra Emergency Trauma Solution)

Trauma within the human system occurs on all four PEMS levels when we experience a sudden and shocking situation or event. The key words with trauma are "sudden and shocking." Let's say a man has a car accident and is injured. He has several broken bones, cuts that will require a lot of stitches, torn muscles and severe bruising. This is the list of what has happened to his body as a result of the accident. It's not the trauma. The trauma is the immediate reaction on his PEMS levels from having just experienced the shock of an accident and from the sudden assault on his body and his life. The trauma comes from the sounds and sights of the accident as it's happening. It comes from seeing glass fly all over the place. It comes from seeing blood. It comes from hearing people shout as they run toward him to help. It comes from the sudden awareness that he is in trouble and could possibly die. And it comes from knowing that his life, which was scheduled and orderly just two seconds ago, is now turned upside down and in total chaos. These reactions are part of what constitutes trauma. They are not the injuries themselves. Although directly related to the cause of the trauma, the injuries are the *result* of the accident, not the immediate *reaction* to the accident.

Our unfortunate fellow and his body are now dealing with two separate and distinct situations: (1) His immediate reaction to the accident that's triggering the trauma, and (2) the injuries that are the result of the accident. His electric system is also dealing with two separate and distinct situations: (1) The circuits connected with each of the injury areas have suffered considerable damage and are in need of repair. (2) The damaged circuits related to the trauma he experienced at the onset of the accident need repair *before* the body can activate the full healing process to deal with the injuries.

Reacting to a sudden and shocking event is normal. We each have a PEMS unit of circuits that fully supports this activity. When the trauma response circuits hold their balance, we react well to a shock and are still able to think, ask and answer questions coherently, and make good decisions. When these circuits are balanced and functioning well, they automatically activate at the onset of a traumatic event and deactivate once the body has stabilized and the trauma period has passed. At that point, the body's electric system is able to fully activate the circuits that support the healing process for each injury. The trauma circuits and the healing process circuits are two different units of circuitry within our electric system that support two different operations in our body. When dealing with a traumatic event and its damaging impact on the human system, the body responds best when these two units of circuits remain separate.

But just like any other circuits, the trauma circuits may need balancing, stabilizing and repair following the impact of a sudden and severe situation. When those circuits are damaged, we are seen as someone who is suffering from shock or said to be in a state of shock. The body and mind are fully focused on the trauma and a person's actions and reactions reflect the damage in those circuits: He is listless, dazed, his face is drained of color, he's unable to speak clearly or answer questions, he slides in and out of consciousness...

That first twenty minutes is a critical window when dealing with trauma. During this time, the trauma symptoms and the injury symptoms remain separate electrically, making the trauma circuits easier to isolate and repair. However, when damaged trauma circuits aren't addressed in the first twenty minutes, they do not deactivate. Instead they begin to overlay, connect to and weave with the damaged circuits connected to the area that has been injured, thus complicating the injury. It's not a "clean" injury any more. Now it's an injury that carries with it the damaged trauma circuits and its symptoms. This impedes the normal healing process, and it is more difficult for the body to recover. Instead of dealing with two separate and distinct situations, each with its own set of circuits, we are now dealing with one larger and more complex situation made up of the damaged circuits connected with the trauma response and damaged circuits that are in the body area that has been injured. A more extensive healing process and medical approach are now needed and there is a greater chance for complications to occur.

So what I'm suggesting (in a not too subtle way) is that it's important to take ETS Plus, the Perelandra solution that was developed to repair damaged trauma circuits, and address trauma's symptoms within the first twenty minutes. At first blush, this seems insane even to consider. For example, our unfortunate accident victim is sitting in his wrecked car reeling from the impact of the accident and feeling a lot of pain from the injuries. At the very least it's rude to tell him to pull himself together and find the Essence bottles that are now rolling around the car floor just so he can do an Essence test. That's not going to work. This is where the Perelandra Emergency Trauma Solution (ETS Plus) comes in. It is just one bottle with a pre-mixed solution that requires no testing, and it was specifically developed to balance, stabilize and repair trauma circuits. He doesn't have to dink around with testing fifty-one Essence bottles. He only needs to reach in his pocket or that special spot in the car where he's stored his ETS Plus bottle for just such an emergency, unscrew the cap and take one dropperful of the ETS solution. He's going to feel the stabilizing effects immediately. While waiting for the emergency response team, he'll take two or three more doses of ETS Plus approximately five minutes apart. He has now spent that critical twenty minutes stabilizing himself and repairing the damaged trauma circuits. This will prevent those damaged circuits from linking with and complicating the injury circuits.

BASIC ETS PLUS DOSAGE. Within the first twenty minutes of experiencing a trauma, take three to four doses (one dropperful or ten to twelve drops each dose), waiting five minutes between each dose.

I know you're still thinking that what I'm suggesting for a trauma victim is crazy. And if I didn't have years of stories from people using ETS Plus right after an accident or other shocking event, I would have agreed with you. But here's the deal. Included in the PEMS circuits for emergency reaction are the circuits that support the human drive to do whatever he can to help himself in an emergency. It's all part of our reactions when suddenly faced with a crisis. We call it names like "the survival instinct" and "the fight or flight instinct." When we're not actually in trouble, we grossly undersell our ability to act when faced with a crisis. We tend not to understand just how much we are capable of at these times. Think little, ninety-pound grandmothers lifting the family SUV off their grandson's legs with no help. Let me give you some examples of what I mean.

> A woman told me that after being put into an ambulance after a car accident, she realized she was clutching her bottle of ETS Plus. She did not know how she got it out of the glove compartment, but there the bottle was in her hand so she began taking the oral doses in the ambulance. By the time she got to the hospital, she was alert, comfortable, and able to answer questions and make clear decisions.

Another woman reported that she was mowing the lawn and cut a finger completely off when she accidentally put her hand near the blade. She remembered sitting down on the lawn in shock. Then she got up, went into the house and got her ETS Plus. She took one dose and went back outside to pick up her finger and wrap it in a paper towel. She took the other three doses while driving herself to the hospital. She said she remained alert and conscious the whole time, and was able to present her finger to the doctors for reattachment. She was told she would probably never feel anything in that finger and that her range of movement would be very limited. She moved through the recuperation period testing the Essences for the finger. In about six months, most of the feeling had returned and she was now able to play the piano again. (Honest. This isn't a joke. She really played piano.)

Here's the rest of why it's important to take ETS Plus. *The body must balance, stabilize and repair the trauma circuits before it can address any injuries.* The healing process cannot adequately begin until those trauma circuits are balanced, and the body "knows" this. When we're talking about the body's healing process, the natural sequence of the electric system is to fully focus on the trauma circuits first. As long as the trauma circuits are in need of repair, the body is unable to draw crucial white blood cells into the areas surrounding the injuries. The healing process is dramatically slowed down, even delayed, and auxiliary conditions connected to the injuries continue to develop. For example, there's more swelling, continued bleeding and deeper bruising. When we take ETS Plus, we repair those circuits and prevent the complications caused by trauma. The healing process for the injuries can begin and the injuries can be addressed right away.

We don't realize how much damaged trauma circuits interfere with the healing process until we repair them within that early twenty-minute window and experience the dramatic differences in the body's natural healing response. Remove the trauma complications and the healing process can commence unfettered. An uncompromised healing process is truly a proverbial sight to behold.

> I use ETS Plus for any ouch situation and it seems to start healing immediately, such as when I burn myself or cut a finger. I take the dropperful of ETS Plus and stick my finger under cold water if I've burned myself. When I remove the finger, there is no sign of a burn. It heals very quickly in a day

or two. I always keep ETS Plus within reach. After falling and breaking my wrist I took it on the way to the hospital, asking the ambulance person to hold the bottle as I used the dropper with my one good hand. I also used a homeopathic solution for healing. After three weeks, I was at the doctor's office. Two X-ray technicians were walking by with the X-rays, and since I was the only one in the waiting room I knew they were talking about my X-rays. I heard one insist, "It can't happen, a bone healing this fast." The doctor confirmed he couldn't understand how I could have healed so fast, but he was going to keep me in the cast for three more weeks anyway!...

— F.H., Morris, NY

QUICK THINKING, QUICK HEALING

Earlier this year, in the dark of winter, on my way to feed the horses, I stepped off the middle step and fell into space. It was a spectacular fall onto concrete. I skidded across the floor and ended up with my lips smashed against the old coffee can I carry the feed in and with my head against the dog door. I was terrified that I had truly injured myself this time. I picked myself up and immediately went inside.

I shakily grabbed the ETS Plus... and took stock of my injuries. My knee was throbbing and beginning to swell. My ribs hurt where my elbow had smashed into them. My neck and back muscles were already beginning to tighten up. My thumb and wrist were scraped, purple and already swelling. And my upper lip was ballooning up.

I was so scared I felt like crying. I knew I was going to be sore and stiff enough that it would be almost impossible to care for the horses in the bad weather. (I needed to carry five-gallon buckets of water up the hill for them twice a day.) I worried that I would miss work, as well. What happened was astonishing. Almost immediately upon taking the ETS Plus, the bruised places stopped swelling and actually began clearing up. I became calm. My lip, which I fully expected to balloon up terribly, stopped swelling. Twenty-four hours later there was only a thin blue bruise and a hard lump under the skin—nothing like what you would have expected a smashed lip to look like. There was a bruise on my knee cap, only about the size of a quarter or so. And that very morning, I was able to care for the horses and go to work as if nothing happened!

I had stepped off into space a foot and a half above the concrete floor with no warning, hitting the floor with full force. I should have been soaking in a hot tub, lying around with hot and cold packs on my neck, back, knee and lip for at least a couple of days, maybe longer. I am 54 years old, overweight—not in great physical shape—and I realize not so smart. At least now I turn the lights on if it is still dark when I leave for the barn!

— J.H., Paxico, KS

I stated that the key words for trauma are "sudden and shocking." But the wild card with ETS Plus is an individual's definition of trauma. In my years of working with ETS Plus and watching how others successfully use it, I've come to the conclusion that we underestimate what constitutes trauma. Added to this is the human element when trying to define trauma. It is literally a matter of personal opinion. It's easy for us to recognize that someone in a bad car accident, falling out a window, or getting hit by a bus has experienced a sudden and shocking event. But "sudden and shocking" covers a wide range of situations. At one end of the spectrum there's the person who has been smashed by a bus and at the other end of the spectrum we include all those times we feel a slight kick in the gut or wince or quietly gasp. Plus something can be traumatic for one person and not traumatic at all for another. Some people can respond well to some crises without suffering damage to their trauma circuits, and others have blown circuits flying around all over the place. Some people just know how to navigate through trauma. Still others have developed none of these skills. I've decided the best way to use ETS Plus is to take it for any incident or event, large or small, and let the body's circuits sort it out. ETS Plus contains 153 electrical patterns that are combined to specifically address the full range of trauma-circuit damage. If circuits need repair, they've got the ETS Plus to do it with. If they are fine, there's no foul and no harm.

WHEN TO TAKE ETS PLUS

*Trauma and
ETS Plus*

● ACCIDENTS AND ATTACKS (serious and small). Cuts, burns (including tongue burns from hot food or beverages), sprains, falls, bites, sports injuries, spinal cord injuries, car accidents and near accidents, heart attacks, strokes, seizures, asthma or allergy attacks, insect stings, equipment/tool accidents, severed limbs/fingers, broken bones, sexual assault . . .

● ILLNESS. Food poisoning, radiation sickness, reaction from medication, sudden appearance of a rash, an allergic reaction from an insect sting, allergies (food and others), sudden craving, sudden nausea/pain/exhaustion, heat stroke or heat exhaustion, feeling faint/light-headed/dizzy . . .

● SITUATIONS. After hospital visits and/or visits to a sick friend resulting in exposure to disease-causing viruses, fungi and bacteria; exposure to industrial and home chemicals, cleaners, insecticides, herbicides, fertilizers and pesticides; exposure to high levels of air or water pollution; right after taking serious or strong medications (whether you have had a reaction or not); after receiving difficult, scary or invasive medical treatments, either in a physician's office or in the hospital, including vaccinations or shots, radiation and chemotherapy treatments, receiving stitches; dental appointments; after getting a sunburn; after each counseling/therapeutic session; after physical therapy sessions; during and immediately after a PTSD attack; when experiencing fears or phobias; after a difficult family visit or discussion/argument; grief; the anniversary of a personal crisis or the death of a loved one . . . If you are a parent, you will want to have ETS Plus available for your child for the countless accidents and illnesses he/she goes through, as well as for yourself for getting through the trauma of dealing with your child's accidents and illnesses.

● SHOCKING PERSONAL, LOCAL AND GLOBAL NEWS. You've just heard someone you know has died or been killed, another terrorist attack has occurred, war is breaking out, people (especially children) are suffering from famine and starving to death, a natural disaster has destroyed everything in its path and killed many, a nuclear reactor is damaged and could result in a meltdown . . . You've just been fired, failed a test, received bad news about a family member or friend, received a call from a bill collector or the bank, been told you have a serious illness or disease, been told your spouse wants a divorce, your car has been stolen, you've been robbed, you've just been told you've been exposed to something toxic . . .

99

TRAUMAS
WITHIN TRAUMAS.
Take the basic ETS Plus
dosage within the first twenty
minutes of each new trauma.

● TRAUMAS WITHIN TRAUMAS. Example: You had an accident or illness for which you took your ETS Plus during the first twenty minutes. The ETS Plus stabilized you well. And now it's a day later or weeks later and you are recuperating from that injury or illness. You wake up one morning and realize that you have taken a step backward in your recuperation process and are feeling ill or pain. Or you suddenly feel awful during the day. Assume you have experienced another trauma that is impacting your healing process and take ETS Plus again three or four times within the first twenty minutes of experiencing the new discomfort.

ANOTHER EXAMPLE: We have the same scenario as described above. Only this time you are not near your ETS Plus bottle for hours. If you still experience the new discomfort once you have access to ETS Plus again, consider that your first twenty minutes of the trauma within a trauma begins at that point and take ETS Plus three or four times within the next twenty minutes.

> *Even though it was six hours after the initial injury, once I took the ETS Plus, the pain, which had continued to be pretty strong, almost immediately went away. Not only that, I was able to let go of my exaggerated fears (Oh no, what if I broke my toe? Should I go to the ER?) and move into a very positive mental/emotional space where I could at last begin to clearly visualize a positive outcome and very tangibly feel my own powerful healing energies "come online" and begin moving throughout my body.*

> —K.G., Bend, OR

DAILY DOSES
OF ETS PLUS.
Take three or more doses
throughout the day,
including one dose
at bedtime.

● DAILY DOSES OF ETS PLUS. If your workplace or home are regularly exposed to chemicals, biological agents, cleaners, insecticides, herbicides, fertilizers, pesticides or radiation, take three or more doses of ETS Plus (ten to twelve drops) throughout the day, including one dose in the evening before bedtime. You would also take these daily doses any day(s) your area has high levels of air pollution or if you are exposed to water pollution on a regular basis. And if you work in a "sick building," you will also benefit from taking ETS Plus three or more times a day, including at bedtime. Should you experience stress or unusual difficulty in your job or home situation (e.g., fears and concerns about a member of the military who is deployed in a war zone, a family member is an alcoholic or is taking drugs, or you are taking care of a chronically ill or elderly person...), your health and well-being will benefit from several doses of ETS Plus throughout your day, including one dose at bedtime. People who work in high-intensity jobs such as EMT response, trauma care, hospital

emergency rooms, police, firefighters, 911 operators, suicide hot line operators…
These kinds of jobs have trauma built into them.

● EXTENDED TRAUMA TIME FRAMES. Sometimes a "sudden and shocking" event is a trigger for something that lasts for more than a few minutes. Moving through the fallout from a trauma can require that we address a non-stop series of related traumas. For example, the period of time it takes to deal with the details and rebuild *after* you've lost your home to fire, foreclosure or flood; the personal and legal process one goes through *after* being told by your spouse he or she wants a divorce; the scary two weeks you spend in the hospital *after* a serious accident… These situations provide ongoing traumas that seem like they'll never end. When we find ourselves in an Extended Trauma Time Frame, we're not just taking ETS Plus the first twenty minutes. We did that when we experienced the trauma trigger—the very first sudden and shocking event. For Extended Trauma Time Frames we need to take ETS Plus differently—three to five doses daily, including one dose at bedtime. Continue taking ETS Plus daily until you feel your changed or new life has settled in for you. If you've miscalculated and you realize you're not out of the Extended Trauma Time Frame yet, just go back to the three to five daily doses of ETS Plus. Your goal for taking the daily doses is to keep the constant daily barrage of challenges from crippling your ability to make the right decisions and do the right things for yourself and your family.

● EMERGENCY FIRST RESPONSE FOR OTHERS. I generally carry a bottle of ETS Plus with me. I never know when I'm going to do something to myself. I'm pretty creative with my own klutziness. But I also don't know when someone I'm with or who is nearby is going to have an accident or suddenly become ill. So I carry the bottle as an emergency first response, as well. Over the years I've had several opportunities to offer it to people in trouble. Each time they've let me administer the doses to them. Each time the ETS Plus clearly helped them. And each time they were grateful for the help.

> I was on a hike when a man behind me started screaming that we had to get to the road fast because he couldn't breathe well and his chest was hurting. Someone said he was a diabetic and needed sugar. I looked back at the white sweating face and had another opinion. I fell back to walk next to him and ask if he'd take this emergency stuff I had. He said he was hurting so bad he'd take anything to feel better. I warned him it tasted like vinegar but wouldn't have any chemical effect. I administered the first dropperful to him and five minutes later asked him to take the second, which he did.

Trauma and ETS Plus

EXTENDED TRAUMA TIME FRAMES.
Take three to five doses of ETS Plus daily, including one dose at bedtime.

EMERGENCY FIRST RESPONSE FOR OTHERS.
First, take one dose of ETS Plus for yourself.

Then administer the basic ETS Plus dosage within the first twenty minutes upon your arrival.

101

After that when I tried to give him the third, he said he thought he was okay. His color had returned and he had stopped sweating. I suggested, but didn't push the third and fourth dosage. We finally got to the road where others had called ahead for the ambulance. It was later confirmed that he had had a heart attack.

Two weeks later, the man was in the parking lot where we gather for our hike. When he saw me, he walked over and said, "It was you who gave me that stuff, wasn't it?" I smiled and said "yes," and he smiled. It made me feel very special to have been able to help him with the ETS Plus. That week he wasn't hiking—he just wanted to see the group, and I feel he wanted to acknowledge to me that he and I knew what had stopped the heart attack. I tell people about ETS Plus and have given many bottles away. Sometimes someone will tell me they took it and it seemed to help. I know it does but it sounds strange to others, so now I wait until I see the right opportunity to pass the message.

— F.H., Morris, NY

TRAUMA CARE, ETC. Administer the basic ETS Plus dosage within the first twenty minutes upon your arrival.

● TRAUMA CARE / EMERGENCY ROOM RESPONSE / EMT RESPONSE / BATTLEFIELD TRIAGE. I urge those of you who work in these kinds of emergency areas to administer ETS Plus to patients in these extreme situations. I understand it is tricky trying something new in a highly regulated and overly litigated environment, but I'm hoping that some of you will figure out how to introduce ETS Plus and start using it—for the sake of the patient.

DOSAGE: Immediately upon arriving on the scene, administer one dose of ETS Plus three times, five minutes apart during the first twenty minutes.

ETS PLUS BATHS. Add ¼ cup (two ounces) of ETS Plus to a full bath and soak for twenty minutes.

● ETS PLUS BATHS — THE FULL-IMMERSION EXPERIENCE. An ETS Plus bath works wonders for everything from general stress to periods of extreme stress to tired, sore or injured muscles, sunburn, heat exhaustion, recovering from surgery or illness, or just recovering from life...

For an ETS Plus bath, put ¼ cup (two ounces) ETS Plus in a full bath and soak for twenty minutes. Do not add any other bath ingredients such as bubble baths, salts, oils, etc. If you use PKTT, you can test for how many nights you would benefit from an ETS Plus bath. Everyone who has tried the bath swears by it!

> TO USE ETS PLUS BEST, it's important to have a bottle within easy reach should a trauma occur. Really. It's so annoying to have to go on a search mission while we're bleeding all over the place or we've just knocked ourselves senseless. Think about the danger zones for you and your family and put a bottle of ETS Plus in each location. This would include having a bottle in the kitchen, bathroom, workshop, office, each car, bike bag, backpack, gym bag, purse and briefcase. Also include a bottle by the television and phone to use when receiving or hearing bad news. And if you're like me, you also may need to carry a bottle around in your pocket so that you'll have your ETS Plus handy at all times throughout the day.

If you hate sitting in a tub or don't have time for this, but you know you could benefit from a full immersion, put undiluted ETS Plus in a spray bottle and spray the solution over your whole body. (You need to be naked for this!) Then air dry. It should take just a few minutes. (Pour any remaining ETS Plus back into its dropper bottle each time you have finished spraying. Don't let it sit in the spray bottle.)

● TOPICAL APPLICATIONS. This is an ETS Plus use that has become quite popular over the years. It goes like this:

> If you get a cut: Take ETS Plus orally. Then place a drop(s) or spray ETS Plus directly on the cut and let it air dry.

> If you burn yourself: Take ETS Plus orally. Then place a drop(s) or spray ETS Plus directly on the burn and let it air dry.

> If you sprain a muscle: Take ETS Plus orally. Then place a drop(s) or spray ETS Plus directly on the damaged muscle area and let it air dry.

> If you get an insect sting or bite: Take ETS Plus orally. Then place a drop(s) or spray ETS Plus directly on the bite or sting and let it air dry.

Get the rhythm? This two-prong application of ETS Plus helps reduce pain more quickly and speeds the healing process even more. NOTE: If you set up an ETS Plus spray bottle, don't leave the plastic pipette submerged in the bottle once you are finished applying the ETS Plus. Remove the spray cap and replace it with a spare dropper cap with the glass pipette until you need to spray ETS Plus again.

> JUST TO MAKE SURE WE'RE CLEAR ABOUT THIS: ETS Plus does not take the place of needed and qualified medical attention such as having a broken bone set, receiving stitches or taking needed medications. In such cases, take ETS Plus immediately after the trauma, then call for help.

USING ETS PLUS AND THE PERELANDRA ESSENCES

ETS Plus and the Perelandra Essences function extremely well together. When something happens, take ETS Plus first. Dealing with the simplicity of a single, pre-mixed bottle while our eyes are crossed and we're screaming with pain makes life quite a bit simpler. As I've said, ETS Plus takes care of trauma circuit damage. Once that's done, we can address the injury or health issue and facilitate the body's healing process by working with the Perelandra Essences. Because you've already stabilized the trauma circuits, you'll need fewer Essences.

Before I introduced ETS Plus, I had to provide Essence protocols for a bunch of different scenarios for you to use that were complex enough to make Rube Goldberg smile. Lordy, have mercy on us all. Then along came ETS Plus and life's complexities got reduced to a beautiful simplicity. Here's a list of some different situations we might face. To give you a sense of how to approach them, I've included the sequence for addressing them with ETS Plus and the Perelandra Essences.

● INJURIES

    1. ETS Plus—Take three or four doses during the first twenty minutes.

    2. Do the Basic Telegraph Test.

● INJURIES NEEDING MEDICAL ATTENTION

    1. ETS Plus—Take three or four doses during the first twenty minutes.

    2. Call for help immediately.* Go to the hospital.

    3. If you are incapacitated, take ETS Plus daily until you are able to test.

    If you can do a little testing: do a daily Basic Essence Test (no dosage testing needed).

    4. Once you can resume full testing: do the Basic Telegraph Test for the injuries.

> * Immediately after taking the first dose of ETS Plus, call for help. Don't wait until after the full twenty minutes to seek assistance.

● SERIOUS OR COMPLEX INJURIES

    1. ETS Plus—Take three or four doses during the first twenty minutes.

    2. Do the Basic Telegraph Test.

    If the injury includes seizures or attacks:
    1. ETS Plus—Take three or four doses as soon as you feel a seizure/attack coming on.

    2. ETS Plus—Take three or four doses right after a seizure/attack.

    3. Do the Basic Telegraph Test. Should a related injury occur, add it to your BTT checklist and telegraph test this new injury right away and do all the follow-up testing. It is now a regular part of your BTT checklist.

● MISALIGNMENTS AND CHIROPRACTIC WORK. By "misalignment" I mean something like a vertebra that is not seated or anything in the rest of the skeletal system that has been knocked, pulled, banged or emoted out of its correct alignment.

    1. Take three or four doses of ETS Plus during the first twenty minutes when the problem occurs or when you first recognize the problem.

    2. Make a chiropractor appointment as soon as possible, if needed.

    Sometimes a misalignment will automatically adjust on its own if treated with ETS Plus and Essences right away. In this case a chiropractor appointment is not needed.

    3. While waiting for the appointment day, do daily Basic Essence Tests.

4. Immediately after the appointment, take three or four doses of ETS Plus during the first twenty minutes.

5. Post-appointment, do the Basic Telegraph Test for the misalignment.

- PHYSICAL THERAPY SESSIONS

1. Use ETS Plus during the session whenever there is unusual difficulty, stress or pain. Take one dose only.

2. Use ETS Plus immediately after the session. Take three or four doses during the first twenty minutes.

3. Consider including the Perelandra Essences in your daily regimen for whatever is causing the need for physical therapy. Look at the Basic Essence Test, the Basic Telegraph Test and Telegraph Testing for Chronic Illness and decide which testing approach best suits your situation.

- COUNSELING SESSIONS

1. Use ETS Plus during the session whenever there is unusual emotional difficulty or pain. Take one dose only.

2. Use ETS Plus immediately after the session. Take three or four doses during the first twenty minutes.

3. Consider including the Perelandra Essences in your daily regimen for whatever is causing you to need counseling. Look at the Basic Essence Test and the Basic Telegraph Test and decide which approach best suits your situation.

- ANY SITUATION OR EVENT THAT MADE YOU GRAB YOUR ETS PLUS

1. ETS Plus: Take three or four doses during the first twenty minutes.

2. As soon as possible *(within twenty-four hours)* and if needed, follow up with the appropriate Essence testing. A lot of times ETS Plus will take care of a problem and nothing more is needed. However, for the situations that go beyond the initial trauma and require more attention, decide which Essence testing is best for you to use. If you're not sure if a follow-up is needed, do a Basic Essence Test about an hour after taking the ETS Plus doses. If ETS Plus took care of it, the Basic Essence Test will test clear and no Essences are needed. If you did not test clear, take the Essences that tested positive. Then decide which Essence testing best addresses the situation and either switch to the Basic Telegraph Test or continue doing the Basic Essence Test (daily or with dosage testing) until you test clear.

ADDITIONAL PERELANDRA PROCESSES THAT HAVE BEEN STREAMLINED BY ETS PLUS

ETS Plus Birth-Stabilizing Process*

We can now greatly expand the range of support for both mother and child during the birthing process by taking ETS Plus.

- LABOR AND BIRTH. As soon as contractions begin, take two doses (ten to twelve drops per dose) of ETS Plus. Focus on yourself for the first dose and on the baby for the second dose. If labor proceeds naturally and without any problems, this initial dose of ETS Plus is all you and the baby will need. However, should a problem arise or should you feel overly stressed or panicked during labor, take another dose of ETS Plus immediately for yourself and a second dose for the baby.

- TELL DAD (or whoever is assisting or coaching you) to take a dose of ETS Plus once labor begins so that he can be more helpful during the process and less annoying. Should he faint or become overwhelmed at any time during the process, he's to take another dose.

- AS SOON AS POSSIBLE AFTER THE BIRTH

  - MOM. Take one dose of ETS Plus for your part of the birthing process. If you received stitches or experienced any other problem during the birthing process and you work with the Perelandra Essences, plan to telegraph test using the surgery guidelines** once you are up to testing the Essences again.

  - BABY. Tell someone to place ten drops of ETS Plus on your forehead and gently rub the drops into the skin. (It would help if they held the bottle in their hands to warm the solution before putting the drops on your forehead. After all, you're brand new to this life and deserve a little extra TLC.) Then tell them to let your forehead air dry. Finally, tell them to cuddle you like crazy and tell you how perfect you are. (If they don't say any of this to you, throw up on them.)

  - DAD. Take one dose of ETS Plus to balance out the intensity of your own experience during the birthing process and the shock of realizing the baby is finally here and is actually lying there and staring at you.

* Formerly known as the Cauliflower Essence Birth-Stabilizing Process.

SEE APPENDIX A for updated information on the following Essence processes:

- Calibration Process
- Miasm Process
- Restabilizing Process for the Perelandra Essences
- Past Problems
- Peeling Process
- Two-Week Essence Process

SEE CHAPTER 17 for the updated Post-Death Essence Process.

** See chapter 10 for the surgery guidelines.

At some point the baby will get sick. They like to do this because it makes their mom and dad crazy. When they get sick, treat them first with a dose of ETS Plus, then do a Basic Essence Test or a Telegraph Test, whichever process is best for the situation. Be sure to follow the guidelines for testing infants.* Up to nine months of age you can place ETS Plus and Essence drops on the baby's forehead and gently massage them into the skin. After that point, they will need to take all drops orally.

* See chapter 15, *Surrogate Testing Children.*

Extreme-Trauma Repair Process**

** Formerly known as the Body/Soul Fusion Process.

In chapter 3, I describe how the circuits on each of the PEMS levels connect and support one another. The soul level is connected electrically with each of the other three levels. When the body's circuits are balanced and operating well, the dynamics and information that are unique to the soul level flow into and support the other three levels. Our overall balance as a human being depends on the soul-level information that provides the range and scope of what constitutes balanced activity on all our levels.

But we are talking about biological electric circuits and these can become damaged. If the flow from the soul level is impeded, the consequences are significant and the person will experience problems on all PEMS levels. Circuit damage that impedes the currents and flow from the soul level are caused in two ways: (1) The circuits have irregularities or mechanical damage that need repairing, or (2) a person experiences a trauma that is so severe, so shocking that it has significantly damaged the circuits that fuse, connect and seat the soul level with the emotions, mental and physical levels. This intense level of trauma is so great that, as part of the trauma response, a person will desperately attempt to withdraw or disconnect from the event to protect himself, resulting in even greater damage to his trauma circuits. The kinds of trauma an adult or child may experience that can cause such extreme damage include incest; child abuse; adult abuse; dealing with an alcoholic or drug addicted parent, child or spouse; rape; the sudden loss of a child; a sudden injury that has left the person severely injured or paralyzed; a horrific accident in which someone was killed or witnessed someone dying.

After a person has suffered this degree of trauma, he can appear listless, unable to speak coherently, unable to cope with daily routine, flaky or depressed. He has trouble focusing and his eyes can appear glassy or distant. He shows no interest in what is positive in his life. These symptoms are severe and the person will show no interest in lifting out of them. They are providing the person a sense of comfort and protection. We tend to say this person is in severe shock and/or depressed. The symptoms will last as long as his circuits are in need of repair. That can be a matter of weeks, months or years, depending on his body's ability to naturally repair the circuits and the person's will to re-enter life and live again.

Sometimes, depending on the nature of the extreme-trauma event, a person is able to take ETS Plus within that initial twenty-minute window. When this is possible, the damaged extreme-trauma circuits on all four PEMS levels are repaired right away, thus enabling the person to turn his attention in clear and grounded ways to the serious situation in which he now finds himself.

However, what is more likely to happen is that you will not be the victim but, rather, the one administering ETS Plus to a friend or loved one who is suffering from extreme trauma. And that initial twenty-minute trauma window will be long gone before you are able to get to his bedside. Treat this situation as an *Extended Trauma Time Frame.*

When Coming to a Friend's Aid

- When you first arrive, administer the initial four doses of ETS Plus five minutes apart. If he is unconscious or otherwise unable to open his mouth, just put the drops on his lips, two or three drops at a time, until you've administered a total of ten drops *(Fig. A)*. The drops will seep into his mouth and mix with his saliva. Repeat this three more times every five minutes.

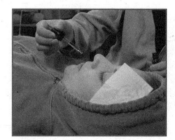

Fig. A

* This is an extreme situation and the only time a diluted ETS Plus will maintain its effectiveness. All other ETS Plus dosages are to be taken undiluted.

- Once he has regained consciousness, have him take ETS Plus five times daily, including one dose at bedtime. The easiest way for him to take five doses each day is to add *twelve drops* of ETS Plus to a half cup of water (four to six ounces) so that he can sip it throughout the day.* It doesn't matter if he takes more than five doses. It does matter if he takes fewer than five doses. Someone needs to make sure they stop by each day to mix the drops and water for him. You may need to organize an "ETS Plus Brigade" among family and friends to make sure each day is covered.

- He is to continue taking ETS Plus daily until he feels he can cope with the situation and begin to participate in his life. ETS Plus will provide the support and circuit pathways for him to reconnect with his life on all four PEMS levels, but it will not override his sense of timing or his feeling that he is not yet ready to leave the comfort of his detached state. In short, ETS Plus removes the obstacles and resets all the damaged circuits so that they will be ready for him when he wishes to reconnect to life. By repairing the damaged circuits, the time he spends in the detached state will be shortened. But when those circuits are not repaired, the wild wiring sets up an electrical environment that continues to reflect his experience of the extreme-trauma event and says to him that it's not safe to re-enter life. Plus, he doesn't have the connections and pathways to move out of the state until the circuit damage is repaired. The circuit damage literally supports and encourages him to remain in his detached state.

● When he feels he's back on track and interested in life again, he can stop taking the daily ETS Plus doses. But if he miscalculates and rushes the timing, he'll realize it pretty quickly. The feelings of detachment, listlessness and disinterest will return letting him (or those around him) know he's not out of the Extended Trauma Time Frame yet. Should this occur, he only needs to return to the five daily doses of ETS Plus.

● His goal for taking ETS Plus is to provide his damaged extreme-trauma circuits what they need to balance, stabilize and repair the hit they took from the event and to provide himself the encouragement and pathways he needs for reestablishing himself in life.

* See chapter 13, *Surrogate Basic Telegraph Test*.
● After ETS Plus is no longer needed, you can surrogate telegraph test* any remaining issues and symptoms. List them on the BTT checklist.

● OLD EXTREME-TRAUMA EVENTS

If an extreme-trauma event occurred in your life years ago and you notice that you are now perpetually spacy, frightened, shy, flaky, aggressive or acting out in other ways that you know are not who you are, you could be carrying forward damaged extreme-trauma circuits that need repair right away. Not only are they causing you to act, think or feel in odd ways, but they are interfering with your overall health. Don't forget that the body's natural healing process is impaired if the trauma circuits are damaged. In this case, the original event, the memory of it and your thoughts keep adding extreme trauma on top of extreme trauma. You're in a perpetual trauma loop, and the original circuit damage has never had a chance to repair. This has caused the healing process for all other health issues to be compromised. For this situation, do the following:

- Take ETS Plus *five times daily,* including once at bedtime. Once you repair these trauma circuits, how you think about the event and how those memories impact you will change and you'll notice that the behavior that you know is not really you will be gone.

- After ETS Plus is no longer needed, you can telegraph test any remaining issues and symptoms. List them on the BTT checklist.

- Go on the vacation of your dreams to celebrate that the extreme-trauma event is no longer dominating you and use the bundle of money you save from all the therapy sessions you no longer need thanks to your newly repaired circuits to pay for that vacation.

● NEWBORNS AND INFANTS UP TO NINE MONTHS

If your child seems detached and/or developmentally slow, she may have suffered mechanical circuit issues that occurred in utero as the electric system developed or circuit damage that occurred during the birth process. She may also have shifted into an extreme-trauma protection mode that damaged circuits if she sensed she was about to enter a jarring, violent, loud world caused by a troubled, addicted or angry parent, or a hostile family situation. (She may have been in utero, but she could still hear and she could sense the environment that was immediately outside and surrounding Mom's body.) In either case, she's born with damaged trauma circuits. If she has been given ETS Plus when her mother went into labor and again right after birth, the trauma damage will be taken care of. If she hasn't had this benefit:

- Apply ten drops of ETS Plus on her forehead, gently massage in and allow her forehead to air dry *(Fig. B)*.

- Repeat this routine *once daily* for the next four days.

- After four days, the trauma circuits will be repaired and she'll have the pathways she needs to fully integrate into her life on all PEMS levels.

- Do whatever is necessary to make her environment baby friendly. If you don't, she may need doses of ETS Plus on a regular basis just to survive the unfriendly home situation.

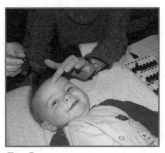

Fig. B

● FOR TODDLERS AND CHILDREN UNDER AGE TWELVE

I'll give you an example of identifying possible trauma circuit damage in toddlers and older children. A mother took her seven-year-old daughter to a practitioner who offered the Body/Soul Fusion Process (the old version) as part of her service. The daughter had never spoken—not to her family and not to her friends. She had been examined by many specialists and given a bunch of tests, but they could find nothing physically wrong with her hearing or her ability to speak. She just wasn't speaking. The practitioner felt the Body/Soul Fusion Process was worth a shot and put her through the steps right then. Immediately after the process was completed, the daughter looked at her mother (something she hadn't done very often) and calmly stated, "This is boring. Let's go home." Then she got up and started toward the door, leaving Mom and the practitioner sitting in shocked amazement. According to the practitioner who told me this story, the daughter never stopped talking again.

We can say that this child was just stubborn or uninterested in verbal communication. Or we can say she either was born with damaged trauma circuits or she developed a problem early on after birth that, when finally repaired, immediately supported her ability and desire to communicate verbally. Throughout the seven years, she had shown no signs of being defiant or playing games with her parents or the doctors. She also showed no signs of being mentally disabled. She was one of those patients who caused the doctors to scratch their collective heads and mumble, "I don't know."

☾☾☾

After birth, children may experience extreme-trauma circuit damage in any number of ways. Frequent screaming at a child, physical and mental abuse, threatening physical or mental abuse, a traumatizing adoption situation…anything that would over-activate the child's trauma and self-protection circuits. For these children, do the following:

- Administer *two doses* of ETS Plus daily, including once at bedtime.

- Treat this as an Extended Trauma Time Frame and continue the daily ETS Plus doses until the damaged trauma-circuit symptoms are gone. This may take a matter of days or a few weeks—or it can happen right away.

- After ETS Plus is no longer needed, you can do a surrogate Basic Essence Test,* including all the follow-up testing for addressing any residual electric system damage.

- Straighten out the home, your life and the child's situation so that she doesn't have to experience trauma and need to function with damaged circuits. Really, enough is enough.

* See chapter 12, *Surrogate Basic Essence Test.*

- Have them take *four doses* of ETS Plus daily, including once at bedtime.

- Treat this as an Extended Trauma Time Frame and continue the daily ETS Plus doses until the damaged trauma-circuit symptoms are gone. This may take a few weeks or a few months.

- After ETS Plus is no longer needed, you can do a surrogate Basic Essence Test, including all the follow-up testing for addressing any residual electric system damage.

- This still applies: Straighten out the home, your life and the child's situation so that she doesn't have to experience trauma and need to function with damaged circuits.

NOTE: When a child is experiencing trauma-circuit damage, you will need to focus first on repairing those circuits. For this, you will be using ETS Plus only. Once the Extended Trauma Time Frame is over and you wish to address any lingering symptoms, set up to do a surrogate Basic Essence Test first and do all the follow-up testing until the child tests clear. For any persistent symptoms, set up a surrogate Basic Telegraph Test and include each remaining symptom on the BTT checklist.*

* See chapter 15, *Surrogate Testing Children* for information and steps.

Coping with the Adolescence from Hell

If your son or daughter is experiencing the adolescence from hell, try an ETS Plus regimen following the guidelines for children twelve to eighteen. If your child's adolescence has caused you to beat your head against a wall more than three times, you might need ETS Plus for yourself as well. Plan to take doses three or more times daily until you feel you can cope comfortably and nonviolently. Anytime the old urges come up again for you, resume the daily ETS Plus dosages.

Primary Electric System Repair Package

By this point, you have learned the tools in the Primary Electric System Repair Package:

> Basic Essence Test
> Basic Telegraph Test
> ETS Plus

You will be using the information and testing processes from those three chapters (chapters 6, 7 and 8) for nearly all your health needs throughout the rest of your life. You can stop right here and concentrate on working with the Primary Electric System Repair Package for as long as you wish.

The next two chapters (chapters 9 and 10) address Essence testing for special situations: chronic illness, surgery, active scars, amputation and phantom limb syndrome. You don't have to deal with the information contained in chapters 9 and 10 unless you need to address one of these special situations. Be sure you are comfortable with the testing and information in the Primary Electric System Repair Package before moving on to the information and testing for those special situations.

You may want to read Part Four: *Surrogate Testing* sooner rather than later. I've already mentioned this testing several times and if you wish to offer the Perelandra Essences and their health benefits to family and friends, you'll need to learn surrogate testing.

Part Three

ESSENCE TESTING
FOR SPECIAL SITUATIONS

POINTS TO REMEMBER FOR
TELEGRAPH TESTING CHRONIC ILLNESS

- THE ILLNESS NORM FACTOR makes dealing with chronic illness challenging—but not impossible. With the Essences you have the best tool you could want for balancing, stabilizing and repairing the damaged circuits that are behind the illness and the best tool for shifting the electric system back to its original state of balance and strength. You'll be working with the Basic Telegraph Test but, in order to address the unique elements of a chronic illness, some of the steps have been slightly modified. With the Essences and the Telegraph Test, you will be changing the illness norm factor into a "gone norm factor" and return your circuits and system back to the original "health norm factor."

- THE "PATIENCE FACTOR." As I've said, dealing with chronic illness can be challenging. To work with the electric circuits underlying a chronic illness, you will need patience. I say this because the last thing people who are chronically ill want to be is patient. They want to be healthy and have a normal life. They don't want to be ill. The hell with patience. But telegraph testing isn't magic and you will not have a 100 percent instantaneous turn around. You will be embarking on a well-organized healing process that will incrementally shift your electric system and circuits towards a new health norm. You *want* this to be gradual for the sake of your body and state of mind. If you could push a magic button and eliminate a chronic illness in fifteen seconds, no matter how appealing this might sound, your body would violently spasm and you'd just faint—or die. It's too great a shift, and you and your body haven't had time to adjust to the incremental changes and to strengthen in the necessary ways. So I urge you to respect your body, your body's electric system, your personal rhythm, your sanity, the Essences and the Basic Telegraph Test. I also urge you to respect the timing that's involved with repairing and restoring a complexly damaged electric system and its circuits. It took some time for the illness norm factor to establish itself. Be prepared to provide the time and attention it takes to repair what's needed and to establish the new health norm factor.

Having said all this, allow me to contradict myself and give you some hope. Time is relative. It may have taken ten years for the electrical structure of a chronic illness to establish into place, but by using the Telegraph Test process and Essences, it probably won't take ten years to unravel everything and establish the electrical structure for the health norm factor. The Perelandra tools are exceptionally effective, and you will be moving a healing process along a lot faster than would occur if the system and circuits were left to repair, if they could, on their own.

● WORKING WITH PHYSICIANS. If you are chronically ill, I assume you are under a doctor's care (or the care of a team of doctors) and receive regular treatment. *You don't have to back away from or change this in any way when incorporating the Perelandra Essences and telegraph testing.* You will now be providing something that doctors, medicine and hospitals don't provide. You will be monitoring the state of your electric system and moving it forward through its own healing process. With a strengthened electric system, all the treatment and medication you take for the illness can become more effective and efficient. The entire healing process is speeded up, all because you are moving the key element, your electric system and illness-related circuits, simultaneously through the healing process.

Generally it's best to deal with your electric system on your own and not talk to your doctors about it. Alternative treatment and new ideas tend to make them nervous. (Remember Björn Nordenström.) It's not that this work should be secret. It's just that a lot of doctors still don't recognize there is an electric system or that it could play a vital role in your healing process. In order to get the best help from your doctors, you don't want to antagonize, annoy or scare them. Nor do you want them to categorize you as a nut. If they think you're crazy, they'll stop listening to you. So I recommend you do the electric-system work quietly. But be aware that your medication and/or treatment may need to be adjusted faster than the doctor expected because you've kicked in the electric work. When you feel a change should be made in either the medication or treatment, don't hesitate to make an appointment and talk to your doctor about the changes you are feeling.

Your doctors may not see that electric-system ship on the horizon yet, but they do care about you and they do want you to improve. Despite all the bad press doctors get, they actually don't like to see a patient drop dead on them. When a doctor sees a patient with a chronic illness improve, the doctor smiles and does some version of a high-five with the patient. They really are pleased for you, and you have clearly made their day. They say things like, "I don't know what you are doing, but keep it up." And they truly mean this. They don't know what you are doing, and they honestly do want you to keep it up. But—and this is a big but—they also don't want you to tell them what you are doing. If they did, they would say to you, "Tell me what you are doing." Keep in mind that your goal is to restore your health and not to educate or convert your doctors. If they want the information, they'll ask for it.

● THE HEAD-START PROGRAM FOR CHRONIC ILLNESS. If you want to get a head start and provide yourself some relief while you are putting together your chronic-illness checklist (see below), do a Basic Essence Test right away and include dosage and follow-up testing while working on the checklist. Once you have completed the chronic-illness checklist, you may begin telegraph testing even if you are still taking an Essence dosage from the "Head-Start Basic Essence Test." Continue taking that dosage and move through all the follow-up testing for the Head-Start Basic Essence Test until you test clear while simultaneously moving through the telegraph testing for chronic illness. This may look like a daunting task, but the Head-Start Essences will weave through and support the Telegraph Test Essences. Your payoff will be less complex telegraph testing results.

"Command Central" — the Symptoms Checklist for Chronic Illness (CI Checklist)

Telegraph testing for chronic illness is a Basic Telegraph Test that has built into it a special focus for a serious health situation. Except for a couple of tweaks, the steps are the same. But because of the seriousness of the situation, the CI checklist will be more extensive than a regular BTT checklist.

To move successfully through the healing process for a chronic illness, you need a detailed CI checklist. This becomes your "command central" whenever you do any testing for the illness. It isn't going to be like the transient-illness BTT checklists you put together in about five minutes. With a chronic illness, more symptoms are involved, some are not easily identifiable — for example, you may not be paying any attention to the little red blotch on your arm, but your doctor knows this is a symptom of your illness — and some symptoms are internal and complex. So be prepared to take all the time you need to build a quality CI checklist that covers the full range of symptoms for your illness. The CI checklist is what you'll be using for all telegraph testing and follow-up testing.

● TO START THE CI CHECKLIST, write "full electric system" at the top of the paper. The telegraph testing process begins as usual with a Basic Essence Test to clear your electric system. This addresses your electric system as an independent unit. But because of the illness norm factor, you will also need to telegraph test the electric system as a regular "symptom." There's a problematic relationship between those circuits and the system that has to be straightened out in order to restore balance.

121

● YOU MUST KNOW SOMETHING about the disease and how it manifests. If you haven't done this already, it's time to Google, go to the library and contact an association that "specializes" in supporting those with your disease. Your quest is to find out what symptoms are part of *your* chronic illness. Add these to your CI checklist. A chronic illness can have a wide range of symptoms. Two people can be diagnosed with the same illness and manifest different symptoms. So you need to determine which ones apply to you.

● CONSULT WITH YOUR DOCTOR. Ask your doctor to explain your illness in more detail and to help you list the symptoms that apply to you. His perspective will probably point you to some symptoms you had not already included on your CI checklist.

Some doctors get annoyed when you ask these kinds of questions. (God forbid you should ask them to explain your illness to you.) But more and more doctors are learning that they need to talk with and listen to the patient. If you have a friendly doctor who exhibits enlightened people skills, you can find out a lot about your symptoms just by asking them questions.

> NOTE: If your doctor doesn't want to talk to you about this, then talk
> to one of your nurses. They are an unrecognized font of information,
> and they tend to excel in people skills.

● *THE ANATOMY COLORING BOOK.* That's right. Buy an anatomy coloring book. I'm serious. Know the anatomy of your illness. There are several versions of anatomy coloring books listed on Amazon.com. The one I use is *The Anatomy Coloring Book* by Kapit and Elson. I urge you to purchase a nice set of felt-tip color pens or splurge on the biggest box of crayons or color pencils you can get. Just because you're sick doesn't mean you can't have a little fun.

Your anatomy coloring book may be the best friend you have when dealing with a chronic illness and telegraph testing. When you're consulting with your doctor (or nurse) and you don't understand what he's talking about or what part of the anatomy he's referring to, open your anatomy coloring book and have him point to it.

> HINT: Put a check mark next to whatever he's pointing to and dog-
> ear the page. Later, you'll be able to easily locate all the different pages
> he pointed out and you can color the checked "items" in question. I
> recommend that you not color anything else on the page other than

the checked item. You want the part of the anatomy in question to be highlighted and quickly distinguishable from everything else on the page. Remove the page from the book (or photocopy the page first and color the photocopy) and keep these pages with your CI checklist.

When your CI checklist is finally set, organize the coloring pages according to the order of symptoms listed on the CI checklist and staple the ordered stack to the back of the CI checklist. Whenever you telegraph test each of those symptoms, just refer to that page and focus on what you colored. This gives you a good, clean focus for testing and when taking the Essence dosage. HINT: You don't have to confine your coloring to just the symptoms the doctor points out. You have all those other symptoms on the CI checklist to color as well. As I said: Know the anatomy of your illness.

● THE PERELANDRA ESSENCE TELEGRAPH TEST CHECKLIST.* This is a chart that lists all the body's systems and what is included in each system. By PKTT testing this chart, you discover what areas and parts of your body are involved in your illness. At the top of the chart write the name of your chronic illness. Do a Basic Essence Test to clear your electric system for telegraph testing the Telegraph Test Checklist. Then ask:

> Which systems and areas of my body are included in my illness [insert the name of your illness] and need telegraph testing?

Test the list and place a check beside anything that tests positive. Then add whatever tested positive and isn't already included to the CI checklist.

● LASTLY, ADD THE MAGICAL CHECKLIST INGREDIENT. Find out if you have any mystery symptoms that are connected to your illness but have yet to be recognized by you, your doctor or even medical science. To do this, read aloud the list you've made, then ask:

> Is there a symptom that is part of my chronic illness [insert the name of your chronic illness] that I don't know about? (Test.)

If the result is negative, you have no mystery symptoms. However, if you get a positive response to the question, something else needs to be included on the CI checklist.

With your focus on the first mystery symptom, state:

> I name this symptom "Factor-X." **

* You may purchase a pack of fifty of the Perelandra Essence Telegraph Test Checklists from us or download and print it at no charge from our website. Our web address is on the Contacts page at the end of the book.

** You may use any names for your mystery symptoms. Just be sure they are clear and easy to remember.

Write Factor-X on your CI checklist. You asked, "Is there a symptom that is part of my chronic illness that I don't know about?" If you got a positive response to your question, one mystery symptom was highlighted. You assigned an identifying name to it when you stated, "I name this symptom 'Factor-X.'" Now "Factor-X" identifies the circuits that are the electrical foundation of that mystery symptom.

You may have more than one mystery symptom. Ask again:

> Is there another symptom that is part of my chronic illness that I don't know about? (Test.)

If you get another positive response, state:

> I name this symptom "Factor-Y."

Continue asking the question and assigning names (just keep assigning letters) until you get a negative to the question.

You have now identified all the mystery symptoms and included them on your CI checklist. And you have successfully gotten around any roadblocks that pop up when working with a chronic illness that may not be fully understood or defined by today's medical science. Maybe someday you and the researchers will find out what those mystery symptoms are but, for now, what's important is the task of balancing, stabilizing and repairing all the circuits connected with your illness, including the ones underlying the mystery symptoms.

● AUXILIARY SYMPTOMS. These are symptoms that are not officially part of the illness, but you are experiencing them *because* of the illness and the treatment: bed-sores, muscle tightness, joint pain, sleeplessness, general pain, bloating, hair loss, stress from money worries, weight loss, nausea...

It is important to distinguish between the main symptoms that make up the chronic illness and the auxiliary symptoms that are the crappy things you have to deal with because you are sick and receiving some serious, tough, expensive treatments or medications. On your symptoms CI checklist page, *make a separate column* for the list of auxiliary symptoms.

Once you begin taking the Essence solutions for each of the symptoms that make up the illness, *wait two weeks from that start date* before you review the auxiliary symptoms list. Some of the things you've listed will show signs of improvement. This means that they are directly connected with one or more of the chronic-illness symptoms and are already being addressed. You can remove those symptoms from the auxiliary list. You don't have to identify which chronic-illness symptom is connected with an improved auxiliary symptom.

● TESTING THE AUXILIARY SYMPTOMS. You will need to telegraph test each of the remaining auxiliary symptoms. Do a Basic Essence Test first to clear the electric system, then telegraph test each auxiliary symptom. Take those Essences and test for dosage. You now have two sets of Essence solutions running simultaneously on parallel tracks: the Essences for the chronic-illness symptoms and the Essences for the auxiliary symptoms. You will be working with both tracks at the same time and maintaining the rhythms set by the dosage and follow-up testing for each symptom on each track. Complete all the follow-up testing for both the auxiliary symptoms and the chronic-illness symptoms.

Treating auxiliary symptoms ensures that they don't complicate or interfere with the circuit repair for any of the chronic-illness symptoms. It also dramatically lessens or eliminates the auxiliary symptoms that are causing so many of the painful and annoying elements of your illness. If you can feel more comfortable, get more sleep and maintain a more positive frame of mind, your healing process will move along that much more quickly. Tackling the auxiliary symptoms gives you some control over this part of your illness.

EXAMPLE: CI CHECKLIST FOR TYPE 2 DIABETES*

Chronic illness symptoms

1. Full electric system ☺
2. Feeling very thirsty
3. Frequent urination
4. Irritability and mood changes
5. Blurred vision
6. Slow-healing wounds and bruises
7. Tingling in the hands

[from the Essence Telegraph Test Checklist]
8. Gall Bladder, Pancreas, Spleen ☒

9. Factor-X
10. Factor-Y

Auxiliary symptoms

11. Depression ☹
12. Fear of losing job $
13. Anger at the inconveniences 💣

---

* Although the symptoms I've listed on this CI checklist are consistent with type 2 diabetes, they are not the only symptoms a person can experience. If you have type 2 diabetes, do not rely on this list for your testing. You will need to put together your CI checklist that accurately reflects your symptoms.

The other CI checklists and examples I use in this chapter are also not to be used for treatment. All the testing results have been fabricated.

REMEMBER TO ADD THE ORGANIZATION AID TO THE CI CHECKLIST. Number everything that is listed on the CI checklist. The numbers allow for easy referencing when working with the Perelandra Essence Record Chart and writing down the dosage and follow-up information on separate sheets of paper.

CAUTION: You may include the number on the solution bottle label, but when actually taking the doses from that bottle you will need to set your focus by stating the symptom or reason for that solution and not just the number.

● ORGANIZE! Get a desk calendar and use it for nothing else but tracking your telegraph testing, dosage periods and follow-up testing! An iPad or other electronic device that includes a calendar would be brilliant for this work. Also, if you are handwriting your notes and don't plan to computerize them, now's the time to get a binder notebook for centralizing all your notes, charts, testing results and your CI checklist. Here's another nifty idea: Carry-on luggage on wheels with a collapsible handle and several compartments normally designed for hauling around a computer and office files makes a great telegraph testing "office." Not only can you store your paperwork, pens and blank charts, but it will also hold your boxes of Essences. While I'm at it: You do a lot of testing when dealing with chronic illness. I recommend that you download (available at no charge) and print off a bunch of the Essence Record Charts from our website. It lists all the Essences, and all you have to do is put a check next to the ones that test positive for each symptom. It saves you time and writing wear and tear. Really. Just how many times do you want to write "Gruss an Aächen"?! Now you are properly organized and have your Essence office on wheels.

Tricks and Aids for Focusing

● I'VE ALREADY TALKED ABOUT one fine focusing tool: the relevant colored pages from *The Anatomy Coloring Book*.

● CODE WORDS AND SYMBOLS. You may have a symptom with a location that's difficult to pinpoint and doesn't easily lend itself to the coloring book. And some symptoms may be difficult to see or feel, or even imagine. For each of these you will need a focus aid. Choose a visual symbol or code word that for you describes the symptom in relationship to your body and/or illness. Or it can be any symbol or code you personally like and just feel like using. Draw the symbol or write the code word next to that symptom on your CI checklist. Then "officially" link your symbol or code with the symptom by stating out loud:

> I assign this [symbol/code] to [the name of the symptom as described on the CI checklist].

If it's a symbol, be sure to keep the symbol in your mind as you state the sentence aloud and name the symptom it represents. If it's a code word, insert the code and the symptom/injury as it's written on your CI checklist when you read the sentence out loud.

When you are telegraph testing a symptom with a code word or symbol, keep the word or symbol in mind as you do the testing *and* as you take the Essences. This focuses your mind and activates the circuits for one thing (the symptom/injury) to the exclusion of all else. Keep the word or symbol in mind when you take the Essences so that the Essence patterns shift to the circuits affected by the symptom/injury. The focus on the symbol or word has set up all the needed pathways and connections for shifting the Essence patterns.

If all of this sounds familiar to you, it's probably because it is. You are working with the same process you used when assigning "Factor-X" to a mystery symptom. The symbols and codes use the same physical-circuit/mental-circuit connection. A chronic-illness symptom is generally manifested on the physical PEMS level. Code words, symbols and focus are all mental-level activities. You can't think about, visualize or focus on a symptom without those circuits activating on each of the PEMS levels. It's all part of the same PEMS package.

You may know this better as the body/mind connection. A variation on the body/mind theme is visualization therapy. Physicians have found that treatment is much more effective if the patient visualizes what the treatment is supposed to be doing in the body. They give the patient all the clinical information that is needed and then let the patient go to work developing a visualization that embodies either symbolically or in realistic terms what is supposed to be happening to them. The visualization (mental circuits) links the treatment right into the problem areas (physical circuits), which then enhances the effectiveness of the treatment. The relationship between the focused visualization and the physical movement of the treatment and its impact on the body is not a chance thing. It is a discernable, viable relationship that is set up through the use of focus and the body's electric system.

● POKING: ANOTHER SIMPLE FOCUSING TRICK. If you are having difficulty holding your focus on a specific physical symptom, just touch it or lightly poke it. Even allow yourself to make it hurt *a little.* By doing this, you are activating that specific symptom and adding a sensory stimulus to your focus, and for a short period of time (about fifteen minutes), your ability to hold the focus is much easier. The main thing to remember is that the touch must be enough to create some physical sensation. To "deactivate" a touched spot in order to move on and test the next symptom, just touch the next spot or focus on the next description, picture, code or symbol. You and your electric system will immediately shift focus.

● A FOCUS REMINDER. In the beginning, achieving and maintaining focus is going to be a little challenging. But developing focus is like developing muscle. If you work at it, the ability to focus strengthens. The body and mind learn what needs to happen in order to do this kind of focus. I'm not talking about some mystical or paranormal achievement here. I'm literally talking about what you would need to do in order to fully hear someone who is speaking to you in the midst of chaos. We can all do this. Mothers and teachers do it all the time.

● BEFORE YOU GET OVERWHELMED with the tedious tone of all of this, we are further ahead in our ability to focus than we are in muscle development! We are a mentally oriented society and, for the most part, we already have the tools in place for the kind of focus I'm talking about. The tools just need to be sharpened so that we may use them at will. If you can read an interesting book for thirty minutes straight and be aware of nothing else but what you are reading, you know how to focus. There is nothing between you and the book. It's the same focus that is used when listening to someone in a chaotic atmosphere—only you have to work harder to achieve a focus that excludes everything but the person to whom you are listening.

When I describe focus in these terms, all I am doing is giving you an idea of what to shoot for when you sit down to telegraph test the Essences. But because testing Essences is different from reading a terrific book or listening in a chaotic situation, the focus ability that you already possess is going to be applied to the Essence testing and developed accordingly. It's a new situation and just requires some practice. In a short period of time, you'll notice that your ability to focus will feel more agile, more in control, and more laser-beamed.

Telegraph Test for Focus

You try mightily to focus on a symptom from your CI checklist, you've tried every trick I've listed and even some you've come up with on your own, and still you can't stop your mind from wandering aimlessly around the room. If solving this problem involves more than just getting a good night's sleep, remember to telegraph test the circuits that support your focus. Here's a repeat of the Telegraph Test steps for focus:

1. Set up a Telegraph Test by doing a Basic Essence Test first. Take any needed Essences. Do not test for dosage.

2. State:

I want to test the circuits that are connected with and support my ability to focus. I need for these circuits to remain activated throughout the entire test, even if I am unable to properly hold the focus.

Based on what you've just stated, you have set the intent and purpose of this Telegraph Test. In short, you have defined the scope and parameters of the test up front and the targeted focus circuits will remain activated throughout the entire test.

3. Test the Essences. Take any needed Essences and test for dosage.

4. Test your focus circuits whenever needed. And remember to do any needed follow-up testing once a dosage period ends.

● IMPORTANT: When you are doing a Telegraph Test, you are not focused on the test or the PKTT. You are focused on the *symptom.* What's perverse but helpful is that the more severe the symptom, the easier it is to hold the focus. It dominates, and all you can do is think about it and be aware of it during testing and when taking the Essences for that symptom. The challenge here is to block out the dominating symptom(s) in order to isolate and test the other symptoms that also make up the chronic illness.

STEPS FOR TELEGRAPH TESTING CHRONIC ILLNESS

SUPPLIES:
- the five sets of Perelandra Essences
- pen, paper, calendar and your completed CI checklist
- option: a blank Perelandra Essence Record Chart
- a blank Perelandra Essence Telegraph Test Checklist
- a watch or clock with a second hand
- a clean spoon
- clean solution bottles
    (one bottle for each symptom on the CI checklist)
- brandy or distilled white vinegar preservative
- blank labels

PREPARE FOR TESTING: Be as alert and as well-rested as possible. Find a quiet spot. Drink water. Go to the bathroom. Be comfortable: Sit in a comfortable chair or propped up in bed.

1. State your intent:

> I want to set up for a Telegraph Test for [name of chronic illness].

2. Clear your electric system: Do the Basic Essence Test (steps 2–5, pp. 54–55). Take any needed Essences. Do not test for dosage.

If you test clear and you need no Essences, proceed with the telegraph testing. Not needing Essences for clearing the electric system but needing them when telegraph testing the symptoms is not unusual.

3. Place your completed symptoms CI checklist in front of you. (Also include the colored pages from the coloring book.)

4. Begin by telegraph testing your body's full electric system. Treat it as a symptom. Ask:

> What Essences are needed for my electric system as it relates to
> [insert name of illness]? (Test.)

Keep your focus on your electric system while following the Basic Essence Test, steps 2–5. (Creating a symbol for your full electric system acilitates focusing.) Take the needed Essences and find out how many times a day and how many days/weeks/months you are to take these Essences (Basic Essence Test: Dosage, steps 6–10, pp. 60–62). Record the information. Do not make any solution bottles until step 7.

5. Telegraph test each remaining symptom on the CI checklist, one by one. Keep your focus on each symptom while following the Basic Essence Test, steps 2–5.

- Use an assigned code or symbol as a focus aid. Touch or poke the spot if you need help focusing on it.

- Take the needed Essences after each test.

- Dosage: Find out how many times a day and how many days/weeks/months you are to take these Essences (Basic Essence Test: Dosage, steps 6–10) before moving on to the next symptom.

- On the CI checklist, be sure to record all Essences needed and the dosage information for each symptom, including the beginning and end dates of the dosage and how many times a day you are to take it. Also include the times of day you are to take it (morning, afternoon, evening).

• If you are to take Essences just one time for a symptom, you don't need to do any further dosage testing and you can move on to the next symptom on the CI checklist.*

* However, the follow-up test for that symptom will need to be done within the next forty-eight hours.

If you need to make any solution bottles, wait until step 7 after all the telegraph testing is completed and make any needed solution bottles at one time.

IMPORTANT: Once you make a solution bottle, the Essence drops have been diluted and are no longer concentrated. For each dosage, you will need to take ten to twelve drops (one dropperful) of each solution.

6. When you've finished testing every symptom on your CI checklist,** complete the Telegraph Test for your chronic illness by doing a final Basic Essence Test for your full electric system. This will provide balancing and stabilizing for your system as a unit after doing all the circuit repair. *Do not check for dosage. These Essences are to be taken one time only.*

** Wait two weeks after the initial CI starting-gate testing before reviewing your auxiliary symptoms list and testing the symptoms that are still present.

7. Make any needed solution bottles (Basic Essence Test: Solution Bottle, steps 1–3, p. 63). You may need to make one solution bottle for each symptom or issue listed on the CI checklist. To avoid mistakes and confusion, *label each bottle right after making a solution.* Include the solution's focus, the beginning and end date of the dosage and how many times a day you are to take it. Also include the times of day you are to take it (morning, afternoon, evening).

Sample label

1. Full electric system ☺
2 wks/3 days (5/1 to 5.17)
2x daily: A.M. & P.M.

Pat yourself on the back. Put your Essences away and store your CI checklist. Take a well-deserved coffee/tea/beer/chocolate break. Now you can get on with the rest of your day.

Dosage and Follow-up Testing

- REMEMBER TO TAKE all needed dosages (one dropperful per dose) for the full period of time prescribed. It'll help you to remember if you set your solution bottles in an obvious place such as on your bedside table or in the kitchen or bathroom. Also, record the end date for each solution on a calendar or computer so that you will know when to do the follow-up testing.

- ADMINISTERING DOSAGES. Each time you take a solution dosage, you are to first activate the circuits the solution is addressing. To do this, read what symptom/ injury, symbol or code is written on the solution bottle label and keep it in mind while taking a dropperful (ten to twelve drops) of the Essence solution. That will automatically activate the targeted area and set up the connections for shifting the Essence patterns to those circuits.

- COMPLETING A DOSAGE PERIOD. Once you complete a dosage period for a symptom, you'll need to do a new Telegraph Test for just that one symptom *within forty-eight hours* as a follow up to find out if any additional Essences might be needed. Continue doing follow-up testing at the end of each dosage period until you test clear.*

* This includes symptoms that require Essences one time only. The follow-up test is done within forty-eight hours after taking that one required dose.

- AFTER A SYMPTOM ON THE CI CHECKLIST TESTS CLEAR, do a new Telegraph Test for that one symptom for the next seven days. When it tests clear for seven days straight, you know that you have completed the work for that particular symptom and no additional Essences are needed at this time. Cross the symptom off your CI checklist. If you tested positive for any Essences on any one of the seven days, assume the follow-up series is not complete and continue with the follow-up testing as usual until the symptom tests clear for seven days straight.

- RETURNING AND NEW SYMPTOMS. Should a symptom that tested clear return, just list it again on the CI checklist and do a new Telegraph Test for chronic illness for this one symptom, starting with step 1 and testing through step 6 (pp. 130–131). Move it completely through the dosage periods and follow-up testing. Continue this until it tests clear again for seven days straight.

If the returning symptom exhibits any changes or anomalies that differentiate it from the old one in any way, consider this a new symptom that needs to be added to the CI checklist. Do a new Telegraph Test for that one symptom and move it completely through all dosage periods and follow-up testing. Continue this until it tests clear for seven days straight. If you used a code or symbol on the CI checklist for the old symptom, *do not* use that same one for the new symptom. It will need its own code or symbol and you will need to "officially" assign the code/symbol (pp. 126–127).

A symptom that has returned or a new symptom that suddenly pops up while moving a health issue through a telegraph testing regimen means that (1) the circuits that tested clear for a symptom were unable to maintain their balance and now need to be addressed again, and/or (2) while moving through the healing process for this issue, new circuits that are related to the issue were strained and need attention.

☾☾☾

I know this may seem like a lot of Essence testing. In fact, if you feel no one in their right mind could do the testing needed to move through a serious illness, you most likely have not been diagnosed with a serious illness. I have found that the people who are faced with this situation, by necessity, have their life centered around their illness. This isn't a curiosity or a lark or a game to them. It is a priority. Should you have the misfortune of being diagnosed with a chronic illness and you want to include Essences in your treatment, you will find the time, energy and determination to get on with the telegraph testing. Once you get set up with the initial testing that addresses the full list of symptoms—the Telegraph Test starting gate—you never address the full list at one time again. Each symptom has its own Essence solution, its own dosage period and its own follow-up testing. So once you get past the starting gate, you will be addressing one symptom at a time as each dosage period ends. Now moving a Telegraph Test for chronic illness through to its completion will feel quite manageable.

<h1 style="text-align:center">INSPIRATION,
ENCOURAGEMENT
AND HOPE</h1>

A number of years ago, while I was giving an Essence workshop, I wanted to demonstrate how to set up telegraph testing for serious illness. I asked if there was anyone in the crowd who had a serious illness and who would allow me to test them in public. A woman raised her hand and I asked her to come up. As she approached, I noticed that she walked carefully and with a bit of a limp. When she got to me, I sat her down and asked some questions. I'll call her Martha and here's her story.

Martha lives in Germany but she and her family (husband and two sons) were visiting friends who lived about an hour from Perelandra. When they arrived for the visit, the friend told Martha that she had registered for a workshop at Perelandra that was scheduled during their visit and invited Martha to join, if she wished. Martha had not heard of Perelandra or Essences or Essence testing. But she was kind of intrigued, so she came along.

Martha had multiple sclerosis. She had been diagnosed eight or nine years before. By the time she came to the workshop, the illness had forced her to step back from her profession (she was a physician), and it was interfering with the activities she could do with her two young sons.

I asked her to give me a list of all her symptoms. I had wanted to show the people at the workshop how detailed a symptoms list for a chronic illness needed to be, and I knew I had lucked out with Martha because she was a physician and she was going to give me a comprehensive symptoms list. I wrote the symptoms on a Mylar board as she listed them off—it totaled thirteen symptoms in all. Since I would be doing the actual testing for her, I set up for a surrogate Telegraph Test.* Then, with the Essences, I tested her symptoms, going down the list one by one. I gave her one drop of each Essence that tested positive for a symptom before moving on to the next one. (I administered the drops directly from the Essence bottles and they were in concentrate form.) Most of the symptoms needed six or eight Essences and a few needed twenty-five or more.

* The surrogate Basic Telegraph Test is discussed in chapter 13.

The testing I did for one of the symptoms—exhaustion—jumped out when I saw the results. When I wrote "exhaustion" on the board, I didn't think too much about it. I even thought it might be an auxiliary symptom. After all, it made sense that someone dealing with multiple sclerosis would experience exhaustion from time to time. But the test results indicated that this was a primary symptom and when she became exhausted, she needed to take that very seriously. When I said something to her about it, she explained that exhaustion was a major factor in the type of multiple sclerosis she had.

We finished the testing and she had taken all the needed Essence drops. I was using the five sets of Perelandra Essences preserved in brandy. Both she and I were a little concerned that she might be tipsy at the end, but she was fine!

We met after the workshop and I made the thirteen solution bottles she needed. Some dosage periods were for two or three weeks and a few she would be taking for two or three months. I sent her off with a full set of Perelandra Essences, the thirteen solution bottles and instructions for taking each one, plus instructions for how to do follow-up testing. We decided that it would be important for her to do a Basic Essence Test each day just to make sure nothing interfered with the healing process that would go on with the circuits connected with the multiple sclerosis.

I also asked her to stay in touch and let me know how she was progressing or if she was running into a problem. Because of the scope of her illness, I was concerned about triggering a significant physical reaction just from balancing, stabilizing and repairing all these circuits simultaneously. I knew that if this occurred it would be a good thing and indicate that her circuits were repairing, but it might give her some discomfort. She had two weeks left before returning to Germany, and I suggested that she consider waiting until she got back home before continuing with the work. She didn't want to wait.

I wasn't sure if she would follow through on everything. After all, that workshop was the first time she had heard about Essences and it was all brand new to her. But she taught me something about the determination people with chronic illness can have.

I heard from her again just before she and her family returned to Germany. She was following the protocol and doing everything exactly as I had said. She told me that the next day after leaving Perelandra, she experienced such significant improvement that she went on a hike with her family and friends. It was several miles long and it had been years since she had been able to do something like this. Needless to say, she was amazed. However, the day after the hike she became sicker than she had experienced in years. She said it was like she had been hit with a very bad flu and she just went down. Luckily, her positive response in the first twenty-four hours encouraged her to continue with the Essences even though she was now sick. Here's where she really made me smile. She didn't just try to wait out her sickness. Instead, she tested the Essences for her "flu." And she kept the testing going each day until she came out of the "flu" six days later. When I spoke to her about it, we decided that the "flu" was her body responding to taking the thirteen solutions and eliminating different aspects of the chronic disease from her body. I felt it was that reaction I had suspected might occur. Once she came out of the "flu," her strength returned.

She returned to Germany with much of her health restored. She continued taking her solutions, did all the follow-up testing, and she continued the daily Basic Essence Test. I heard from her several times over the next few years. She was happy with her progress and she had resumed practicing medicine again. Her health held up well until about three years down the road. All of a sudden some of the old symptoms returned and a large number of Essences tested positive each day. She couldn't get control of the symptoms again and she was frustrated. She was also angry that the Essences had not pulled her out of this current problem. Her pain got so bad that she had to have hospital tests done. That's when she found out the symptoms were not caused by a return of the multiple sclerosis. She had a vertebrae pressing in on nerves which required surgery. The daily Essence testing had picked up the new problem, but surgery was needed to alleviate the problem. The Essences couldn't do it alone. She resumed the Essence testing and, as far as I know, recuperated from the surgery and returned to an active life again.

☉☉☉

As I've said, telegraph testing Essences for a chronic illness takes determination and diligence. You need to follow through with the testing all the way to the point where each symptom tests clear for seven days straight. And, like Martha, you cannot let something like her "flu" experience stop you. But remember, everyone is different and the circuits connected with a chronic illness operate differently from person to person. Martha's experience is an example of what *can* happen and not what *will* happen. Also, since that workshop so many years ago, I have fine-tuned the telegraph testing process for chronic illness. I have included all the fine-tuning and years of research since working with Martha in this book. What I didn't know to do for her back then was test the electric system as a symptom on its own. It should have been the very first "symptom" and had its own solution bottle. I also should have done a final balancing and stabilizing for the electric system once all the starting-gate circuit work had been completed (step 6). I don't know how these two refinements would have changed her progress, but I feel certain they would have added a stabilizing force that would have been helpful.

The CI Checklist & the Starting Gate Tests

Date: 6/1/11

for myself

Focus: Type 2 diabetes

Symptoms:

1. Full electric system ☺
   Nymphenburg, Celery, Tomato
   6 weeks/4 days, 1x daily: P.M.
   6/1 to 7/16

2. Feeling very thirsty
   Tomato, F-1
   3 weeks, 2x daily: A.M. & P.M.
   6/1 to 6/21

3. Frequent urination
   Blaze Imp., Maybelle Stearns, Sobopla
   2 weeks/1 day, 1x daily: A.M.
   6/1 to 6/15

4. Irritability and mood changes
   #3, #5, #6, Chives
   1 week/5 days, 2x daily: A.M. & P.M.
   6/1 to 6/12

5. Blurred vision
   Betty Prior, Cauliflower, Zinnia, #6
   1 week/2 days, 2x daily: A.M. & P.M.
   6/1 to 6/9

6. Slow-healing wounds & bruises
   V-2, B-1, B-2, Tomato
   13 weeks/1 day, 1x daily: P.M.
   6/1 to 8/31

7. Tingling in the hands
   Blaze, Sonia, Tiffany, Peace, Eclipse
   4 weeks/6 days, 2x daily: A.M. & P.M.
   6/1 to 7/4

8. Gall Bladder, Pancreas, Spleen ☒
   Nymphenburg, Celery, Tomato, #1
   3 weeks/4 days, 2x daily: A.M. & P.M.
   6/1 to 6/25

9. Factor-X
   Cauliflower, Chicago Peace, Dill
   14 weeks/4 days, 2x daily: P.M.
   6/1 to 9/10

10. Factor-Y
    #7, Nasturtium, Cauliflower,
    Moon, Sobopla, #3, #1, F-1,
    Royal Highness, Tomato, Snap Pea
    26 weeks, 4 days, 1x daily: A.M.
    6/1 to 12/3

Auxiliary List after 2-week delay:

11. Depression ☹
    6/15: Clear ✔✔✔✔✔✔
    (No longer experiencing depression!)

12. Fear of losing my job $
    Royal Highness, F-1
    1 week
    6/15 to 6/21

13. Anger at the inconveniences 💣
    Chives, F-1
    3 days, 2x daily: noon & P.M.
    6/15 to 6/18

NOTE: The Essence names listed in all the examples throughout the book are from the five sets of Perelandra Essences. They were chosen randomly and do not reflect actual testing results.

Perelandra Essence Telegraph Test Checklist

Name: _for myself_

Intent: _Type 2 diabetes_

Date: _6/1/11_

First, do a Basic Essence Test to clear yourself. Then focus on the intent and ask, "Which electric circuits need telegraph testing for [read intent]?" Test the list.

___ ___ Cell division/mitosis
___ ___ Tissues: Epithelium
___ ___ Tissues: Connective Tissue
___ ___ Tissues: Muscle Tissue
___ ___ **SKELETAL SYSTEM: unit**
___ ___ Bones of the Skull
___ ___ Vertebrae and Vertebral Column
___ ___ Thorax
___ ___ Upper Limbs: Pectoral Girdles and Arms
___ ___ Forearms
___ ___ Bones of the Hands
___ ___ Lower Limbs: Pelvis and Pelvic Girdle
___ ___ Thighs and Legs
___ ___ Bones of the Feet
___ ___ Joints: unit
___ ___ **MUSCULAR SYSTEM: unit**
___ ___ Head (including face and mastication)
___ ___ Neck
___ ___ Torso
___ ___ Upper Limbs (shoulders, forearms, wrists, hands, fingers)
___ ___ Lower Limbs (gluteal region, thighs, legs, feet)
___ ___ **CARDIOVASCULAR SYSTEM: unit**
___ ___ Blood and Blood Cells
___ ___ Mediastinum
___ ___ Heart
___ ___ **LYMPHATIC SYSTEM: unit**
___ ___ Thoracic Duct and Tributaries
___ ___ Lymph Nodes
___ ___ **RESPIRATORY SYSTEM: unit**
___ ___ External Nose, Nasal Septum, Nasal Cavity
___ ___ Paranasal Air Sinuses
___ ___ Pharynx and Larynx
___ ___ Lungs and Bronchial Tree
___ ___ Mediastinal Surface of the Lungs
___ ___ **INTEGUMENTARY SYSTEM: unit**
___ ___ Skin
___ ___ Sensory Receptors of the Skin
___ ___ **DIGESTIVE SYSTEM: unit**
___ ___ Mouth and Tongue
___ ___ Teeth
___ ___ Pharynx and Esophagus
___ ___ Peritoneum
___ ___ Stomach
___ ___ Small Intestine: Duodenum, Jejunum, Ileum
___ ___ Large Intestine
___ ___ Liver
___ ✔ Gall Bladder, Pancreas, Spleen

___ ___ **URINARY SYSTEM: unit**
___ ___ Kidneys, Abdominal Cavity Vessels
___ ___ Kidney, Coronal Section
___ ___ Uriniferous Tubule
___ ___ **REPRODUCTIVE SYSTEM**
___ ___ Male: unit
___ ___ Testes
___ ___ Urethra, Penis, Urogenital Region
___ ___ Female: unit
___ ___ Ovaries
___ ___ Uterus and Uterine Tubes
___ ___ Breasts
___ ___ Embryo/Fetus, Fetal/Maternal Coverings, Placenta
___ ___ **ENDOCRINE SYSTEM: unit**
___ ___ Pituitary Gland and Hypothalamus
___ ___ Thyroid Gland and Parathyroid Glands
___ ___ Adrenal Glands
___ ___ Gastrointestinal Hormones and Pancreatic Secretions
___ ___ **NERVOUS SYSTEM: unit**
___ ___ Neurons, Nerve Endings
___ ___ Reflex Arcs
___ ___ Central Nervous System: unit
___ ___ Ventricles
___ ___ Meninges of the Brain and Spinal Cord
___ ___ CSF (cerebrospinal fluid)
___ ___ Cerebral Hemispheres
___ ___ Diencephalon
___ ___ Brainstem/Cerebellum
___ ___ Spinal Cord
___ ___ Ascending (Sensory) Tracts
___ ___ Descending (Motor) Tracts
___ ___ Spinal Nerves
___ ___ Nerves to Upper Limbs
___ ___ Nerves to Lower Limbs
___ ___ Dermatomes
___ ___ Cranial Nerves
___ ___ Autonomic Nervous System (ANS)
___ ___ Visual System
___ ___ Auditory System
___ ___ Taste and Olfaction
___ ___ **IMMUNE SYSTEM: unit**
___ ___ Thymus and Red Marrow
___ ___ Spleen
___ ___ Lymph Node
___ ___ Mucosal Associated Lymphoid Tissue (M.A.L.T.)
___ ✔ **FACTOR-X**
___ ✔ Factor-Y
___ ___ Factor-Z

Follow-up Testing

Focus: Type 2 diabetes

1. Full electric system ☺
    Betty Prior, Yellow Yarrow, Bowl
    3 weeks, 1x daily: P.M.
    7/17 to 8/6

    8/7: clear ✔✔✔✔✔✔

2. Feeling very thirsty
    Corn, Zucchini, Ambassador, #7
    8 weeks, 3 days, 2x daily: A.M. & P.M.
    6/22 to 8/19

    8/20
    #6, #7, Moon, V-2, B-1
    1 week, 1x daily: A.M.
    8/20 to 8/26

    8/27: clear ✔✔✔✔✔✔

3. Frequent urination
    Bowl, Mr. Lincoln, White Lightnin'
    2 weeks, 1x daily: A.M.
    6/16 to 6/29

    6/30
    clear ✔✔✔✔ (7/4 not clear!)

    7/5
    Ambassador, #7
    6 days, 2x daily: A.M. & noon
    7/5 to 7/10

    7/10
    V-1, F-2, Royal Highness,
    Orange Ruffles
    3 weeks, 1x daily: noon
    7/10 to 7/30

    7/31
    clear ✔✔✔✔✔✔ (finally!!)

4. Irritability and mood changes
    #3, #5, #6, Chives
    6 weeks/5 days, 1x daily: P.M.
    6/13 to 7/29

    7/30
    Comfrey, Royal Highness, Bowl,
    Orange Ruffles, V-1, Nasturtium
    3 weeks, 1x daily: P.M.
    7/30 to 8/19

    8/20
    Mr. Lincoln
    4 days, 1x daily: P.M.
    8/20 to 8/23

    8/24: clear ✔✔✔✔✔✔

5. Blurred vision
    Peace, Royal Highness, #6, #4
    2 weeks/6 days, 1x daily: A.M.
    6/10 to 6/29

    6/30
    Chicago Peace, Betty Prior, Tiffany
    2 weeks, 1x daily: A.M.
    6/30 to 7/13

    7/14
    F-2, B-1, Bowl
    5 days, 1x daily: A.M.
    7/14 to 7/18

    7/19: clear ✔✔✔✔✔✔

6. Slow-healing wounds & bruises
    9/1: clear ✔✔✔✔✔✔

Follow-up Testing

Focus: Type 2 Diabetes

7. Tingling in the hands
   Eclipse, #6, Orange Ruffles, Bowl
   Chicago Peace, Sonia, Comfrey
   6 weeks/4 days, 1x daily: noon
   7/5 to 8/19

   8/20
   Dill, Okra, Tiffany, Zucchini
   2 weeks, 1x daily: noon
   8/20 to 9/2

   9/3
   Blaze, Okra, Dill, #8, #4
   2 weeks/3 days, 1x daily: noon
   9/3 to 9/19

   9/20: Clear ✔✔ (not yet)

   9/23
   Salvia, Comfrey, Yellow Yarrow
   1 week/1 day, 1x daily: noon
   9/23 to 9/30

   10/1
   Dill, Zucchini
   1 week/3 days, 1x daily: noon
   10/1 to 10/10

   10/11: Clear ✔✔✔✔✔✔

8. Gall Bladder, Pancreas, Spleen ⧖
   Zucchini, Dill
   18 weeks, 2x daily: A.M. & P.M.
   6/26 to 10/30

   10/31 Clear ✔✔✔✔✔✔

9. Factor-X
   Sobopla, Nymphenburg, Tiffany,
   Dill, F-1
   4 days, 1x daily: A.M.
   9/11 to 9/14

   9/15 Clear ✔✔✔✔✔✔

10. Factor-Y
    12/4 Clear ✔✔✔✔✔✔

Auxiliary symptoms

11. Depression ☹
    Gone by 6/15.

12. Fear of losing my job $
    Snap Pea, Bowl, Zucchini
    1 week/2 days, 1x daily: P.M.
    6/22 to 6/30

    7/1
    Clear ✔✔✔✔✔✔
    (Got a promotion and a raise!!)

13. Anger at the inconveniences 💣
    6/19: Clear ✔✔✔✔✔✔

Chapter 10

Surgery, Scars, and Phantom Limb Syndrome

BEFORE SURGERY

WHEN CONSIDERING SURGERY, it's important that we remain calm and balanced emotionally and mentally so that we can hear everything that is being said to us about the procedure, consider all the options available and make the decisions that best address the problem. So the focus for using ETS Plus and the Perelandra Essences prior to surgery centers around the need to stabilize ourselves on the PEMS levels. A positive outcome hinges in large part on how well we've prepared as we enter a surgical procedure.

● TRAUMA MOMENT #1. When you are first told by the doctor that you need surgery, you have just been smacked with a trauma moment. Hopefully you will have a bottle of ETS Plus with you and can take the first dose in the doctor's office right after he's given you the news. Everything he says to you after that point must be heard. You need to have your wits about you. You need to understand what he's talking about. So stop him after he gives you the news, take a dose of ETS Plus and then tell him to continue. Right after you leave his office, take three or four doses of ETS Plus, five minutes apart.

● TRAUMA MOMENT #2. This occurs when you are told the date of your surgery. You're hit with the realization that it's really going to happen. When you are given the date, take ETS Plus again. If you are in the doctor's office or you are talking to

TRAUMA MOMENT #1.
Take one dose of ETS Plus when the doctor gives you the news. Take three or four doses, five minutes apart, right after leaving the doctor's office.

TRAUMA MOMENT #2.
Take one dose of ETS Plus when you are given the date for surgery. Take three or four doses, five minutes apart, right after leaving the doctor's office or hanging up the phone.

141

him by phone, repeat the routine you did when he told you that you needed surgery. Stop him for a second, take a dose of ETS Plus, then tell him to continue. After the conversation, take ETS Plus three or four times, five minutes apart.

If you are having elective surgery in which you are the one initiating the need for an operation, your first trauma moment will be different and perhaps a bit more subtle. It may include the moment when you made that decision, so take ETS Plus then to make sure all the trauma circuits are balanced and stabilized. But most likely the more intense trauma moment for you will come when you are first told the date of the operation. That this-thing-is-really-happening moment can be surprisingly traumatic even when you are the one requesting the surgery.

WAITING FOR THE DAY. Do a daily Basic Essence Test until you enter the hospital for the surgery.

Add a Basic Telegraph Test to prepare your electric system for the surgery.

● WAITING FOR THE DAY. During the waiting period, your focus is to achieve and maintain as deep a level of stability as possible. For this, do a daily Basic Essence Test until you enter the hospital for the surgery. This will keep your electric system stable, clear out any damage caused by the inevitable emotional stress around the surgery, and make sure you aren't impacted electrically by anything that might be swirling around you at home, at work or at the doctor's office.

Add a Basic Telegraph Test with just one focus to telegraph: "My electric system and circuits in preparation for the [insert the surgical target name]." (Ex., gall bladder removal, valve replacement, appendectomy...) Take the needed Essences and do any follow-up testing until the day you leave for the hospital. At that point, consider the preparation period over and stop taking Essences. Leave your Essence sets at home but take a couple of bottles of ETS Plus with you to the hospital.

TRAUMA MOMENT #3. Take one dose of ETS Plus after each hospital test is completed. Continue the daily Basic Essence Test as well.

● TRAUMA MOMENT #3. You will probably need to have tests done in preparation for surgery. No matter how a test registers on the "annoyance, fear and pain scale," take one dose of ETS Plus immediately after the test is completed. Continue doing the Basic Essence Tests each day throughout the entire period before surgery. Especially don't skip the days when you have appointments for tests.

TRAUMA MOMENT #4. Take one dose of ETS Plus after guests leave.

● TRAUMA MOMENT #4. This has to do with your family, loved ones and friends. They will worry, cluster around you, try to do things for you that at times are not very helpful, give you advice that at times isn't very helpful... Well, you get the idea. I know they don't mean to add to your stress level, but they do. Any time you are not laughing and having a good time during a visit, take a dose of ETS Plus after the guests leave. This might be the right time for you to introduce ETS Plus to them and suggest they take it several times a day to calm *their* nerves!

THE HOSPITAL

Once you enter the hospital, assume that you have entered an Extended Trauma Time Frame and take three to five doses of ETS Plus daily, including one dose at bedtime. Take an additional dose anytime you feel "hit" by the experience as you wait for surgery. Include visits from your group of well-meaning but overly emotional family and friends. Don't hesitate to take an additional dose of ETS Plus after they leave. (Or while they are still there, if they're making you crazy and they won't leave.) This might be another opportunity for you to introduce ETS Plus to them and suggest they take it several times a day to calm their nerves!

However, if you are close to the time you'll be going into surgery and you've been told you can't eat or drink anything, *don't take ETS Plus orally.* Instead, *apply one drop** topically to your forehead, lightly rub it in and then let it air dry. You may not get the full effect of the ETS Plus, but you'll receive some benefit without breaking that pre-surgical fast.

● EMERGENCY SURGERY. There's no time for preparing prior to surgery. For the entire time you are dealing with this emergency up to the time of surgery, assume you are in an Extended Trauma Time Frame. Take ETS Plus three to five times each day prior to surgery. If your emergency doesn't include that kind of time, take as many of the three to five doses as possible prior to going into surgery. Once the surgery is over, follow the listed protocol starting with "Post-surgery in the hospital."

If your surgical emergency was caused by an accident that left you with multiple injuries, you'll need to telegraph test those injuries along with the surgery testing. Follow the steps as outlined for telegraph testing multiple injuries (pp. 79–80).

AFTER SURGERY

● POST-SURGERY IN THE HOSPITAL. Take three to four doses of ETS Plus, five minutes apart, after surgery. Here's where a family member or friend can help by administering these doses to you. Set this up with them prior to your surgery. NOTE: ETS Plus will not interfere with anesthesia or pain medication.

While recovering in the hospital, you are still in the Extended Trauma Time Frame and need to take ETS Plus three to five times daily, including one dose at bedtime.

Surgery, Scars, and Phantom Limb Syndrome

THE HOSPITAL.
Take three to five doses of ETS Plus daily, including one dose at bedtime. Take an additional dose anytime you feel "hit" by the experience.

* HEADS UP!
Apply only one drop to your forehead, not the ten to twelve drops you would normally take. A full dose of ETS Plus at this point could interfere with whatever you will be given during surgery.

EMERGENCY SURGERY.
Take ETS Plus three to five times daily prior to surgery.

FOR OUTPATIENT SURGICAL PROCEDURES.
Consider this surgery (which it is even though it is not done in a hospital) and follow the Essence protocol for surgery. The "Hospital" steps will apply to your time in the doctor's office or clinic.

POST-SURGERY IN THE HOSPITAL.
Take three to four doses of ETS Plus, five minutes apart, after surgery.

DURING THE HOSPITAL STAY.
Take ETS Plus three to five times daily, including one dose at bedtime.

Should you experience sudden pain or discomfort, take an additional dose of ETS Plus immediately and buzz for the nurse.

AT HOME. Continue taking ETS Plus three to five times daily, including one dose at bedtime. Take an additional dose when you experience discomfort.

● RECOVERY AND RECUPERATION AT HOME. If you don't have the strength to resume testing when you first get home, assume you are still in the Extended Trauma Time Frame and continue taking ETS Plus three to five times a day, including one dose at bedtime.

READY FOR TESTING. Discontinue the daily doses of ETS Plus and set up for the Basic Telegraph Tests #1 and #2.

● THE EXTENDED TRAUMA TIME FRAME HAS ENDED AND YOU CAN TEST AGAIN. When you are able to test again, discontinue the daily doses of ETS Plus and set up two separate Basic Telegraph Tests *to be worked simultaneously.* During surgery, the surgeon didn't just cut into the body and repair or remove "stuff." The surgeon also sliced through your electric system and disrupted circuit connections. Each Basic Telegraph Test will have a different intent and focus: (1) the surgical goal—the circuits in need of repair as a result of the original problem and the targeted work, and (2) the surgical procedure—the circuits that were severed by the incision(s) or damaged during the overall surgical procedure.

> IMPORTANT: If you need help getting the information about your surgery for the BTT checklist, don't forget to ask your doctor to explain what was involved in the surgery and what parts of your body were affected. Unless he's the strong, silent type with the doctor/patient manners of a kumquat, he'll tell you. However, if you see a kumquat forming over his head as he looks at you with annoyance, bid him adieu and go ask one of the nurses to help you. Take notes.

Basic Telegraph Test #1: Set up the first Basic Telegraph Test by stating the intent:
> Intent: Balance, stabilize and repair the electric system and circuits connected with and impacted by the original problem and the work done in the targeted surgical area.

> *The BTT checklist:* Include both the areas/organs targeted by the surgery plus everything that is connected with the original diagnosis that led to surgery. Test the Perelandra Essence Telegraph Test Checklist to identify the additional areas that need to be included on the BTT checklist for this first testing intent.

> Proceed with the Basic Telegraph Test steps and do the needed follow-up testing within *forty-eight hours* after each dosage period ends. Continue doing this until you test clear for seven days straight for each thing listed on

your BTT #1 checklist. At that point, it's safe to assume you have completed your recovery and recuperation period, as far as the first test and intent are concerned.

Basic Telegraph Test #2: Set up the second Basic Telegraph Test and state the intent:
Intent: Balance, stabilize and repair the electric system and circuits connected with and impacted by the incisions and surgical procedure.

The BTT checklist: Include the "external" incision and the deeper "internal" incision. If more than one external or internal incision was made, list each separately. Also include any injuries resulting from post-surgical treatment (sore or inflamed injection sites or where tubes were inserted, bruising, sore skin areas from bandages, etc.), areas of pain, difficulties in mobility… And test the Perelandra Essence Telegraph Test Checklist to identify additional areas that need to be included on the BTT checklist for this intent.

Symptom Identification: If you have a symptom and you're not sure which BTT checklist you should list it on, test the symptom this way. Ask:
Does [symptom in question] belong on the Basic Telegraph Test #1 checklist? (Test.)

Does [symptom in question] belong on the Basic Telegraph Test #2 checklist? (Test.)

Include the symptom on the BTT checklist that tests positive. If both tested positive, this means the symptom needs to be included on both checklists.

Proceed with the Basic Telegraph Test steps and do the needed follow-up testing *within forty-eight hours* after each dosage period ends. Continue doing this until you test clear for seven days straight for each thing listed on your BTT #2 checklist. At that point, it's safe to assume you have completed your recovery and recuperation period, as far as the second intent is concerned.

● ABOUT THE RECOVERY AND RECUPERATION PERIODS. They last longer than we expect, imagine or desire. We complicate the recovery and recuperation periods by pulling out of them before they have completed and trying to resume our daily routine as if nothing happened. Consequently, we end up in "damage control" and end up dealing with health issues we would not be experiencing had we applied patience and completed the full "R&R" period. The surest way to know if we are fully recovered is to continue with the telegraph testing all the way to the end when we test clear for seven straight days.

ACTIVE SCARS

This is something that may require an additional Basic Telegraph Test after surgery. Once you have completed your full recovery and recuperation period, take a good look at your scar. If it still looks inflamed or raw, set up a Basic Telegraph Test with the focus and intent just on the scar. The electric circuits in the area of the scar still need to be repaired and most likely are still severed. In the medical world some call this condition "ugly scars." I like to think of them as "active scars." All kinds of health issues, serious and not so serious, can result from an active scar. The scar itself is not the cause of a health problem. Rather, it's a symptom. The actual cause is the damaged and severed electric circuits connected with the scar.

Over the years, I have heard some amazing stories about health issues that were eliminated once an active scar was successfully treated. One physician told me about an older woman who came to him for a checkup. She was wheelchair bound and had been unable to walk for years. She was in luck because he was one of the few physicians in the world who recognizes and treats active scars. After checking her, he asked if she had any old scars that looked raw or red. She said no. At the next appointment, he asked her again. She still said no. But this time he needed to examine her chest. When she opened her blouse, he later said to me that he saw a long, vertical, raw scar that ran from her clavicle right down to her abdomen. He was surprised, to say the least. He said it was amazingly ugly and apparently she had somehow managed to block its existence all these years. He asked her about that scar, and she explained that she had open heart surgery in the Soviet Union thirty years prior. Not long after the surgery, she began having difficulty walking, which eventually led to the wheelchair. After he addressed the damaged circuits connected with her scar for a couple of months, it changed color and appearance. He said it was now a "healthy scar." And in a matter of few weeks, she got out of the wheelchair and began walking again.

The story I've just told you is probably the most dramatic example of active-scar problems I've heard over the years. Again, it's not the scar that is the issue. It's the electric system and the damaged circuits that are causing the active scar and the other health problems. Address the damaged circuits and the scar heals—and we clear up the other health problems related to those damaged circuits.

The excellent news in all of this is that we don't have to search out a physician who treats active scars. We can take care of them ourselves by addressing the electric circuits directly and working with the Perelandra Essences and the Basic Telegraph Test. The scars and the related circuits respond extremely well to this treatment.

If you'll remember, I had you list "external incision" and "internal incision" on the Basic Telegraph Test #2 checklist. This should take care of repairing all the circuits that were severed when the surgical incisions were made. But once you complete your full recovery and recuperation period and you notice that your scar still looks raw, red or swollen, set up a new Basic Telegraph Test right away. State the intent:

> Balance, stabilize and repair the electric system and circuits that are underlying and still causing this active scar.

The Active Scar Checklist

Include the active scar that you can see along with the other incisions/scars (internal and external) that were included in the Basic Telegraph Test #2 checklist (p.145). Now see if there were any incisions that you needed to include on the BTT #2 checklist the first time around but missed because you were not aware of them. Ask:

> Were there any incisions that I did not include on the original BTT #2 checklist? (Test.)

If the result is negative, you have all of the incisions and scar locations on your BTT checklist for the active scar and you are ready to telegraph test that list. However, if you get a positive response to the question, a mystery scar location needs to be included on the BTT checklist for the active scar. Remember, had it been included on your original BTT #2 checklist (p.145), you would have referred to it as an incision. Now it's no longer an incision. It's a scar.

> With your focus on the first mystery scar, state:
> I name this scar the "Factor-X scar."

Write "Factor-X scar" on your BTT checklist for the active scar.

> You may have more than one mystery scar. Ask again:
> Is there another scar that I haven't included on the BTT checklist?
> (Test the question.)

If you get a positive response, state:

> I name this second scar the "Factor-Y scar."
> Include that on your BTT checklist.

Continue asking the question and assigning names (just keep assigning letters) until you get a negative to the question: "Is there another scar that

I haven't included on the BTT checklist?" Now all the scars have been included in your new BTT checklist.

Proceed with the Basic Telegraph Test steps and do the needed follow-up testing *within forty-eight hours* after each dosage period ends. Continue doing this until you test clear for seven days straight for each item listed on your BTT checklist. At that point, it's safe to assume you have completed your recovery and recuperation period, as far as the active scar is concerned.

Give the active scar five more weeks to finish its shift from active to healthy. If, after that time, it still looks raw, set up the telegraph testing for an active scar again and do a new round of testing. Something was missed. See if you need to add another mystery scar to the checklist. This second round of active-scar testing will not be a frequent occurrence.

When I have publically discussed active scars in the past, it usually inspires people to run home, strip, stand in front of a mirror and look for what they expect is a lifetime collection of active scars. Relax. First, they call it "ugly" for a reason. An active scar is so distinct from a healthy scar, you will know if you've got one — unless you've blocked it out of your mind like the woman in the wheelchair. So it's going to be easy to spot an active scar. If you do have one, just set up a Basic Telegraph Test as outlined above. If you're unsure (any scar looks ugly to you so you're not sure if what you're seeing is active or not), set up the Basic Telegraph Test anyway. If it's not active, everything on the BTT checklist will test clear, no Essences needed.

> Stretch marks are a form of scarring. If you have stretch marks that have not diminished over a reasonable amount of time and still look "active" to you, set up a Basic Telegraph Test for scars. Treat the stretch marks within a certain body location as a unit. For example, the stretch marks on your abdomen, or the marks on your arms, or your legs. The localized collection of marks constitute one "item" and one focus on your BTT checklist. Include on the BTT checklist any other symptoms you are experiencing that might be connected to the stretch-mark scarring.

PHANTOM LIMB SYNDROME

Phantom limb syndrome is pain (or other sensations such as tingling, cramping, heat, cold and squeezing along with pain) that is felt in the area where an arm or leg has been amputated. Phantom limb pain can be mild to agonizing and disabling, and it may lead to a lifelong battle with chronic pain. Women who have had a breast removed because of breast cancer may also feel phantom pain. Some amputees may experience residual limb pain or "stump pain" at the actual site of the amputation, such as cramping, burning, aching, or sensations of heat or cold in the remaining stump. Phantom limb syndrome is relatively common in amputees, especially in the early months and years after limb loss.

When a limb is amputated, we are left with an electrical situation that is very different from a surgical incision. With an incision, you end up with electric circuits that have been severed, but the disconnected ends remain in place and can reconnect either naturally or with the help of ETS Plus and the Essences, thus closing the circuitry again. With an amputation, an entire section of a person's electric system is completely removed and the person is left with only one end of the remaining severed circuits.

But as you know by now, every bodily action, reaction and ability is supported by electric circuits on the *four* PEMS levels and not just the physical level. The circuits on each of these four levels are also connected with the brain circuits. If this were not the case, the limb would not have been able to experience full-range function prior to the amputation.

It's also important to understand that some of the PEMS circuits that support one area of the body may not be physically located in that specific area. It has to do with how the circuits function on each of the PEMS levels in relationship to the one location (i.e., a limb) and with the rest of the body. For example, all the PEMS circuits that support the right-arm functions and sensations may not be located in the right arm. Because of the nature and intricacy of a biologically closed system of electric circuits, it doesn't matter if the circuit supporting one function of the right arm is actually located somewhere around the left toe. It's a completely closed system with connected and closed electric circuits that remain active and shoot impulses in less than a nanosecond. The right-arm circuits sitting somewhere around the left toe are a non-issue when considering distance and speed. However, the fact that some right-arm circuits may be connected with circuits located around the left toe does say something about the intricacy of these electrical connections and the complexity of support present within the electric system as a whole. Electric circuits are not "laid out" randomly. There is a reason some circuits that support one area or function of the body are located in a different area and connected with other seemingly unrelated circuits.

When a limb is removed, we are left with four major electrical issues to deal with:

1. The removal of a significant portion of the person's electric system that has left open circuits and severed circuit ends.

2. The removal of circuits that impact the balance, function and general health in areas of the body that were not amputated.

3. The PEMS circuits that are part of the supportive foundation for the now-removed limb that remain untouched, active and still connected with the body's remaining electric system, its nervous system and brain.

4. The need to establish a new range and balance for the remaining electric system as a functioning unit.

Phantom limb syndrome (including "stump pain") is the result of problems that arise primarily from #1 and #3.

Treating Amputation and Phantom Limb Syndrome

When faced with amputation, follow the surgery guidelines as written up to and including "Recovery and recuperation at home" (pp. 141–144). Up to this point, you are working with a straight surgical procedure. Once you can resume testing, you will discontinue the daily doses of ETS Plus and set up four Basic Telegraph Tests that specifically address the amputation and its resulting unique electrical issues. *Work with these four Telegraph Tests simultaneously.*

● THE SURGERY EXTENDED TRAUMA TIME FRAME HAS ENDED AND YOU CAN TEST AGAIN.

Each Basic Telegraph Test will have a different intent and focus:
1. Balance, stabilize and repair the open circuits and severed circuit ends caused by the amputation and the removal of a significant portion of the electric system.

2. Establish alternate electric circuit connections and pathways to restore the balance, function and general health in areas of the body that were not amputated but suffered circuit damage resulting from the amputation.

3. Shift the function of the remaining PEMS circuits that were part of the supportive foundation for the now-removed limb but are still active and connected with the body's remaining electric system, its nervous system and brain to reflect the overall new balance of the electric system as a unit.

4. Balance, stabilize and repair the remaining electric system as a unit with a new range of function, strength and balance.

Basic Telegraph Test #1 for an amputation: Set up the first Basic Telegraph Test by stating the intent:

Intent: Balance, stabilize and repair the open circuits and severed circuit ends caused by the amputation and the removal of a significant portion of the electric system.

The BTT checklist #1: Unlike other BTT checklists, the ones for amputation repair will not be a detailed collection of symptoms and parts. Instead, you will set up the BTT checklist to reflect the overall intent and focus of the test. Write:

Focus: All the open circuits and severed circuit ends caused by the amputation and the removal of a significant portion of the electric system.

Proceed with the Basic Telegraph Test steps and do the needed follow-up testing *within forty-eight hours* after each dosage period ends. Continue doing this until you test clear for seven days straight. At that point, it's safe to assume you have completed your recovery and recuperation period, as far as the first test and intent are concerned.

Basic Telegraph Test #2 for an amputation: Set up the second Basic Telegraph Test and state the intent:

Intent: Establish alternate electric circuit connections and pathways to restore the balance, function and general health in areas of the body that were not amputated but suffered circuit damage resulting from the amputation.

The BTT checklist #2, write:

Focus: Establish all needed alternate electric circuit connections and pathways to restore the balance, function and general health in areas of the body that were not amputated but suffered circuit damage resulting from the amputation.

Proceed with the Basic Telegraph Test steps and do the needed follow-up testing *within forty-eight hours* after each dosage period ends. Continue doing this until you test clear for seven days straight. At that point, it's safe to assume you have completed your recovery and recuperation period, as far as the second test and intent are concerned.

Basic Telegraph Test #3 for an amputation: Set up the third Basic Telegraph Test by stating the intent:

Intent: Shift the function of the remaining PEMS circuits that were part of the supportive foundation for the now-removed limb and are still active and connected with the body's remaining electric system, its nervous system and brain to reflect the overall new balance of the electric system as a unit.

The BTT checklist #3, write:
Focus: Shift the function of all the remaining PEMS circuits that were part of the supportive foundation for the now-removed limb and are still active and connected with the body's remaining electric system, its nervous system and brain to reflect the overall new balance of the electric system as a unit.

Proceed with the Basic Telegraph Test steps and do the needed follow-up testing *within forty-eight hours* after each dosage period ends. Continue doing this until you test clear for seven days straight. At that point, it's safe to assume you have completed your recovery and recuperation period, as far as the third test and intent are concerned.

Basic Telegraph Test #4 for an amputation: Set up the fourth Basic Telegraph Test by stating the intent:

Intent: Balance, stabilize and repair the remaining electric system as a unit with a new range of function, strength and balance.

The BTT checklist #4, write:
Focus: Balance, stabilize and repair the remaining electric system as a functioning unit with a new range of function, strength and balance.

Proceed with the Basic Telegraph Test steps and do the needed follow-up testing *within forty-eight hours* after each dosage period ends. Continue doing this until you test clear for seven days straight. At that point, it's safe to assume you have completed your recovery and recuperation period, as far as the fourth test and intent are concerned.

IMPORTANT: Anytime you experience pain or any other phantom-limb symptoms, take a dose of ETS Plus as soon as possible. If the symptom doesn't subside right away, take two to three more doses five minutes apart. These doses of ETS Plus are in addition to the Essences and ETS Plus you'll be taking as part of the treatment regimen.

ᦅᦅᦅ

● A RECURRENCE OF PHANTOM LIMB PROBLEMS. Should you experience symptoms after you've completed the amputation and phantom-limb syndrome treatment, just set up a Basic Telegraph Test. Now the BTT checklist will include all the symptoms you are currently feeling and experiencing. Test each symptom and do all the needed follow-ups until you test clear for seven days straight.

● YOU HAD THE SURGERY SOME TIME AGO. If you have already had an amputation, it is still important to balance, stabilize and repair any remaining electrical damage, no matter how long ago the surgery was performed. This is especially important for those still suffering phantom limb pain, stump pain, discomfort caused by an artificial limb or any other discomfort. The continuing problems indicate continuing electrical damage. It is also important for those experiencing little or no after-effects. Checking the state of your electric system and repairing any remaining circuits that are still damaged is the final step and completes your healing process.

To do this, set up the four post-surgery Basic Telegraph Tests for treating amputation and phantom limb syndrome (pp. 150–153). *Work with the four BTT checklists simultaneously.*

1. Balance, stabilize and repair any remaining open circuits and severed circuit ends caused by the amputation and the removal of a significant portion of the electric system.

2. Establish alternate electric circuit connections and pathways to restore the balance, function and general health in areas of the body that were not amputated but suffered circuit damage resulting from the amputation.

3. Shift the function of the remaining PEMS circuits that were part of the supportive foundation for the now-removed limb but are still active and connected with the body's remaining electric system, its nervous system and brain to reflect the overall new balance of the electric system as a unit.

4. Balance, stabilize and repair the remaining electric system as a unit with a new range of function, strength and balance.

Proceed with the Basic Telegraph Test steps and do the needed follow-up testing *within forty-eight hours* after each dosage period ends. Continue doing this until you test clear for seven days straight. At that point, it's safe to assume you have completed the healing process centered around the amputation.

Should you experience any problems after completing these four telegraph tests, set up a new Basic Telegraph Test. Now the BTT checklist will include all the symptoms you are currently feeling and experiencing. Test each symptom and do all the needed follow up until you test clear for seven days straight.

PKTT and Testing for Amputees

If you are missing an arm or hand, you have a little logistical problem when it comes to PKTT. There are ways to solve the problem. I encourage you to call our Question Hot Line so that we can talk with you directly and come up with the best solution for you to use in light of your specific situation. Our Question Hot Line contact information is at the end of this book.

Part Four

SURROGATE ESSENCE TESTING

Chapter 11

About Surrogate Essence Testing

ONCE YOU EXPERIENCE THE RESULTS of using the Perelandra Essences for yourself, you will want to help those around you who are having health difficulties. As you have probably figured out by now, this is not something that is likely to be offered as a regular part of mainstream medicine—at least not for awhile.

If you learn to Essence test for yourself and learn to use them well for your own health issues before attempting to surrogate test another, 98 percent of your questions about surrogate testing will already be answered. Most of the questions we get are from those who jumped the gun, didn't go through their personal learning curve and dove into surrogate testing before they were ready. This is guaranteed confusion. If you're new to the Perelandra Essences, just reading this chapter about surrogate testing can feel overwhelming.

However, once you are comfortable with the Essences, it's really quite easy to surrogate test another person—adult or child—using the PKTT method you have been using to test yourself. In surrogate testing, you set up a controlled link with the other person's electric system and read all their test answers through your electric system. Your two electric systems are "plugged" into one another, and this allows only the other person's electrical responses to feed into your system, thus enabling you to PKTT using *your* fingers but reading *the other person's* responses.

● THE KEY TO ACCURATE SURROGATE TEST RESULTS. The key to making sure you are reading the other person's responses and not your own is step 1 of the surrogate testing process setup:

If you do not clear your electric system first (using the Basic Essence Test), whatever Essences you need and whatever part of your electric system that is not in balance will "bleed" into the surrogate testing. Should this happen, the other person's electric system will test positive for the Essences *you* need. If your electric system is cleared first, it will not override the surrogate test or be a factor in the test results and you will get clean responses from the person you are testing. So don't be sloppy about step 1 in surrogate testing. The integrity of the rest of the testing depends on it.

● PHYSICAL PRESENCE OF THE TESTER. It is important for the integrity of the testing and for the support of the other person, that you always be physically present with anyone you are working with. Do not try to Essence test someone "long distance" or over the phone. The Perelandra Essences were not "designed" to include this kind of testing, and accuracy will not be consistent or guaranteed.

If you know someone in need and you can't be physically present for Essence testing, send them a bottle of ETS Plus and instruct them to take a dose (a dropperful) three to five times a day, depending on the severity of their situation. They should continue the daily doses of ETS Plus until they have fully recovered or until you can get to them for surrogate Essence testing. By providing them with ETS Plus, their electric system is supported, and any trauma they might experience while recovering will not complicate the overall healing process. However, by including surrogate testing, the circuits connected to the health problem will receive the individualized treatment they need and the healing process will be greatly assisted.

SURROGATE TESTING GUIDELINES

● Don't try to do surrogate testing until you're comfortable doing Essence testing (the Basic Essence Test and the Basic Telegraph Test) for yourself.

● If you are helping someone who has just suffered a trauma of any kind, administer the three to four doses of ETS Plus first. Follow this up with the appropriate surrogate testing (the Basic Essence Test and the Basic Telegraph Test) fifteen to twenty minutes after the last dose of ETS Plus. Your testing for the person's illness or injury will be less complex if you address the trauma elements with ETS Plus first.

● Make physical contact with the person you are testing: his* hand on your knee, his foot touching your foot, or his hand on your shoulder. Maintain that contact throughout the testing, unless otherwise directed in the surrogate testing steps.

● If possible (if he is not unconscious, too young or disabled), the person must keep his attention on the testing. To help him maintain focus, read the steps aloud as you go through them and explain some of what you are doing. This will engage the person's interest and help him hold his focus.

● All Essences that test positive are given directly to the person you are testing. You do not take them for him.

● Test the Essences as that person would test for himself. The only difference is that you'll be reading his test results through your electric system.

● When surrogate testing, it's important to record what Essences test positive and the dosage information.

● Both of you should drink water before you start to make sure your bodies and electric systems have the water they each need for giving strong test results.

About Surrogate Essence Testing

* For the sake of my sanity and your reading ease, I have written this surrogate testing information from the perspective of the reader testing a man. If you are testing a woman, mentally change all the pronouns to the appropriate feminine form. I am not making a political statement by having chosen to write this section in the masculine. I tossed a coin to see which way I would go, and tails came up.

Eliminate Distractions

While moving through any surrogate testing, it is important that the person you are testing be relaxed yet quietly focused on what you are doing.

● He can't read a book, listen to music, watch television, listen to the radio, be distracted by children or be allowed to fall into daydreaming.

● His attention on what is happening allows for accurate testing. If his mind is engaged in something else, your testing will be more difficult and possibly inaccurate.

● The easiest way to keep his attention is to include him in the process by telling him what you are doing or which Essences have tested positive. Listening to you will help keep him focused. (It also makes focusing easier for you.)

● If either of you is distracted, make sure both of you bring your attention back to the matter at hand before you continue with the testing.

The Surrogate Essence Testing Dance

When surrogate testing, you'll need to move the Essence boxes and bottles around. Some liken it to a dance. To help you with this dance, I have **emphasized the pertinent position phrases** (like that) in the steps that let you know where the boxes and bottles are to be sitting at that given point. After a few tests, the dance begins to make sense and you'll look like John Travolta (in *Saturday Night Fever,* not *Michael).*

Controlling the Surrogate
Testing Learning Curve

If you know someone who is in serious need of the Perelandra Essences but you've just purchased the Essences for yourself and don't know how to use them, you need to weave your learning curve with your desire to help that person. First, while you're learning to test for yourself, your friend in need can be taking ETS Plus four to five times daily to help stabilize him and to provide some comforting support while he waits for you to test him. Then synchronize the testing you do for him with your personal learning curve.

1. LEARN THE BASIC ESSENCE TEST. > THEN DO SURROGATE BASIC ESSENCE TESTING. Once you become comfortable and confident working with the Basic Essence Test for yourself, you are ready to do a surrogate Basic Essence Test for the other person. Plan to test for dosage to reduce the number of tests you'll need to do by making a solution bottle to leave with him. Also plan to return once each dosage period is complete for the important follow-up tests. When the follow-up testing and dosages have been completed and the person tests clear (no further Essences are needed) for three days straight, you have successfully moved the person and his electric system as a unit through a Basic Essence Test.

2. LEARN BASIC TELEGRAPH TESTING. > THEN DO A SURROGATE BASIC TELEGRAPH TEST. Once you become comfortable and confident with the Basic Telegraph Test, you are ready to do a surrogate Basic Telegraph Test for the other person if he has any persistent symptoms. For that, you will need to be prepared to make a solution bottle for each symptom listed on the BTT checklist and return once each dosage period is complete for the follow-up testing. When all the dosage periods for each BTT checklist symptom have been completed and the person tests clear (no further Essences are

needed) for seven days straight, you have successfully moved the person through a full Basic Telegraph Test. (Congratulations! And take a bow.)

3. IF SURROGATE TELEGRAPH TESTING FOR CHRONIC ILLNESS IS NEEDED before you are comfortable with and confident using the Basic Essence Test or the Telegraph Test for yourself, follow these guidelines:

> *Basic > Basic:* If you want to help someone who is chronically ill but you have not yet gotten comfortable with the Basic Essence Test, first give him a bottle of ETS Plus and have him take five doses daily while you learn Basic Essence Testing. Once you are comfortable with and confident using the Basic Essence Test, you are ready to do a surrogate Basic Essence Test with him. Include testing for dosage and make a solution bottle to leave with him. Plan to return once each dosage period is complete for the follow-up testing.

> *About ETS Plus:* You and the chronically ill person will need to make a judgement call as to whether to continue taking the daily doses of ETS Plus once you do the surrogate Basic Essence Test. The two (ETS Plus and the Essences) will not interfere with one another. If he experiences traumas within traumas or has to suffer through painful tests and therapy, continuing the ETS Plus would be good. Also, if he says he doesn't want to give up the ETS Plus because of the quality of stabilization it has given him, then do the surrogate Basic Essence Test knowing that his daily ETS Plus doses will not interfere with those Essences.

> *Telegraph > Telegraph Test for chronic illness:* Once you become comfortable with and confident using the Basic Telegraph Test for yourself, you will need to shift your surrogate work and do telegraph testing for chronic illness. The main difference between the Basic Telegraph Test and telegraph testing for chronic illness is the setup for the two checklists.

> NOTE: If the person is still taking Essences from the Basic Essence Test once you begin the surrogate telegraph testing, he is to continue taking those Essences until he tests clear for three days straight. For awhile he may be taking doses from the first Basic Essence Test as well as the doses of new solutions from the telegraph testing for chronic illness. It may sound tedious beyond words to work the two testing processes simultaneously, but you and he will come out way ahead if you proceed with both tests.

● ABOUT THE SURROGATE TESTING PROCESS STEPS. In the following steps, I am assuming that you have familiarized yourself and are comfortable with the testing steps and information in chapters 6, 7 and 8. This includes the hints, notes, bells and whistles I included in these chapters. Even if you haven't memorized all the information (That would be scary and sad if you have!), at least you know where to turn should you have a question. Finally, to help you help others, I've set up the surrogate process steps to include the wording you will need for the statements and questions.

Follow the same guidelines you used for yourself when determining the best Essence test to use for the other person's health issue.

Chapter 12

Surrogate Basic Essence Test

Supplies:

- the five sets of Perelandra Essences
- pen, paper and calendar
- option: a blank Perelandra Essence Record Chart
- one clean solution bottle*
- brandy or distilled white vinegar preservative (his choice)
- a blank label
- a watch or clock with a second hand
- a clean spoon and several clean paper towels

Both of you prepare for testing:

- Drink some water. Go to the bathroom, if needed. Find a quiet spot and sit comfortably. Place the boxes of Essences and the other supplies within easy reach for you.

- At the top of a clean sheet of paper or a new Perelandra Essence Record Chart, write the person's name and the date.

You're ready to proceed with the surrogate Basic Essence Test.

1. *Always clear your electric system with Essences just before testing another person.* For this, the person cannot be touching you *(Fig. A)*. State aloud or to yourself:

> What Essences do I need to prepare for surrogate testing the Perelandra Essences?

Then do a Basic Essence Test for yourself (steps 2–5, pp. 54–55) and take any needed Essences. Do not test for dosage. These will be taken one time only. If you test clear and you need no Essences, proceed with the surrogate Basic Essence Test.

* To reuse solution bottles, wash the bottles and droppers in hot, soapy water *two times,* rinsing them well, and air dry on a clean paper towel. Do not touch the glass dropper with your fingers (or anything else). But it's okay if the glass dropper lightly touches the clean paper towel during the drying process. Always handle the dropper by the rubber bulb.

Fig. A

Fig. B

2. Physically make contact with the person you are going to test and remain physically connected throughout all the surrogate testing, unless otherwise instructed. Have him place a hand on your knee or touch your foot with his foot or rest his hand lightly on your shoulder *(Fig. B)*.

Focus on the person for five seconds. The easiest way to do this without creeping one another out or giving one another a fit of the giggles is for both of you to look at (focus on) where you are physically connected and hold that focus for five seconds. This touching and focusing connects his electric system with yours.

> Okay. Let me be more clear about this five-second business. If you are in love with this person (and/or he/she with you), now's not the time to gaze longingly at one another and get all gooey-eyed. You are connecting your two electric systems for a health test. Try to keep that in mind. Once all the testing is completed, then you two can get goofy. But not during the testing. Over the years I've surrogate tested people (strangers!) who thought the thing to do during the test was "lovingly" massage my knee. I had to tell them to cut it out and pull themselves together. So I'm blabbering on and on about this because I know from experience that some people don't have the sense God gave a kumquat. Be prepared to draw a line. (But I digress...)

Test the connection by asking (aloud):

> Are our two electric systems connected for this surrogate Basic Essence Test? (Test the question.)

If negative, spend a few more seconds focusing on the individual—and make sure you are physically touching. You both also need to relax. If either of you is being distracted, move to a quieter room or quiet the environment you are in. Encourage him to keep his mind focused on the testing or on the hand (or foot) that is touching you. A wandering mind for either of you will cause fuzzy test results. (Actually it's a lot like trying to test a drunk driver who is swerving all over the place.) Test your connection again. This time you should get a positive result. If not, keep adjusting your physical connection (you may need to change how he is touching you) and applying a sharper focus until you get a positive response to the question.

3. State your intent:

> I want to do a surrogate Basic Essence Test for [person you are testing].

4. Place each box of Essences, one at a time, *in his hands or lap (Fig. C)*. Ask:

> Does he need any Essences from this box? (Test.)

If you get a negative, you don't have to test the bottles from that box because none are needed.

If you get a positive, move the box off to one side and test each bottle from that box individually by placing the bottle *in your lap* to determine which ones are needed *(Fig. D)*. For each bottle, ask:

> Does he need _____ Essence? (Test.)

A positive test result indicates that this particular Essence balances, stabilizes and repairs *his* electric system. You have already cleared yourself of any need for Essences in step 1. So when you place the Essence bottles in your lap for this part of the process, you are literally testing the results of how that Essence is affecting his electric system.

5. Check your results by placing *in his hands or lap* just the bottles that tested positive *(Fig. E)*. Ask:

> Are these the only Essences he needs? (Test.)

If the response is positive, that's a "yes." Go to step 6. If only one Essence is needed, skip step 6 and go to step 7.

If you get a negative, retest the other Essences. A negative means you missed an Essence and need to find what was missed. After retesting, ask the question once more:

> Are these the only Essences he needs? (Test.)

If the response is still negative, keep testing the Essences until you get a positive response to the question. This will verify that you have identified all the needed Essences.

6. If you have more than one Essence, check them as a combination by placing all of them *in his hands or lap** and asking:

> Is this the combination he needs? (Test.)

If you get a negative even though the Essences tested positive when tested individually, you need to adjust the combination. It's a case of the whole being greater than the sum of its parts.

Fig. C

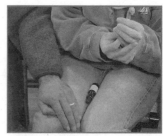

Fig. D

Fig. E

* There is no shortcut for checking the Essence combination in step 6. The bottles that test positive must be taken out of the box(es) and placed in his hands or lap in order to test them properly as a combination.

165

Fig. F

Just test each of the combination bottles separately by having *him hold each bottle (Fig. F)* while you ask:

> Should this bottle be removed from the combination? (Test.)

Whatever tests positive gets removed. Then put the remaining combination bottles *in his hands or lap* and ask:

> Is this combination now correct? (Test.)

You should get a positive. If you don't, test the *original* combination again (the combination before you removed any bottles), and keep working at it until they test positive as a unit.

7. Administer these Essences to him orally, *one drop each.* You may put all the combination Essence drops on a spoon for him to take at one time or place each drop directly on his tongue. Record the Essences that tested positive.

When surrogate testing, most people prefer to put the Essence drops on a spoon. This way he won't accidentally touch the dropper with his tongue or get his saliva on the dropper and you won't have to wash off the dropper before putting it back in the bottle. People can be a little nervous when they are not familiar with Essence testing or having someone put drops into their mouths. Accidents are likely to happen.

Dosage: Number of Days

Fig. G

8. Have him hold *in his hands or lap* the bottle(s) that tested positive as a combination or unit *(Fig. G).*

9. Ask:

> Does he need the Essence(s) more than one time? (Test.)

*If negative, that means he has already completed the dosage in the above step 7 and you have completed the surrogate Basic Essence Test.** To disconnect the two electric systems, just stop touching. Once you two are no longer touching, the electric systems are no longer connected and the two of you are free to continue on with your day.

* If he needed Essences one time only, you will need to do the follow-up testing within the next forty-eight hours.

> NOTE: If the person you are testing is addressing an illness or condition that you feel should logically require Essences for more than one day, yet you tested negative for step 9, he may need another testing approach. To determine if this is so, PKTT test the options.

• *Daily surrogate Basic Essence Test:* In order to move successfully through the problem, he may need different Essences each day. He has already taken the Essence(s) he needs today in step 7 and he needs a new Basic Essence Test tomorrow. You need to consider whether you are in a position to test him daily until he tests clear, no further Essences needed, for seven days straight. Now may be the time to teach him how to test Essences for himself so that he can do the daily testing.

• *Surrogate Basic Telegraph Test:* His health issue may need to be addressed in more detail. Let his electric system adjust to the first Basic Essence Test for a couple of days before doing a surrogate Basic Telegraph Test.*

* If he has a chronic illness, you will need to shift the testing to Telegraph Testing for chronic illness. See chapter 14.

Whatever tests positive is the next step for testing this person.

10. If the result for step 9 is positive, remain connected and find out how many days he should take these Essences and how many times per day.

Do a sequential test. With the needed Essence(s) *in your lap (Fig. H)*, ask:

   Does he need these one day? (Test.)
   Two days? (Test.)
   Three days? (Test.) And so on.

Do a count until you get a negative response.** Your last positive will tell you how many days he is to take the Essences. Record the number of days.

Fig. H

** If he needs to take the Essences for three days, you will test positive when you ask, "one day?" "two days?" "three days?" When you ask, "four days?" you will test negative. That will tell you that his electric system will be assisted by having the Essences available for three days, not four days.

Dosage: Number of Times per Day

11. Using the same format with the bottle(s) still *in your lap,* ask:

   Should he take them one time daily? (Test.)
   Two times daily? (Test.)
   Three times daily? (Test.)

Your last positive will tell you how many times per day they are needed. Record this dosage information.

12. Generally, Essences are to be administered in the morning and/or in the evening and/or in the afternoon. If you wish to be more precise, test to see if it is best for him to take them in the morning, afternoon or evening, or any combination of the three. Ask:

Should these Essences be taken in the morning? (Test.)
In the afternoon? (Test.)
In the evening? (Test.)

Whatever tests positive is when he should take one of his dosages.

Making a Solution Bottle

Fig. I

Make a solution bottle for him if the Essences are to be taken more than one time (and you won't be around to administer the Essences to him) or if he needs to take it several times throughout the day and must carry the solution around.

● Add five drops of each needed Essence to a clean half-ounce bottle *(Fig. I)*.

● Then add one teaspoon of brandy or distilled white vinegar (his choice) if he needs to preserve the solution, and fill with spring or untreated water. If this is unavailable, tap water will do. He can refrigerate the solution, thus eliminating the need for preserving it.

● Label the bottle with the testing purpose/focus ("Basic Essence Test") and dosage information so that he'll know how many days and how many times per day he's to take the solution and not have to rely on memory.

Making a Solution in a Glass

Fig. J

● Add nine drops of each needed Essence concentrate to *four ounces* of water *(Fig. J)*.

● Add three teaspoons of brandy or distilled white vinegar if he wants to preserve this solution. Refrigerate it if no preservative is added.

● Be sure to write down the dosage instructions to leave with him so that he'll know when to take his solution and what to focus on while taking them, and not have to rely on memory.

Dosage and Follow-up Testing

● HELP HIM REMEMBER to take his dosages (one dropperful per dose) for the full period of time prescribed. It'll help him to remember if one of you sets his solution bottle in an obvious place such as on his bedside table, in the kitchen or bathroom. Also record the end date for the solution on a calendar or computer so that you will know when to do the follow-up testing.

● ADMINISTERING DOSAGES. Each time he takes the Essence solution during the prescribed dosage period, he is to first activate the circuits the solution is addressing. He does this by reading the focus/intent ("Basic Essence Test") written on the bottle label.

> IMPORTANT: Once you make a solution bottle, the Essence drops have been diluted and are no longer concentrated. For each dosage, he will need to take ten to twelve drops (one dropperful) of each solution.

● COMPLETING A DOSAGE PERIOD. Once he completes a dosage period, do a new surrogate Basic Essence Test *within forty-eight hours* as a follow up. Continue doing follow-up testing at the end of each dosage period until he tests clear.*

● AFTER TESTING CLEAR, do a new surrogate Basic Essence Test for the next three days. When he tests clear for three days straight, you have completed the series of follow-up testing and he needs no additional Essences at that time.

● PERSISTENT SYMPTOMS OR INJURIES. Should a Basic Essence Test and the follow-ups not take care of all the symptoms or injuries, set up for a surrogate Basic Telegraph Test and list the remaining symptoms on his BTT checklist. Move the telegraph testing completely through all dosage periods and follow-up testing. Continue this until each listed symptom tests clear for seven days straight.

* This includes symptoms that require Essences one time only. The follow-up test is done within forty-eight hours after taking that one required dose.

Chapter 13

Surrogate Basic Telegraph Test

Sᴜᴘᴘʟɪᴇs:

- the five sets of Perelandra Essences
- pen, paper and calendar
- option: a blank Perelandra Essence Record Chart
- a blank Perelandra Essence Telegraph Test Checklist
- a watch or clock with a second hand
- a clean spoon and several clean paper towels
- clean solution bottles (one bottle for each symptom on the BTT checklist)
- brandy or distilled white vinegar preservative (his choice)
- blank labels

Bᴏᴛʜ ᴏꜰ ʏᴏᴜ ᴘʀᴇᴘᴀʀᴇ ꜰᴏʀ ᴛᴇsᴛɪɴɢ:

- Drink some water. Go to the bathroom, if needed. Find a quiet spot and sit comfortably. Place the boxes of Essences and the other supplies within easy reach for you.

- At the top of a clean sheet of paper or the Perelandra Essence Record Chart and a Perelandra Essence Telegraph Test Checklist, write the person's name and the date.

You are ready to proceed with the Surrogate Basic Telegraph Test steps.

1. *Always clear your electric system with Essences just before testing another person.* For this, the person cannot be touching you. State aloud or to yourself:

I would like to clear my electric system and prepare myself for surrogate testing the Perelandra Essences. (Test the Essences.)

Then do a Basic Essence Test (steps 2–5, pp. 54–55) and take any needed Essences. You do not need to test for dosage. These will be taken one time only. If you test clear and you need no Essences, proceed with the surrogate telegraph testing.

2. Physically make contact with the person you are going to test and remain physically connected throughout all the surrogate testing, unless otherwise instructed. Have him place a hand on your knee or touch your foot with his foot or rest his hand lightly on your shoulder.

Focus on the person for five seconds. The easiest way to do this without creeping one another out or getting the giggles is for both of you to look at (focus on) where you are physically connected and hold that focus for five seconds. This touching and focusing connects his electric system to yours. Test the connection by asking aloud:

> Are our two electric systems connected for the Basic Telegraph Test?
> (Test the question.)

If negative, spend a few more seconds focusing on the individual—and make sure you are physically touching. You both need to relax. If either of you is being distracted, move to a quieter room or quiet the environment you are in. Encourage him to keep his mind focused on the testing or on the hand (or foot) that is touching you. A wandering mind for either of you will cause fuzzy test results. Test your connection again. This time you should get a positive result. If not, keep adjusting your physical connection (you may need to change how he is touching you) and applying a sharper focus until you get a positive response to the question.

ADD THE ORGANIZATION AID TO THE BTT CHECKLIST. Add a number in front of everything that is listed on the BTT checklist. The numbers allow for easy referencing when working with the Perelandra Essence Record Chart and writing down all the dosage and follow-up information on separate sheets of paper.

CAUTION: You can include the number on the solution bottle label, but when actually taking the doses from that bottle he will need to state the symptom and not just the number.

3. Before doing any of the surrogate telegraph testing, you must first clear his electric system. To do this, state aloud:

> I want to do a Basic Essence Test to clear [name of person] in preparation for telegraph testing for [state problem]. What Essences does he need? (Test.)

Do a surrogate Basic Essence Test (steps 4–7, pp. 165–166). Administer to him any needed Essences. He only takes these one time, so there's no need to test for dosage. Not needing Essences for clearing the electric system but needing them when telegraph testing the symptoms is not unusual. NOTE: *With the statement in step 3, you also set the intent for the Telegraph Test.*

4. Together make a BTT checklist of all the symptoms and/or injuries connected with the issue he is addressing. Include any symptoms or injuries that he is experiencing but eliminated from consideration because he felt they were not connected. Include any mystery symptoms/injuries (pp. 76–77) and test the Perelandra Essence

Telegraph Test Checklist. Then add whatever tested positive and isn't already included to the BTT checklist. Assign any needed codes or symbols. Also, when dealing with an accident, separate the injuries according to their different locations. (NOTE: You can put the BTT checklist together anytime prior to beginning a surrogate Basic Telegraph Test.)

5. Focus on the first symptom or injury on his BTT checklist and ask:
> What Essences are needed for [insert symptom/injury as listed on the BTT checklist]? (Test the Essences.)

Instruct him to keep his focus on the symptom or injury while you do the surrogate Basic Essence Test, steps 4–7 (pp. 165–166). He may touch or poke the spot if he needs help focusing on it. Remind him to focus on the assigned symbol or code for each out-of-sight symptom.

6. Administer to him the needed Essences for this first symptom/injury. Record the Essences alongside the symptom listed on the BTT checklist or check the needed Essences on the Essence Record Chart. Remember to note on the Record Chart which Essences apply to which symptom.

7. Test for dosage (surrogate Basic Essence Test, steps 8–12, pp. 166–168): Find out how many days and how many times per day he is to take the Essences for this symptom/injury.

If he is to take the Essences just one time, you don't need to do any further dosage testing and you can move on to step 8.

If he is to take these Essences more than one time, complete the dosage testing now. On the BTT checklist next to the symptom, record the dosage information.

NOTE: If you need to make a solution bottle, wait until after all the telegraph testing is completed and make all the needed solution bottles at one time.

8. Repeat the surrogate Basic Telegraph Test steps 4, 5, 6 and 7 for every symptom or injury listed on the BTT checklist.

9. When you've finished testing every symptom/injury on his BTT checklist, complete the Telegraph Test for this issue by doing a final Basic Essence Test (steps 4–7, pp. 165–166) for his full electric system. This will provide balancing and stabilizing for his system as a unit after doing all the circuit repair. *Do not check for dosage. These Essences are to be taken one time only.*

10. Make any needed solution bottles (p. 168). To avoid mistakes and confusion, label each bottle right after making the solution. Include the solution's focus, the beginning and end date of the dosage and how many times a day he is to take it. Also include the times of day he is to take it (morning, afternoon, evening).

You have completed this part of the surrogate Basic Telegraph Test. To disconnect the two electric systems, just stop touching. Once you two are no longer touching, the electric systems are no longer connected and you are each free to get on with your day. There's no sin in the two of you taking a well-deserved coffee/tea/beer/chocolate break!

DOSAGE AND FOLLOW-UP TESTING

● HELP HIM REMEMBER to take his dosages (one dropperful per dose) for the full period of time prescribed. It'll help him to remember if one of you sets his solution bottles in an obvious place, such as on his bedside table, in the kitchen or bathroom. Also record the end date for each solution on a calendar or computer so that you will know when to do the follow-up testing.

● ADMINISTERING DOSAGES. Each time he takes a solution dosage, he is to first activate the circuits the solution is addressing. To do this, he's to read the symptom name listed on the solution bottle label and keep it in mind while taking a dropperful (ten to twelve drops) of the Essence solution. That will automatically activate the targeted area and set up the connections for shifting the Essence patterns to those circuits.

> IMPORTANT: Once you make a solution bottle, the Essence drops have been diluted and are no longer concentrated. For each dosage, he will now need to take ten to twelve drops (one dropperful) of solution.

● COMPLETING A DOSAGE PERIOD AND FOLLOW-UP TESTING. Remember to do all needed follow-up testing *within forty-eight hours* after a dosage period ends.* You need to do a new surrogate Basic Telegraph Test (steps 5–7) for each individual symptom as a follow up to find out if any additional Essences are needed. For this, you must be physically present and connected electrically. Clear your electric system first (step 1) and then his electric system (steps 2–3) before doing steps 5–7. Continue doing surrogate follow-up testing at the end of each dosage period until he

* This includes symptoms that require Essences one time only. The follow-up test is done within forty-eight hours after taking that one required dose.

tests clear. When the symptom/injury tests clear for seven days straight, you know that he has completed the series of follow-up testing and no additional Essences are needed at that time. Cross the symptom/injury off his BTT checklist. If he tested positive for any Essences on any one of the seven days, assume the follow-up series is not complete and continue with the follow-up testing as usual until the symptom tests clear for seven days straight.

● RETURNING AND NEW SYMPTOMS. Should a symptom or injury that tested clear return, just list it again on his BTT checklist and do a new surrogate Basic Telegraph Test for this one symptom, starting with step 1 and testing through step 7. Move it completely through all dosage periods and follow-up testing. Continue this until it tests clear again for seven days straight.

If the returning symptom/injury exhibits any changes or anomalies that differentiate it from the old one in any way, consider this a *new* symptom/injury that needs to be added to the BTT checklist. Do a new surrogate Basic Telegraph Test for that one symptom and move it completely through all dosage periods and follow-up testing. Continue this until it tests clear for seven days straight. If you used a code or symbol on the BTT checklist for the old symptom/injury, *do not use that same one for the new symptom/injury.* It will need its own code or symbol and you will need to "officially" assign the code/symbol. (See pp. 77–79.)

Chapter 14

Surrogate Telegraph Testing for Chronic Illness

SURROGATE TELEGRAPH TESTING FOR CHRONIC ILLNESS is a surrogate Basic Telegraph Test that has built into it a special focus on a serious, long-term health situation. Except for a couple of tweaks, the steps are the same. But because of the seriousness of the situation, the CI checklist will be more extensive than the BTT checklist.

I applaud you if you wish to help someone with a chronic illness and you offer to test them for the Perelandra Essences. This is a serious offer on your part, and you are going to have to commit time, caring, emotion, scheduling and effort in order to do the testing and all of the needed follow-up work. You cannot half-ass this. It would be unfair to the person with the illness. Depending on the severity of the chronic illness and the extent of the damage to the electric system, the testing can provide comfort and a better quality of life ranging from a little improvement to a lot of improvement. But what I can say to you is that if there is a chance for *any* improvement, you're going to provide it by helping them balance, stabilize and repair the underlying electric circuits that are connected with the illness.

It is important for him to understand something about what the Essences do and what is involved in the testing. So think about how you can explain that simply and concisely. If you've got someone who shows an interest in understanding more, you could gift them with a copy of this book. (Don't loan them yours! You're going to need it for the testing.)

● BITE THE BULLET AND FINALLY ORGANIZE YOURSELF. It will be important for maintaining *your* sanity if you get serious about organizing your Essence testing setup. You'll need a binder, blank paper, pens, perhaps a small clock with a second hand, a clean spoon, clean paper towels and you'll need to include about twenty clean solution bottles, labels, a preservative... My suggestion is to purchase or commandeer (from a family member and not a store!) a small carry-on business case with wheels and a retractable handle. This is your traveling Essence testing "office" for holding everything you need for surrogate testing. When you're scheduled to test someone, grab your "office," roll it out to the car and off you go. It's a time and stress saver. (By the way, setting yourself up like this also saves time when you have to test Essences for yourself. Everything you need is right there on wheels.)

● THE SURROGATE HEAD-START PROGRAM. When setting up for testing someone who is chronically ill, the most time-consuming thing is putting together a complete CI checklist. You can get a head start and provide him with some relief if you do a surrogate Basic Essence Test right away, and include dosage and follow-up testing while the two of you work on the CI checklist. Once the CI checklist has been completed, you may begin the telegraph testing even if he is still taking an Essence dosage from his Head-Start Basic Essence Test. *He is to continue taking that dosage, and you'll need to move him through all the follow-up testing for the Head-Start Basic Essence Test until he tests clear for three days straight while simultaneously moving him through the telegraph testing.* This may seem like a daunting task, but the Head-Start Essences will weave with and support the Telegraph Test Essences, and your payoff will be a less complex CI checklist and telegraph testing results.

The primary difference between a Basic Telegraph Test and telegraph testing for chronic illness is the CI checklist. If you are helping someone with a chronic illness, you will need to work together to create a good CI checklist that covers the scope of his illness. Do this before you start telegraph testing. Review the instructions and information in chapter 9 (pp. 121–128) on setting up a quality CI checklist. Once the CI checklist is completed, you can start the surrogate Telegraph Test for chronic illness.

> IT WILL BE IMPORTANT for you to take the primary responsibility for holding the focus for all the testing. But you can't let the person mentally drift away from what you are doing. Talk. Say everything out loud. Explain what you're doing. Even though you will be holding the focus, the goal is for the two of you to move through the testing in tandem

mentally and physically. It's important that he stay engaged with the testing the best he can. If you allow his mind to wander, your testing will be compromised, no matter how well you are focused. When this happens, just stop what you're doing and gently bring his attention back to you and the testing. Once you are both re-focused, continue testing from where you left off. Obviously, it's going to be important that this person be well rested for the test. And it's important that you be experienced with both the Basic Telegraph Test for yourself and the surrogate Basic Telegraph Test, as well as familiar with the information on telegraph testing for chronic illness. You need to know what you are doing so you're not requiring him to remain alert while you fumble around trying to figure out what to do next.

SURROGATE TELEGRAPH TESTING FOR CHRONIC ILLNESS — THE STEPS

SUPPLIES:
- the five sets of Perelandra Essences
- pen, paper, calendar and the completed CI checklist
- option: a blank Perelandra Essence Record Chart
- a blank Perelandra Essence Telegraph Test Checklist
- a watch or clock with a second hand
- a clean spoon and several clean paper towels
- clean solution bottles (one bottle for each symptom on the CI checklist)
- brandy or distilled white vinegar preservative (his choice)
- blank labels

BOTH OF YOU PREPARE FOR TESTING:
- Drink some water. Go to the bathroom, if needed. Find a quiet spot and sit comfortably. Place the boxes of Essences and the other supplies within easy reach for you.

- At the top of a clean sheet of paper or a new Perelandra Essence Record Chart and a Perelandra Essence Telegraph Test Checklist, write the person's name and the date.

You are ready to proceed with the test steps.

1. *Always clear your electric system with Essences just before testing another person.* For this, the person cannot be touching you. State aloud or to yourself:

> I would like to clear my electric system and prepare myself for surrogate telegraph testing the Perelandra Essences. (Test.)

Do the Basic Essence Test (steps 2–5, pp. 54–55). Take any needed Essences. Do not test for dosage. These will be taken one time only. If you test clear and you need no Essences, proceed with the surrogate telegraph testing.

2. Physically make contact with the person you are going to test and remain physically connected throughout all the testing, unless otherwise instructed. Have him place a hand on your knee or touch your foot with his foot or rest his hand lightly on your shoulder.

Focus on the person for five seconds. The easiest way to do this without creeping one another out or getting the giggles is for both of you to look at (focus on) where you are physically connected and hold that focus for five seconds. This touching and focusing connects his electric system to yours. Test the connection by asking (aloud or to yourself):

> Are our two electric systems connected for this Perelandra telegraph testing? (Test the question.)

If negative, spend a few more seconds focusing on the person—and make sure you are physically touching. You both also need to relax. If either of you is being distracted, move to a quieter room or quiet the environment you are in. Encourage him to keep his mind focused on the testing or on the hand (or foot) that is touching you. Test your connection again. This time you should get a positive result. If not, keep adjusting your physical connection (you may need to change how he is touching you) and applying a sharper focus until you get a positive response to the question.

3. Before doing any of the surrogate telegraph testing, you must first clear *his* electric system. To do this, state aloud:

> I want to do a surrogate Basic Essence Test to clear [name of person] for telegraph testing for [name of the chronic illness]. What Essences does he need? (Test.)

Do a surrogate Basic Essence Test (steps 4–7, pp. 165–166). Administer to him any needed Essences. He only takes these one time, so there's no need to test for dosage.

Not needing Essences for clearing the electric system but needing them when telegraph testing the symptoms is not unusual. NOTE: *With the step 3 statement, you also set the intent for the Telegraph Test.*

Placing one drop of each needed Essence on a spoon will be the easiest and most efficient way to administer the Essences throughout all of this testing. It will also ensure that your droppers don't become contaminated from his saliva and need washing.*

4. Place the completed CI checklist in front of you. (Also include any colored pages from the coloring book.)

5. Begin by telegraph testing his body's full electric system. Treat it as a symptom. Ask:

> What Essences are needed for [name of person]'s full electric system as it relates to [name of illness]? (Test.)

Keep your focus on his electric system while following the surrogate Basic Essence Test, steps 4–7 (pp. 165–166). Administer the needed Essences and find out how many times a day and how many days/weeks/months he is to take these Essences (surrogate Basic Essence Test: Dosage, steps 8–12, pp. 166–168).

6. Telegraph test each symptom on the CI checklist, one by one. Keep your focus on each symptom while following the surrogate Basic Essence Test, steps 4–7 (pp. 165–166).

- Use the assigned code or symbol as a focus aid, if this has been set up.

- Administer the needed Essences *directly to him* after each test.

- Dosage: Find out how many times a day and how many days/weeks/ months he is to take these Essences (surrogate Basic Essence Test: Dosage, steps 8–12, pp. 166–168) before moving on to the next symptom.

- Be sure to record the Essences needed and the dosage information for each symptom: the beginning and end date of the dosage and how many times a day he is to take it. Also include the times of day he is to take it (morning, afternoon, evening).

- If he is to take the Essences just one time, you don't need to do any further dosage testing beyond step 8, and you can move on to the next symptom on the CI checklist.**

If you need to make any solution bottles, wait until after all the telegraph testing is completed and make all the needed solution bottles at one time.

* Clean the spoon for each Telegraph Test and solution by wiping it with a clean paper towel.

** However, you will need to do the follow-up testing for that symptom within forty-eight hours.

181

* Wait two weeks after the initial starting-gate testing before reviewing and testing the auxiliary symptoms listed on the CI checklist.

7. When you've finished testing every symptom on the CI checklist, do a final Basic Essence Test for his full electric system.* This will provide balancing and stabilizing for his system as a unit after doing all the circuit repair. *Do not check for dosage. These Essences are to be taken one time only.*

8. The surrogate Telegraph Test for his chronic illness is completed. To disconnect the two electric systems, just stop touching. Once you two are no longer touching, the electric systems are no longer connected.

9. Make any needed solution bottles. You may need to make a solution bottle for each symptom or issue listed on the CI checklist. To avoid mistakes and confusion, label each bottle right after making that solution. Include the solution's focus, the beginning and end date of the dosage and how many times a day he is to take it. Also include the times of day he is to take it (morning, afternoon, evening).

● CONGRATULATIONS TO YOU BOTH! I imagine this was quite an adventure for you. And I bet it was easier than you were anticipating. You're past the initial starting-gate testing now and all you have to do is pay attention to the follow-up testing.

You are each now free to get on with your day. There's no sin in the two of you first taking a well-deserved coffee/tea/beer/chocolate/cake break. You've more than earned it.

DOSAGE AND FOLLOW-UP TESTING

● HELP HIM REMEMBER to take his dosages (one dropperful per dose) for the full period of time prescribed. It'll help him to remember if one of you sets his solution bottles in an obvious place such as on his bedside table, in the kitchen or bathroom. Also record the end date for each solution on a calendar or computer so that you will know when to do the follow-up testing.

● ADMINISTERING DOSAGES. Each time he takes a solution dosage, he is to first activate the circuits the solution is addressing. To do this, he's to read the symptom name listed on the solution bottle label and keep it in mind while taking a dropperful (ten to twelve drops) of the Essence solution. That will automatically activate the targeted area and set up the connections for shifting the Essence patterns to those circuits.

IMPORTANT: Once you make a solution bottle, the Essence drops have been diluted and are no longer concentrated. For each dosage, he will now need to take ten to twelve drops (one dropperful) of solution.

● COMPLETING A DOSAGE PERIOD AND FOLLOW-UP TESTING. Remember to do all needed follow-up testing *within forty-eight hours* after a dosage period ends. You need to do a new surrogate Basic Telegraph Test (pp. 171–174) for just that one symptom to find out if any additional Essences are needed. For this, you must be physically present and connected electrically. Clear your electric system first (step 1) and then his electric system (steps 2–3) before doing steps 5–7. Continue doing follow-up testing at the end of each dosage period until he tests clear.* When the symptom tests clear for seven days straight, you know that he has completed the follow-up testing and no additional Essences are needed at that time. Cross the symptom off his CI checklist. If he tested positive for any Essences on any one of the seven days, assume the follow-up series is not complete and continue with the follow-up testing as usual until the symptom tests clear for seven days straight.

* This includes symptoms that only require one dose. The follow-up test is done within forty-eight hours after taking that one required dose.

● RETURNING AND NEW SYMPTOMS. Should a symptom that tested clear return, just list it again on his CI checklist and do a new surrogate Basic Telegraph Test for this one symptom, starting with step 1 and testing through step 7 (pp. 171–173). Move it completely through all dosage periods and follow-up testing. Continue this until it tests clear again for seven days straight.

If the returning symptom exhibits any changes or anomalies that differentiate it from the old one in any way, consider this a *new* symptom that needs to be added to the CI checklist. Do a new surrogate Basic Telegraph Test for that one symptom and move it completely through all dosage periods and follow-up testing. Continue this until it tests clear for seven days straight. If you used a code or symbol on the CI checklist for the old symptom, *do not use that same one for the new symptom.* It will need its own code or symbol and you will need to "officially" assign the code or symbol. (See pp. 126–127.)

Chapter 15

Surrogate Testing Children

A CHILD'S ELECTRIC SYSTEM AND CIRCUITS respond exceptionally well to ETS Plus and the Perelandra Essences. Kids are always "coming down with something" or falling over their own feet. Your first response, of course, is to give them ETS Plus. (Don't forget to take a dose of ETS Plus for yourself right away when dealing with your child's newest catastrophe. Your anxiety and your child's trauma can feed into one another causing each of you to be more stressed and hysterical than the situation calls for.)

If you have small children, you may want to hang a bottle of ETS Plus around your neck so you'll have it available at a moment's notice! This will take care of a lot of the injuries and illnesses children can challenge parents with. If there are lingering symptoms after about an hour, you'll need to surrogate test them for Essences. You will be working with the surrogate Basic Essence Test and the Surrogate Telegraph Test as written. The one you use will depend on the severity of the problem and your judgement call as to which seems more appropriate for the situation. Before surrogate testing, there are some issues that are unique to working with children that you need to know about.

> Before testing a child it is important that you first become comfortable working with the Perelandra Essences by testing yourself. Then surrogate test some willing and needy adults to become familiar with this testing before addressing a child.

In the interest of fair play, I have written the surrogate testing information for children from the perspective of the reader testing a girl. If you are testing a boy, mentally change all the pronouns to the appropriate masculine form for the sake of the child's sanity, self-esteem and future personal identity issues!

WHEN TO TEST CHILDREN

● Anytime they are injured, sick, overly emotional or having a meltdown, overly stubborn, listless, depressed, dealing with sadness or grief… Actually you test children for the same type of PEMS things you would test yourself for—only now the issues tend to be in pint-size form.

● For any situation that hits your child suddenly, like an injury—whether a serious injury or a small nick—give her ETS Plus right away.

> For a child younger than nine months, you may place the ETS Plus drops on her forehead and gently massage them in.

> For a child nine months or older, the drops will need to be administered orally.

Wait about an hour after the last dose of ETS Plus is administered and decide if you need to follow up with a surrogate Basic Essence Test or a Basic Telegraph Test.

After an hour or two, or even the next day after a Basic Essence Test: If there are lingering symptoms that show no signs of improvement, you will need to do a surrogate Telegraph Test for the remaining symptoms. Use your judgement as to the severity of the situation and how long to wait to make these testing decisions.

● Test her whenever some other family member is dealing with a difficult situation, illness or injury. Children tend to absorb the anger, concern and worry that swirls around the home during these times. This also includes anytime local or global news reports cause concern among the adults in the home.

● For preventive care, do a regular surrogate Basic Essence Test checkup to monitor and maintain a child's electric system balance. The frequency of the regular checkup can be weekly, bi-monthly or monthly, depending on the overall state of your child's health.

● Test a child for Essences at the first sign they are getting sick or as soon as they walk through the front door, look up at you with those sad eyes and say, "I don't feel good." With children, a quick ETS Plus and Essence response and a good night's sleep can stop most illnesses in their tracks.

● If you missed the early warning signs and your child is sick, test her *two or three times a day* to help move her through the illness. When possible, use the Perelandra

Essences instead of over-the-counter medications to address the problem. OTC medications mask or suppress symptoms. For Essence testing, the symptoms are considered the road map. You want to let them provide the information you need for smart and effective Essence testing throughout the time it takes the electric circuits and body to process whatever is causing the illness.

● Test anytime your child is exposed to other children who are sick. I know, this sounds a bit insane—especially if your child is in that petri dish we like to call day-care or school. But if her classmates start coming down with something, that's when you want to jump into action. There's no rule written anywhere that requires your child to join the pack and also get sick. Monitor your child's electric system balance by doing a *daily* surrogate Basic Essence Test until whatever is causing the problem with her classmates has run its course. (Don't forget to monitor yourself for Essences daily during this time just in case your child is in the sharing mood!)

GUIDELINES FOR TESTING CHILDREN

● INFANTS. Do not hold an infant while you are trying to test Essences. You can't hold an infant, juggle all those bottles, do PKTT and write down the information. Something or someone is going to end up falling onto the floor.

● CRAWLERS, TODDLERS AND YOUNG CHILDREN. The easiest way to Essence test crawlers, toddlers and young children who will not sit still is to do the testing while they are asleep.

● MAINTAINING PROPER PHYSICAL CONTACT. If it's difficult to maintain physical contact with her (e.g., touching her hand, leg, arm or foot) because she's moving around too much or her crib is in your way, allow her to fall asleep on a blanket on the floor or couch that evening and then do the Essence testing. Sit next to her and be sure to maintain physical contact with her while you test.

● CHILDREN AGE TWELVE OR OLDER should be tested using the regular surrogate procedure for adults. Make the Essence solutions the same as you would for adults. Anyone age twelve or over should be awake and cooperative with the testing.

● IF A CHILD AGE TWELVE OR OLDER IS NOT COOPERATING WITH YOU, then you must consider if it is appropriate to be surrogate testing this young person. You may be placing yourself in an "unethical" position in which you are bypassing her conscious ability to participate in her own health regimen — even if you are her parent, smarter than she is and have only the best intentions. In short, you may be manipulating this young person. (WARNING: If you do manipulate her, when she gets a little older, she'll probably take this out on you!)

● IF YOU ARE NOT THE CHILD'S PARENT. It is also not ethical to do surrogate Essence testing for anyone under age eighteen without first obtaining *verbal permission* from the child's parent(s) or legal guardian.

● CHILDREN WITH SPECIAL NEEDS. For those who are age twelve or older, but who have special needs, such as mental disabilities, autism, severe hyperactivity, Attention Deficit Disorder, or ADHD, that make it difficult or impossible for them to participate in the testing, see chapter 16: *Surrogate Testing Children and Adults with Special Needs.*

ADMINISTERING
ESSENCES TO CHILDREN

● UNDER NINE MONTHS OF AGE AND ASLEEP.
Basic Essence Testing. If she is asleep when you test her, you can give her the first dose of needed Essences immediately by stating, "For _____'s electric system," placing one drop at a time of each needed Essence concentrate on her forehead, and gently rubbing it in with your finger. Allow her forehead to air dry. Her electric system is quite sensitive and can easily receive Essences administered on her forehead. But for a Basic Essence Test you have another option when it comes to administering Essences: You may wait until she's awake the next day to give her the Essences orally or on her forehead, and start her dosage period then. NOTE: If you give her a solution, you will need to apply ten drops of that solution on her forehead each time she takes a dose. To do this, apply three or four drops at a time. Massage them in and then apply the next round of drops. You need to apply a total of ten drops.

Basic Telegraph Testing. When you are telegraph testing her, you'll need to give her the Essences for each symptom *before moving on to the next symptom.* Administer the Essence drops on her forehead. State (aloud) the symptom you are addressing—this sets up her circuits—and place one drop at a time of each needed Essence concentrate on her forehead. Gently rub it in with your finger *(Fig. K)*. Allow her forehead to completely air dry before testing the next symptom. You can wait until the next day to make any solution bottles she needs. (Hope you took good notes during the testing.)

● IF THE CHILD IS OVER NINE MONTHS OF AGE, she will need to take all her Essences orally. If you need her to be asleep because she's so active, don't do a Telegraph Test. You're not going to be able to give her the Essences for each symptom as you do the testing. Instead use the surrogate Basic Essence Test and do all the needed follow-up until she tests clear. It may take longer to move her through an issue this way, but it can be done.

● WHEN ADMINISTERING AN ESSENCE DOSAGE TO A CHILD. You don't need to physically connect with the child when administering an Essence dosage on the days following a test. Nor do you need to clear your electric system first. All of that was done earlier during the test to ensure accurate results. Just before you administer the dose, state aloud the reason for the solution. (HINT: It's written on the bottle label.) Your voice will grab her attention, even if for a moment, and she'll hear what you are saying. This focuses her and her circuits on the purpose of the solution. You can even make a game of it and get her to repeat what you said. These two "tricks" activate her circuits appropriately for shifting the solution into the areas that correspond with the focus. NOTE: Because you are giving her a solution, she will need to take ten to twelve drops (a dropperful) of that solution each time she takes a dose.

● FOR AN INFANT UNDER NINE MONTHS AND AWAKE. State the purpose of the solution aloud just before administering it. Hearing the sound of your voice will focus her attention on what's happening and this will set up her circuits for the solution. NOTE: Because you are administering a solution, you will need to place a total of ten drops of that solution on her forehead each time she takes a dose. To do this, apply three or four drops at a time. Massage them in and then apply the next round of drops *(Fig. K)*. You need to apply a total of ten drops. Allow her forehead to air dry before administering the next solution.

Fig. K

● FOR AN OLDER CHILD YOU CAN TRUST to take the Essence dosages as prescribed, all you have to do is fix any needed solution bottles, label what each bottle

Fig. L

Fig. M

* For children three years or older, you can bypass the preservative taste by making solutions in a dropper bottle or glass and eliminating the preservative. But remember that you must refrigerate these preservative-free solutions.

is for and instruct the child to read the label aloud every time the solution is taken. She is to take one dropperful orally for each dose. If your child tends to be distracted or forgetful, the easiest thing is for you to hand her the bottle each time she needs to take a dose.

● BYPASSING THE BRANDY OR VINEGAR TASTE FOR A CHILD UNDER AGE THREE. Make a solution by adding one drop of each needed Essence to *four ounces* of water. Use water only and not juice or milk. She does not have to drink the entire four ounces to receive the proper dosage. In fact, only *three gulps* are needed for each dose. By mixing the drops in four ounces of water *(Fig. L)*, you will be diluting them to the point where she won't taste the brandy or vinegar that is used to preserve the Essence concentrates but the electrical patterns will still be potent enough for a child under age three. Each time she needs to take a dose, hand it to her for the necessary three gulps while saying out loud what it is for *(Fig. M)*. Keep the remaining solution in the refrigerator for the next dose.*

Some children don't mind the preservative taste at all. If she doesn't mind, give her one drop of each needed Essence concentrate as prescribed in a spoon. Using a spoon keeps the droppers clean. But if she manages to touch a dropper with her mouth, hands, hair, foot, clothes, favorite stuffed bunny or the magic blanket she's been dragging around for a year, be sure to wash the dropper off before putting it back in the bottle.

● YOU CANNOT OVERDOSE A CHILD WITH AN ESSENCE SOLUTION. For a child under age three, if you'd like to mix the four ounces in a sippy cup or baby bottle and let the her drink from it for half an hour every time she needs a dose, this is fine. More than three gulps won't be an issue. However, less than three is not enough.

● BE SURE TO USE WATER and *not* juice or milk for Essence solutions.

● TELEGRAPH TESTING AND ADMINISTERING MULTIPLE ESSENCE SOLUTIONS. After telegraph testing her, you may end up with a solution for each of the symptoms or injuries that were tested. When administering multiple doses, do not mix all these different solutions together into one super solution. You may think this is a time-saving trick, but you will only nullify all the electrical patterns. Consider a solution a unified collection of Essences that should not be "violated" by mixing in any other outside Essences. Keep each solution in its own bottle or glass and administer one dropperful of each one separately.

● ESTABLISHING FOCUS. When you give the child a solution, don't forget to state out loud what it is for. (I'm repeating this because it is the easiest thing to forget, yet it is so important for administering the Essences correctly and effectively. If you forget, you will be required to write the following sentence 500 times: "When I give my child a solution, I will not forget to state out loud what it is for.")

● CHILDREN'S SOLUTION DOSAGES tend to be less complicated than the ones adults test for. Where an adult may need a solution of eight Essences for a week, three times a day, a child may need just two Essences for a couple of days, one time a day.

● DON'T FORGET TO DO FOLLOW-UP TESTING for her *within forty-eight hours* once the dosage period for each solution is completed. For Basic Essence Testing, the follow-ups and dosages are complete when she tests clear for *three days straight.* For the Basic Telegraph Test, each symptom must test clear for *seven days straight.*

Chapter 16

Surrogate Testing Children and Adults with Special Needs

By "SPECIAL NEEDS," I MEAN those individuals who are unconscious; semi-conscious; mentally, physically or emotionally disabled; or who have conditions such as severe autism or Attention Deficit Disorder. This does not include people who are capable of participating in the regular testing with a little help on your part.

● It is not ethical to impose a health regimen on someone eighteen years of age or over without verbal permission—and this includes someone with special needs. If she is capable of understanding a short description of the Perelandra Essences and able to answer for herself, give her that information and ask if she'd like you to test her. If she is unable to make an informed decision and give you permission directly, you will need to get verbal permission from her legal guardian.

● It is also not ethical to do Essence testing for anyone under age eighteen without verbal permission from the child's parent(s) or legal guardian.

● It is important that you be physically present with the person when you obtain her permission, do the testing, administer any multi-day Essence dosages, and do needed follow-up testing. If you are unable to be present for administering the multi-day dosages, instructing someone in the house to do this is fine. Just make sure they are clear about what they need to do each time they administer a dose. It might be helpful if you write down those instructions for them so they don't have to rely on memory. (And let them know that if they forget to state out loud what each solution is for, they will be required to write the following sentence 500 times: "When I give [name of person] a solution, I will not forget to state out loud what it is for." Sometimes outrageous, bald threats are helpful!)

● Do the appropriate surrogate testing and include the guidelines as outlined *for children up to age twelve* in chapter 15.

Fig. N

● If she cannot physically take an Essence dosage (for example, she is unconscious), you may place one drop of each Essence concentrate on her lips *(Fig. N)*. It will mix with her saliva and seep into her mouth. Allow fifteen seconds for the drops to mix with her saliva. This procedure takes a little patience on your part. If she needs a lot of Essences, you'll only be able to place one drop of two or three Essences at a time on her lips. Even if she is unconscious, talk to her and tell her what you are doing. Make sure your intent is to be gentle, not invasive. In this situation, use only the concentrate drops that are administered directly from the Essence bottles.

Chapter 17

Perelandra Post-Death
ETS Plus Process*

* This process was formerly known as the Post-Death Essence Process.

ETS PLUS ALLOWS THIS PROCESS to be simplified while, at the same time, it vastly broadens the scope of support it gives to a family member or friend who has just died. It stabilizes the person during that initial post-death period when he or she is most vulnerable and greatly assists their healing process from the illness or condition that caused death. Your friend or loved one is just finding out that (1) they have died, and (2) life really does go on. This can be confusing and shocking at first. It's one thing to consider, debate and ruminate on what happens after we die. It's quite another thing to suddenly find ourselves in the middle of that reality.

YOU MUST DO THE POST-DEATH ETS PLUS PROCESS
WITHIN SEVENTY-TWO HOURS AFTER A PERSON HAS DIED.

After seventy-two hours, that person's electric system has shifted beyond your range to connect with it, and it is no longer possible for you to administer the ETS Plus drops.

You do not need to be physically touching the person who has died in order to administer ETS Plus. *This is the one Perelandra surrogate procedure that does not require you two to be in the same room.* The circuits that support his soul level will be connected with the circuits supporting your physical level. This will be done by both of you using focus. It's helpful to keep in mind that, although the person has been declared dead and his physical body has ceased to function, he still has an active and alive electric system that has just shifted into "post-death mode." He can still hear you and sometimes he can see you. Plus, he's no longer tied to the room where his body is located. So this surrogate test will seem as if the person is right there with

195

you and cooperating with the testing. That's because he is electrically connected with you and cooperating with the testing.

It is, of course, best for people to be stabilized throughout the entire dying process by having someone do a surrogate Basic Essence Test each day. Whether the Basic Essence Test has been done daily or not, ETS Plus is still important and helpful within the first seventy-two hours after death. However, if it is impossible to do the Post-Death ETS Plus Process, relax. They'll be fine. Many people have died success-fully without assistance and support from ETS Plus.

THE POST-DEATH ETS PLUS PROCESS STEPS

1. To start, take one dose of ETS Plus for yourself. This prepares you and clears your electric system for the process.

2. State your intent:

>I wish to connect my electric system with [person's name]'s electric system for administering ETS Plus.

3. Ask _____ (friend's name) to focus on you while you focus on him. Hold the focus for *ten seconds* while the connection is completed.

Test your connection by asking (aloud):

>Are our two electric systems connected for this Post-Death ETS Plus Process? (Test the question.)

If negative, spend a few more seconds focusing on the individual (think about him)—and relax. If you are being distracted, move to a quieter room or quiet the environment you are in. Remind him to keep his focus on you. Test your connection again. This time you should get a positive result.

4. Now, say hello and tell the person that you would like to offer ETS Plus. In a couple of sentences, explain what ETS Plus does and what it will do for him. Speak to him as if you were talking to him over a telephone. Once you have explained ETS Plus, ask him if he understands what you are explaining. Use PKTT to discern his answer. He can hear you quite well. If he doesn't understand, it's because he needs it explained differently and not because you need to say it louder. Keep your

explanation as simple and direct as possible. You don't have to give a full-blown class on ETS Plus. Just give him an idea of what it is and how it can help stabilize him now and assist in his healing process. Don't be surprised if a person who had no interest in such things prior to death is open to using ETS Plus *after* death. We all tend to change our perspective on things once we've died!

> NOTE: It is not unusual for you to feel deep emotions—and express them—during this process. If you feel at any time that you could use more support, take another dose of ETS Plus, stating as you take it that the ETS Plus is for you. It's also not unusual to feel how special and positive this experience is for the two of you. We've had many reports from people who have done the Post-Death Process for a loved one and talked about what a terrific, warm, practical and sometimes humorous experience it was.

5. Once the person understands, ask:

> Would you like me to administer ETS Plus to you? (Test the question.)

If he does not wish to receive the ETS Plus drops, move on to step 8. Do not try to coerce him into changing his mind. It is important to respect his decision. He knows what he wants. But you might feel his gratitude towards you for caring enough to offer. This alone can be very comforting and healing to him.

6. Administering ETS Plus: With your two electric systems still connected, you will focus on this person and then you take one dose of ETS Plus orally. Your focus will route the ETS Plus through your electric system and into his.

7. Maintain your focus for one full minute. You are waiting for the ETS Plus to transfer fully to his electric system.

After the minute, PKTT test the person to make sure the ETS Plus shift occurred. If not, repeat steps 6 and 7. Once you get verification that the shift has happened, wait five minutes and test to see if he needs a second dose. Most of the time, just one dose will be needed. But if he needs another dose, focus on him and repeat steps 6 and 7. Do this every five minutes until he tests that he does not need another dose. Be sure to verify that each shift has occurred.

8. Once he tests clear, you may spend *up to a half hour* talking to him. You may talk about anything, and you may even ask questions about how he feels, and so forth. You'll probably need to ask simple yes/no questions and PKTT his answers.

The fact that you are still connected to one another electrically facilitates this communication process. Try not to press any feelings of grief and sorrow (or anger) you might have onto the person. This process and time is for the welfare of the person who has died, and it is not appropriate to try to unload your emotions onto that person. Do not spend more than a half hour talking with the person. By this time, you are both getting tired. And he needs to move on. After the half hour is up, tell him you have to close down the process. Wish him well and say goodbye.

9. Close the process by stating aloud:

> I request that our two electric systems be disconnected now.

The disconnection will occur immediately. It's the same as in surrogate testing when the two people stop touching.

10. If you experienced a lot of emotions during the process and after the disconnection, take another dose of ETS Plus. After about an hour or two, if you feel you still need support, do a Basic Essence Test for yourself.

Chapter 18

Surrogate Testing Animals

Aᴌᴌ ᴀɴɪᴍᴀʟs ʜᴀᴠᴇ ʙɪᴏʟᴏɢɪᴄᴀʟʟʏ closed electric systems. If you have an animal with a health problem, you are looking at an electric system in need of balancing, stabilizing and repair. First, every animal-friendly home and vet's office should have a bottle of ETS Plus for Animals. That's right, they have their own ETS Plus that addresses trauma as it is uniquely experienced by animals. So your animal shows up limping or bleeding, or he's over-stressed (think thunderstorms!). Give him ETS Plus for Animals right away — two or three doses, five minutes apart (one dropperful per dose). Much of the time ETS Plus for Animals takes care of the problem, and you need go no further with testing. But just as with humans, should you see that some symptoms are lingering, surrogate test the animal using the Basic Essence Test or Basic Telegraph Test, whichever is more appropriate for the health issue. Set up the testing, go through the steps and administer the Essences orally as you would for a child over age twelve. And be sure to do all the follow-up testing. But because he's an animal, he only needs to test clear, no further Essences needed, *for two days* for both a Basic Essence Test and a Basic Telegraph Test. Then you'll know he has completed that Essence regimen. As with children, treating animals with Essences is less complex than for us adults. The number of Essences needed are fewer, the solutions are simpler and the number of days the solutions are needed are fewer. With rising costs, ETS Plus for Animals and Essences are a godsend.

In general, to incorporate ETS Plus for Animals and the Perelandra Essences into an animal's health regimen, you can look to how both are used with humans for your guidelines. Be sure to include ETS Plus for Animals for vet visits, hospital stays and surgery, as well.

● ADMINISTERING ESSENCES TO A FINICKY ANIMAL. The challenge is the brandy or vinegar smell and taste. A lot of times an animal will learn to willingly take Essence drops directly from your hand if you just work with them a little and encourage them a lot. This is especially effective with dogs. But I had a cat who was very cooperative as well. It depends on their personality and your patience. However, if you can't get an animal to take the drops, here are some suggestions:

● Try bribery. Put one drop of one needed Essence concentrate on a tiny bit of a treat. Repeat this for each Essence that's needed.

Fig. P

● Cats love butter. Place one drop of concentrate at a time on a little bit of butter (about $1/16$ teaspoon). You can even smear a little of this combination on their paw for them to lick off *(Fig. P)*. Or try tiny bits of tuna.

● Dilute the needed Essences by making a solution bottle using just water and no preservative. Be sure to refrigerate it.

● Get a dropper with a plastic pipette and administer one dropperful of a solution directly into the animal's mouth. (Don't store the plastic dropper in the solution bottle. Keep it alongside the bottle.)

ANIMAL DEATH

This is the situation I usually get asked about when it comes to animals. By definition, a pet or companion animal is a friend, a member of the family. Letting go of that friend can be as difficult as letting go of a person we love. By taking advantage of the quality veterinary and health care we have available, it isn't unusual to have an animal as part of our lives for fifteen, maybe twenty years. That's longer than a lot of marriages these days.

When facing animal death, we have several issues coming at us simultaneously. (1) This is our friend. Sometimes, this is our longest-lived and closest friend. (2) Our friend can't communicate in the "normal" way, so we can't sit down and discuss their wishes as to medical process and procedure. And by the fact that this animal is a pet, he looks to us for everything needed for quality survival and quality death. He is in some ways as dependent as a baby. (3) Veterinary medicine gives us about as much option medically as our own medical structure—and as expensively.

Where we used to keep Fido warm and quiet until death after being hit by a car, veterinary medicine can now restore him to health. (4) Veterinary medicine offers euthanasia as a legal and viable option. This throws us right into the middle of the "death with dignity" controversy.

By the time people ask for my advice, they are pretty much frazzled by the impact and emotional cost of dealing with all four of the above issues, usually all at the same time. They have a clear idea that this friend, although an animal, is of value and not something to just be killed and tossed out when care becomes too troublesome.

Within the past thirty years at Perelandra, I've had a number of my animals pass on. I've lived here long enough for the puppies, kittens and other baby animals I got fifteen years ago to live a full life, enter their "senior citizen" days, and pass on. It's never easy emotionally. That's a given, and we who have animals in our lives might as well reconcile ourselves to this fact. When the animal dies, it's going to hurt. Period. End of story. There will be a period of grief and adjustment, no matter how stiff our upper lip is. I often find that people make their pets go through a terrible, drawn-out, and difficult time by relying on their vet to keep the animal alive solely because they (the owner) cannot face the emotional pain of loss. This is a terrible burden to give to an animal.

The grief issue has become so recognized that some vets have on staff a grief therapist to assist the owner once the animal has died. After the death of my sixteen-year-old cat named Fred, my vet told me how difficult it is for him these days to see all the puppies and kittens he treated for fourteen years when he began practicing now come to an age where many have lived out their lives and must be "put to sleep." He said that in veterinary school, they don't deal with the issue of the pain experienced by a vet when an animal they've treated for so long dies or needs to be put down. And they also don't talk about how to deal with the pain and grief of the owner during such times. Consequently, vets may be clear that an animal can no longer sustain a reasonable life and has reached the end of the line, but they may have little knowledge of what to do to help a person face the loss of a friend. Reactions can be quite extreme. Like the time my vet had to tell an ex-marine that his dog needed to be put down as soon as possible—and the rather large, well-developed ex-marine fell apart right on the spot.

Why am I telling you all of this? Well, I feel this grief business is made that much worse when we feel conflict over the depths of what we are feeling and the fact that we are feeling it for an animal. Some people know beyond question that this is a friend. Others get into a push-pull dilemma and resist the emotions, thinking that "regular" people just don't have these feelings about an animal. Well, it's something felt by everyone, including the animal's vet.

I find that the primary thing keeping people from thinking clearly about how to assist an animal through death is their reluctance to accept the sorrow of separation and the inevitable grief. It clouds our ability to make clear decisions based on what is best for the animal. One thing to remember about animals is that they are not at all sentimental about death. From my experience with assisting them during the death process, I feel that they accept death as a natural part of life and, if we allow them, they will move through it with extraordinary grace.

What I encourage people to do and what I do myself is put effort into separating my feelings of personal pain around losing this friend from what needs to be done for the sake of supporting that friend throughout the pre-death and death process. I try my best to make decisions based on what is good for the animal. If it means I will take an emotional hit, so be it. My focus is on the animal and what I am to do, as his friend, to give him the support and quality of life and death he wants and needs. In short, I try my best to keep my focus on the best course of action for the animal.

If the animal has obviously entered the death process and is moving through it in comfort, I will keep the animal physically comfortable and in a quiet, private area. I've seen that animals prefer privacy during this time. In fact, when I suspect that death for an older animal can't be too far off, I watch them for signs of their seeking privacy as an indication that they are now entering the death process.

I think the really difficult experience with animal death is when the issue of euthanasia enters. This puts the decision for death right into our laps, and that's real uncomfortable. I base my decision on two considerations: (1) my vet's information and advice, and (2) the quality of the animal's life if I kept him alive.

First of all, I have a couple of vets I have grown to trust through the years, and I have encouraged them to give me as much information about the condition of my animals as I can understand. In many ways, they have given me a terrific education, which has included letting me look at samples under the microscope and examine X-rays taken after injury. So, when I come to that moment of decision about putting down an animal, they know I want to hear everything about the animal's condition and have the benefit of their (the vet's) opinion.

Secondly, I feel strongly that animals have a right to live a quality life. Just breathing, laying in a corner and watching traffic go by, to me is not an animal's quality life. If they were in the wild, weakness, old age, injury and illness would mean quick death or being killed. But I can protect and sustain them. Sometimes that means they have a chance to heal, recover and continue with a full or partially disabled but acceptable life. At other times it means I can maintain them in a deathlike existence. Sometimes it's a fine line between the two.

I watch for personality changes that indicate to me that my sustaining them has now become an irritation to them. For example, I had a pet skunk (named Louie) who, in his later years, developed a deteriorating spinal column. He slowly lost mobility in his hind legs and, eventually, his entire hind end. He wasn't in pain, and after consulting the vet, I decided to let Louie continue on as long as his life gave him pleasure. In the wild, his lack of mobility would have made him easy prey and he would not have been faced with options of this sort. But because humans were involved, his life took on a greater complexity. For awhile, he continued to enjoy walks in the woods each day. Then he enjoyed drags in the woods—he didn't seem to care that his hind legs weren't working and he'd just drag himself along. He spent more time in the house with me, and I realized it was for both company and the fact that he could easily pull himself around the slick floors. The forest floor was becoming an issue with him. Then his desires and personality changed. He no longer wanted to come out of his den. He only came out to eat and then he'd go right back in. He was irritated anytime I opened the den to see how he was. He was not living, he was existing. As long as I gave him food and water, he could continue existing. It was then I made the decision it was time to put him down and put him through the Animal Death Process.

Just before going to the vet, I explained to him what was going to happen and told him I would be bringing his body back to Perelandra for burial. I also told him I would be giving him the full three-hour transition period for his separation process prior to burial. This way he would know he need not be concerned with anything but transition and that I would still be there in a supportive role.

I go through all of this clarity and explaining business because it keeps the entire process clear and clean for both me and the animal. My verification of this is what occurs at the vet. This is the toughest part of the process for me. I always hold my animals when the vet administers the shot. Going to the vet is usually not a happy time for animals. They all establish their personal patterns of resistant behavior over the years. In every case, when I have had to put one of my animals down, they changed that pattern dramatically. Each animal was quiet, calm and sometimes even helpful. My dog, Jesse, lifted her paw for the injection. Louie had a particularly peaceful and funny transition. The vet administered the usual dose of phenobarbital to him, and we waited for Louie to "let go." But he was a skunk and instead of dying, the phenobarbital moved him into a winter hibernation. He was sleeping away with what seemed like a smile on his face. Finally the vet figured out what happened and administered a second dose. Louie's transition could not have been more peaceful. To me the consistent calm and helpful behavior was a clear indication that indeed these animals were prepared and ready to go.

☾☾☾

In case you are curious, let me tell you about my experience at the vet at the moment of death. My vet injects a massive overdose of phenobarbital into a vein, usually in the foreleg. Sometimes they have to shave a small patch of hair from the foreleg in order to more easily locate the vein. This is especially true when the animal's blood pressure is low. Within seconds, I can feel the animal's body begin to relax. I'll use my hands to gently guide them down to the towel I placed under them before we began. Although I am usually speaking to the animal in a low voice, encouraging him to relax, and assuring him that everything is fine, this has been a very quiet and gentle moment. We wait a few of minutes, then the vet will check for heart activity, verifying death. We spend perhaps another twenty minutes or so in the room, all of us quietly talking, usually reminiscing about my friend, while getting my heart back out of my mouth. Sometimes the animal will twitch or move during this time, but this is just the body and the nervous system naturally letting go. It can be a bit weird to see if you're not prepared for the possibility. Then we wrap the animal in the towel and I take him back to Perelandra for burial.

My experience with this, although tough emotionally, has always been special. I think it is good for my friend to die in loving and caring hands, and I think it is good for me to experience the peace and tranquility of the moment.

I know not all vets are as compassionate as mine toward both the animal and the owner, and some prefer to put an animal down without the owner present simply because it's easier on everyone. I think this is especially true if we owners are not going to be able to maintain a calm composure during the process. Hysterics won't help anyone. Taking three to five doses of ETS Plus daily, starting when I know an animal is dying, really helps me maintain my equilibrium. But if you are inclined to experience this time with your animal, you can request to be present and the vet will agree. Also, if you have property and wish to bury the body there, you can make arrangements with the vet to receive the body back even if you are not present for the injection. Some vets supply body bags for transporting the animal.

Now, I still have the burial part of the process to go through. As I said, I bring my animals back to Perelandra. As soon as I get the body back home, I take a dose of ETS Plus, then I'll administer a dose of ETS Plus for Animals as outlined in the Animal Death Process. I put a dropperful of the ETS Plus on the wrapped body around the chest area. Then I lightly cover them and leave them undisturbed for three hours. I don't make an issue of whether or not the other animals see or sniff the body. I leave that up to them and allow them to move through this period and the burial however they wish.

By the time of burial, I have always been able to sense, to literally feel, that the animal's electric system has fully separated from the body. The body has the distinct feeling of being empty. To me, just to have that stable, clear feeling at the burial is worth doing the Animal Death Process, administering the ETS Plus for Animals doses and taking ETS Plus (for humans) for myself.

At this point, I stop taking ETS Plus daily and concentrate on my own grief process, my feelings of separation. I do a daily Basic Essence Test while moving through the pain. My animals always show signs of missing the one who has died, and I'll watch this to make sure they move through this period for themselves. If they appear to be "stuck," I'll do a surrogate Basic Essence Test for them.

Animal Death Process:
Pre-Death and Post-Death Support

1. When the animal moves into the pre-death period, do a special surrogate Basic Telegraph Test (pp. 171–175), following the steps as outlined for children over age twelve (pp. 187–191).* You will be testing one question as your focus:

What Essences are needed to prepare [animal's name] for death? (Test.)

Include dosage testing to find out the number of days and times per day the Essences will be needed and do any follow-up testing. Also be sure you are taking *three to five doses of ETS Plus for humans daily* for personal support throughout the entire pre-death and death period.

* It's important that you be touching your animal during the testing for step 1.

2. As soon as possible after death, administer one dropperful (ten to twelve drops) of ETS Plus for Animals on the animal's chest area or the towel covering the chest area.*

- For a companion animal, the ETS Plus for Animals must be administered *within three hours* after death.

- For wild or farm animals, it must be delivered *within one hour* after death.

3. If possible, wrap or lightly cover the body. Keep the body in a quiet spot for the required one to three hours.

4. Bury the body. Cover the body with a layer of lime (around a half inch) before covering with dirt. The lime helps with the decomposition of the body and eliminates decomposition odor. It also helps keep curious animals from digging up the body.

For a Quick Death Caused by Injury

If an animal has life-threatening injuries, administer ETS Plus for Animals right away. Then decide if a vet visit will be helpful. Sometimes keeping the animal in a familiar spot and letting them die quietly is the better way to go. Sometimes a vet is needed. You'll need to make a judgement call on this. If the animal remains alive for more than two hours, administer ETS Plus for Animals again to help stabilize him for death. When the animal has died, do the Animal Death Process, starting with step 2. (See above.)

NOTE: If you find your companion animal already dead and you suspect that death occurred within the past three hours, administering one dose of ETS Plus for Animals to the chest area will still be beneficial. After three hours, the animal's electric system has separated from the body.

For Death Including Euthanasia

- Get full information on the situation from your vet, including what lies ahead if the animal is kept alive. Remember that the goal is to do what's best for the animal when making the decision.

- If the animal is young but injured or ill, and the vet isn't sure about the outcome you might sense from the animal that he wants to fight for survival. However, by the time the vet has clearly suggested that the animal be "put down," I have always found that the animal is already fully aware of the situation and waiting to go.

● Make a final decision based on the vet's input, your feelings and what you sense the animal wants. Whatever the decision, inform the animal what it is by speaking to him in a soft, calm voice. The key for the animal's peace of mind is clarity. Include the plans concerning the vet, the shot and what the animal can expect to experience with the shot (your vet can give you details about this), and burial plans. Oftentimes you won't have to go through this step because the animal is in the room when the vet explains all of this to you. At that point, it's safe to assume the animal has a good read on the situation and knows what's happening. (Remember to take ETS Plus for humans after going through this conversation with the vet.)

Animals readily adjust their death transition process to the reality of the situation and to however the body is treated after death. If you plan for the vet to keep the body for disposal, that is a very different situation from your bringing the body home for the three-hour transition period and burial. Animals are pretty pragmatic about life and when it comes to this kind of death-related situation, they don't care. It's up to you to make the decision on this. But you need to keep the animal informed. If you are clear on what is to occur, the animal will adjust his post-death process accordingly.

Move the animal through the Animal Death Process, starting with step 2 (p. 206). If you plan to leave the body with the vet, administer the dose of ETS Plus for Animals on his chest area before leaving the office.

NOTE: It's okay to appear crazy in front of a vet. They are used to all kinds of reactions when a person's companion and friend has to be put down. So do what you have to do with ETS Plus for you and for your friend. If your vet shows interest or is open to taking ETS Plus for humans, go ahead and offer a dose. It's not an easy moment for the vet either, especially if he's known your animal and treated him over the years. But I'll warn you: Usually vets are happy and more comfortable assuming you're crazy and, like physicians, don't want to consider some new-fangled thing.

AN ETS PLUS REMINDER. Support yourself while going through this process with frequent doses of ETS Plus for humans. Take a dose before leaving for the vet, and have anyone else who's going along take a dose, as well. This will help you while at the vet's. And definitely take a dose when the vet tells you it's time and another dose just after the animal has died.

Chapter 19

Professionals and the Perelandra Essences

MAKING THE PERELANDRA ESSENCES available on a professional level is an important development—and a needed one. Quite frankly, every medical office, practice and facility should include quality electric system monitoring and repair as part of what they offer. After all, the healing process requires a fully functioning electric system. But the problem with this grand vision is that in the United States the AMA, ADA, federal and state regulations will not allow such "folly." And there are similar strict regulations in most other developed countries.

Obviously I feel there's equal need for Essence practitioners in hospitals, in ICUs, for neonatal care, in nursing homes and hospices, in all rehabilitation centers, for any medical specialty, and as part of all facilities and practices addressing the wide range of mental and emotional issues. The bottom line: I think a primary focus on a person's electric system when addressing today's health issues should be included in all medical practices. As a professional, if you'll just give it a shot and add electric-system repair to what you already offer, I feel confident that your results and your patients' health will improve faster and in dramatic ways. I'm not sure I'm going to live long enough to see this happen on a broad scale. But I hope I live long enough to see some independent-minded physicians integrate the Essences and electric-system work into their practices.

In the meantime, I concentrate most of my efforts on encouraging the individual, the layperson, to use Essences. This way the individual can do all his own electrical monitoring and repair for any medical situation he needs to address. He doesn't have to rely on each physician or health care provider to offer the Essences to him. Although there's an efficiency and practicality about the number of patients one physician could provide Essences for, there's also an efficiency with one patient providing all the electrical monitoring and repair that's needed for any medical attention he may require throughout his life. In short, the individual doesn't have to wait for physicians to include the Perelandra Essences in their practice.

For you professionals who are ahead of your time, it's easier to incorporate the Essences into your practice once you have learned how to use them and once you have experienced the benefits for yourself. When you get up to speed with PKTT and doing surrogate Essence testing on family and friends, it should take you less than ten minutes to set up a Basic Essence Test with a patient, test all fifty-one Essences, administer any needed Essences and get the dosage information. Add a little more time to that if you are also going to provide a solution bottle for them to take home. Or perhaps an assistant can put together any needed solution bottles for the patient after each appointment.

● Do a Basic Essence Test for monitoring, balancing, stabilizing and repairing a patient's electric system as a matter of course at the end of each appointment.

● The surrogate Basic Telegraph Test will work better in a professional setting when addressing more complex issues that can't be addressed effectively with a simple Basic Essence Test. This may seem like a lot of Essence testing, but balancing, stabilizing and repairing your patient's electric system and circuits for these more difficult health issues may be the most important thing you add to your practice to ensure the patient's recovery.

Appendix A

STREAMLINING THE OLD PERELANDRA ESSENCE PROCESSES

Appendix B

ESSENCE PROCESS STEPS WITHOUT THE BLAH-BLAH

Appendix A

Streamlining the Old Perelandra Essence Processes

I TOYED WITH TITLING THIS CHAPTER "What a Difference Twenty-Five Years Make." Or, "Bringing the Old Essence Processes Kicking and Screaming into the Twenty-First Century." The point is, twenty-five years of refinements and the additional development of ETS Plus have completely changed how to work with the early processes such as the Cauliflower Essence Birth-Stabilizing Process, the Body/Soul Fusion Process and the Calibration Process. In some cases I've streamlined and simplified a process. In other cases I retired the process and put it out to pasture where it will live out the rest of its natural life in peace knowing that it did its job well. Keep in mind that at one point in history the horse-and-buggy was considered the wave of the future. Time marches on.

BEHOLD, THE NEW STREAMLINED PROCESSES

WHEN USING ANY OF THESE PROCESSES,
FOLLOW THE NEW GUIDELINES AND STEPS
AND IGNORE THE OLD STEPS.

ETS Plus Birth-Stabilizing Process
(formerly known as the Cauliflower Essence Birth-Stabilizing Process)

See Chapter 8, *Trauma and ETS Plus* (p. 107), for the new steps.

Perelandra Post-Death ETS Plus Process
(formerly known as the Post-Death Essence Process)

See Chapter 17, *Perelandra Post-Death ETS Plus Process* (p. 196), for the new steps.

Extreme-Trauma Repair Process
(formerly known as the Body/Soul Fusion Process)

See Chapter 8, *Trauma and ETS Plus* (p. 108), for the new steps.

Basic Telegraph Test for Emotional and Mental Issues
(formerly known as the Calibration Process)

I've always had a fondness for the Calibration Process. It was the first "special" Essence process I developed, way back in 1990. The power of the process and the excellent results I experienced encouraged me to go on and develop the other special processes. But now it's time to update my old friend. It has morphed into the Basic Telegraph Test for emotional and mental issues. And, to be honest, it's actually not a special process anymore. It is a regular Basic Telegraph Test that has a person's emotional and/or mental health issues or problems as its focus. If your mind is spinning around the same thought(s) and you can't seem to reach resolution or move on, set up a Basic Telegraph Test with those thought(s) as the focus. If you are emotionally spinning and can't move out of your feelings, set up a Basic Telegraph Test with the emotion(s) as the focus. The BTT checklist replaces the need to verbalize the problem *and* the thirty-minute waiting period in the old process. List everything you are feeling or thinking about an issue on the BTT checklist, one by one. Be sure to check for Factor-X and Y and Z... Then follow the rest of the Basic Telegraph Test steps for each thing you have listed. Don't forget to do all the follow-up testing as outlined for a Basic Telegraph Test, as well.

Approaching mental and emotional issues this new way provides a much broader, more comprehensive and stronger treatment regimen. You'll come out of it with a deeper and longer sense of stability on all your PEMS levels.

● A HEADS-UP FOR MAP USERS. When doing a MAP/Calibration, set up the issue as a Basic Telegraph Test within a MAP session. *Don't use the old MAP/Calibration steps.* However, with this new approach, I think you'll find that you'll need to do a mental- or emotions-focused Basic Telegraph Test within MAP far less often. In fact, it may be eliminated as part of your sessions altogether or just used for infrequent and special situations. The new steps have built into them the elements the MAP team normally provided when you did the Calibration Process during a session. So it's important not to assume you need to do this new testing as part of a session. Check with your team first to find out if you need to set up the Basic Telegraph Test during a MAP session or outside a session and on its own.*

* ATTENTION MAP USERS. The time it takes to do the Basic Telegraph Test within MAP does not count as part of your forty-minute session.

Basic Telegraph Test for Miasms
(formerly known as the Miasm Process)

A miasm is a small energy pocket that exists independently of and within the body. It's a "foreign object" that does not enhance or support the body's balance. It also doesn't draw off or compromise the body's balance. It's dormant and inactive. This is why the electric system isn't picking it up as a problem. The miasm just sits there as a neutral element. That is, neutral until it's triggered. The body itself triggers a miasm when a comprehensive change is initiated by the soul level and integrated into the emotions, mental and physical levels. At this point, the body environment that had enabled the miasm to exist as a neutral entity changes and the miasm reacts to the changed and potentially hostile new environment by activating. That's when a miasm can trigger a health problem. And it's not just any little health problem that will quickly go away. It's a persistent and recurring problem that you can't shake. It can cause allergies, infections, addictions, obsessive issues, skin problems... The point is, if you have a recurring problem that you can't seem to get rid of no matter how hard you try, how many doctors you've consulted and how much money you've spent, you may be affected by an active miasm and not know it.

To treat an active miasm, you will be doing a Basic Telegraph Test. For this new approach, you no longer have to verify you have a miasm. If an active miasm is not causing the health problem you're addressing, #3 (see below) will test clear, no Essences needed. You'll need to pay special attention to the BTT checklist. The main intent and focus for the Telegraph Test will be #1, the recurring physical health issue and all its symptoms. But to check for a potential miasm problem and properly treat it, you'll need to divide the checklist into three different focuses:

1. The recurring physical health issue and all its symptoms. List all the symptoms.

2. The emotions and thoughts you are experiencing because of this health problem and the difficulties you have had trying to deal with it. List your different emotions, including fears.

3. The active miasm. This is all that's written on the BTT checklist for #3.

Essence test the BTT checklist in order, starting with #1, the recurring physical health issue and all its symptoms, testing each symptom that's listed, taking the needed Essences and getting the dosage. Then continue with #2 and test each symptom listed there, take the needed Essences and include dosage. End with #3. There is just one item listed here—the miasm. Take the needed Essences and don't forget to test for dosage.

For all three focuses, make a solution bottle for each symptom/element requiring Essences that are to be taken more than one time. Often, the solution dosages and follow-up testing for the active miasm will extend over a longer period of time than the dosages and testing needed for #1 and #2. But sometimes that isn't the case, so you'll have to let each follow-up testing run its full course.

If the Essence follow-up testing isn't completed for #3, the miasm will remain in the body but in a neutral state. However, there's no guarantee that it won't activate sometime down the road and cause more health problems. So it's important to do all the follow-up testing for each of the three focuses and that each item listed for the three focuses test clear, no further Essences needed, for *seven days straight*.

You will know that the miasm has been completely eliminated when the follow-up testing for #3 tests clear for seven days straight.

A MIASM MORALE BOOST

The following story is from a woman in California who used Essences and the Miasm Process as outlined in Perelandra Paper #3. This paper and all the other Perelandra Papers on Essence Processes have now been updated in *The Perelandra Essences.*

My story began 42 years ago. At about the age of ten, I started getting boils or what some people call carbuncles. At this early age, I would get just one, it would appear on my vagina and was of short duration. Back then, my mother treated it with folk remedies (skins from boiled egg shells and salted pork). In my twenties, the boils no longer appeared on my vagina, but were making their presence known in the underarms—big, painful and messy. I treated them with antibiotics from the physician after having them lanced. It did not work, and I stopped seeing the physician and taking antibiotics for them. They just ran their course. By the time I was 41 years of age, they were continuous, especially large and painful at the onset of menstruation. They'd swell, burst open, discharge, close up and start swelling again. Now, they were appearing under both arms, in the vaginal area and occasionally there were swellings on my breasts and stomach. Though the ones on my breasts and stomach were never great, they'd shrink and leave dark spots.

Need I tell you how devastating this was, especially after the physician told me that he could give me antibiotics for them, but once you were infected with boils, you could not get rid of them. I turned to herbs and spent hundreds of dollars to no avail. Finally, the largest boil under my left arm decided it would show me who was boss in this body. I awakened one morning totally unable to lift my arm without assistance and great pain. I ended up at the hospital on an emergency basis. The physician took one look at the boil and said that it was poisoning my system. I was given an intravenous solution, a hand cast and scheduled for minor surgery. I had the surgery to remove the boil, but knowing well that I had other boils, I asked the surgeon what could be done. He told me that I would have to have the muscles from the underarms removed, which he would not recommend. I drove home drugged and in tears, thinking that I would just have to live with this plague. I certainly couldn't have all the muscles where the boils appeared removed, could I? I had read that boils were a symptom of repressed anger and hurt, so I returned to herbs and started affirmations to help with the emotional pain, hurt and anger. I must have tried every recently announced herb on the market (not to say anything derogatory about herbs, I still use one as prescribed through kinesiology), and I was constantly at the pharmacy buying bandages, tape, peroxide and antibacterial washes, because now that the Great Boil (I called it this because there were other smaller ones still active but to a lesser degree) was gone from the left arm, it appeared that the swellings under the right arm had increased in size and intensity, sometimes to the size of an egg before bursting. Day after day, I applied bandages and tape. My underarm areas were raw and darkened.

Then, thank the gods! I started using MAP. I was using up to thirty essences sometimes and always, always the Nature Program Essences. It made sense. Lots of things were going on with me, I was feeling better, but the pesky boils were still hanging on. While browsing through the Perelandra catalog, my eyes fastened on the offer for the paper about miasms. I ordered it, read it, and it applied to me. I started the program.

Just as you say in your paper, it takes patience and believe me it takes time. But it is well worth it! On April 22, 1996, I identified all the symptoms that I was aware of at the time. There were ten including the emotional factor of prong II, and the miasm itself, prong III. I telegraph tested for each symptom and took the initial dosages; though treatments are not duplicated many of the essences were used over and over again in different combinations. All in all, it took about five hours to work through the procedure. (I was new at this.) I was not prepared, so I was exhausted.

The first round of treatments ran from April 23rd to May 12th. Just as you state in the paper, the dosage for prong II is a one-time dosage while the dosage for the miasm itself extends far beyond that of the other symptoms. For me they ran from 2 to 11 days, and the dosage for the miasm ran for 19 days. All the while, I was still having my MAP coning sessions and taking those prescribed dosages (fortitude), and somehow, I knew that the first round wouldn't be enough. I hoped it would, but I knew better. One evening, while lying on the sofa, I got a "hit" (intuitive nudge) and made a mental note that when it was time to retest, I would include symptoms that I did not think were part of the miasm at first. On May 12th, I ended the first round of treatment and on May 13th, better prepared, with time, water, bottles, frame of mind, patience and all, I retested and understood that I needed to continue. I was willing because finally, I was getting results.

This time, four of the symptoms I had tested for originally tested clear or negative. However, other symptoms were added, namely lack of energy and things I would never have considered prior to the first round of treatment and the MAP conings.

The procedure operated as before with some treatments lasting a shorter duration than others, a one-time treatment for prong II, and an extended period for the miasm itself. However, before I could be through with this energy pattern, I had to address the emotional and mental factor on a deeper level. For about a week, maybe a little longer, I kept feeling this emotional pain in my chest. I talked with my [MAP] Team about it and walked around feeling sad all the time, even though everything was going so well. Lying on the sofa again, I got another intuitive "hit." I was told that I needed to forgive. So I set aside one evening and did just that. I decided to give myself some Reiki energy to facilitate the process and as I touched parts of my body, I forgave and asked for forgiveness from every person and situation I could and could not think of. I was sobbing like a baby and weak as a kitten at the end of the session and could only tumble into bed and sleep. The next day I awakened feeling like a new person.

On May 31, 1996, at the end of treating the miasm itself, there was only a tiny flap of skin, the size of a pea, which the Great Boil had inhabited. I can't begin to tell you how happy I was, but I'll try. First I want to say this: Immediately after this, I had a minor flare-up around the vaginal area. I cursed, went back to the procedure to make sure this energy pattern was dealt with and I got a positive. The flare-up went away, so I think it just wanted to announce its departure. The nodules under my arms continue to shrink. My final test for the miasm was to be the onset of menses. That's when the "big guns" usually came out. They did not show up. I know in my deepest self that I am free. One other thing, medications that I have been taking for other health challenges have had to be adjusted. I don't need as many!

Prior to starting this process, I had little patience and persistence, but that was nothing compared to money and time wasted and pain endured. Now I am one happy woman! In about 39 days of treatment, I ended a 42-year cycle of hopelessness.

—O.G., California

THE RETIREES WHO HAVE BEEN
PUT OUT TO PASTURE

Restabilizing Process for the Perelandra Essences

In the "old days," every time you took the Perelandra Essences through airport security, the electrical patterns were impacted by the X-ray and you needed to restabilize them with this process. Well, no more! I've made the patterns airport and security proof. Your Essences are now safe from any security, military, X-ray or communication checks. This pattern protection covers all Essence sets, old and new. Okay, here's where I have to confess something: I added this protection to the Essence patterns about ten years ago and forgot to say anything to anyone, including my staff. I just want to point out that, even though I was extraordinarily forgetful back then, I'm being exceptionally courageous now. I'm admitting my forgetfulness at the risk of inciting a mob of angry Essence users who have diligently done the Restabilizing Process every time they went through airport security. I beg you to smile about the retirement of the Restabilizing Process and not come after me!

Testing Past Problems

This includes past problems in this lifetime and past problems you feel you are currently dealing with from other lifetimes. Set them up as a Basic Telegraph Test.

Peeling Process

Peeling is a concept I introduced in the book *Flower Essences*. With peeling, you address an issue one "layer" at a time and you do a Basic Essence Test for each layer. Now peeling is automatically included in all Essence testing when you do the needed follow-up and dosages. Each follow-up test is addressing, among other things, the issue or problem, one layer at a time. So don't bother doing the old peeling process as an independent test anymore. Instead, let the follow-up testing automatically address peeling issues. It's a much better approach.

Two-Week Essence Process

I also introduced this process in *Flower Essences*. The concept involves doing a Basic Essence Test each day for two weeks for a single issue. The two-week timing proved to be somewhat magical for many problems. Put it through the process and in two weeks, the problem is resolved or eliminated. Magical though it may feel, it's no longer needed. If a two-week Essence regimen is warranted for resolving an issue or problem, your follow-up testing will last for just two weeks, whether you do a Basic Essence Test or feel the problem calls for telegraph testing. When riding the follow-up testing all the way to the end, you are adding flexibility, fine-tuning and nuance to the Essence treatment by no longer assuming the issue is a two-week problem.

The Definitions of the Individual Bottles of Essences

They are holding you back when it comes to using the Perelandra Essences to their fullest. See chapter 4, p. 40 for more information.

The Perelandra Papers on Essences

The information contained in the Perelandra Papers has been included in this book and it has been updated.

Flower Essences (the Book)

I published this book in 1988. It's hair is grey, whiskers are showing up on its chin and sprouting out its ears, and it's moving a bit stiffly. With the publication of *The Perelandra Essences, Flower Essences* has been turned out to pasture with the other retired processes where they spend their time reminiscing about the good old days when their information was new and relevant. I'm pleased to report they are happy knowing they were a help to people, and they send you their best.

Appendix B

Essence Process Steps
Without the
Blah-Blah

THESE ARE THE STEPS YOU WILL WANT TO USE once you become familiar with the processes as outlined in the preceding chapters. But be warned: If you get impatient and start using these steps before you've gone through the learning curve for the process you wish to work with, you're going to miss important details that are a part of understanding each step and are needed when working with a step successfully. Even when you start using the steps in this chapter, I recommend that periodically you review the chapters on the processes you tend to use. I guarantee you'll find something you have forgotten to do or you'll get an insight that you missed the first time around. By reviewing the chapters, your testing for the processes you work with will continue to become more effective and more fine-tuned.

NOTE: To find the process you wish to work with, see the table of contents, Appendix B. It has been set up to help you move around this appendix quickly and easily.

PKTT SELF-TESTING

For full information, see chapter 4, pp. 29–40.

1. THE CIRCUIT FINGERS. If you are right-handed: Place your left hand palm up. Connect the tip of your left thumb with the tip of the left little finger (finger #4). *Not your index finger.* If you are left-handed: Place your right hand palm up. Connect the tip of your right thumb with the tip of your right little finger.

2. THE TEST FINGERS AND TESTING POSITION. To test the new circuit, place the test fingers, thumb and index finger (finger #1) of your other hand, inside the circle you have created by connecting your circuit thumb and little finger.

3. POSITIVE RESPONSE. Press your circuit fingers together, keeping them in the circular position. *Using the same amount of pressure,* try to press apart or separate the circuit fingers with your test fingers. The circuit will not break and the circuit fingers will not separate or weaken.

4. NEGATIVE RESPONSE. Press your circuit fingers together and, *using equal pressure,* press against the circuit fingers with the test fingers. The electric circuit will break, and the circuit fingers will weaken and separate.

PKTT CALIBRATION

For full information, see chapter 4, pp. 34–35.

1. Ask yourself a question that you know has a positive or true answer and PKTT test for the response. Adjust the pressure between your testing and circuit fingers until you feel the pressure has equalized and you have a strong, positive response. Play with this a bit and get a good feel for the strength of the positive response.

2. Then switch to a question that has a negative or false answer and PKTT test for the response. Play around with the pressure until it has equalized and you clearly feel the circuit break and/or see the fingers separate.

3. Alternate your questions between positive and negative a few times to get the feel of holding the equalized pressure no matter what the question.

THE BASIC ESSENCE TEST

For full information, see chapter 6, p. 51–67.

SUPPLIES:
- the Perelandra Essences
- pen and paper
- option: a blank Perelandra Essence Record Chart

PREPARE FOR TESTING:
- Drink some water.
- Go to the bathroom, if needed.
- Find a quiet spot and sit comfortably.
- Place the boxes of Essences and the other supplies within easy reach.

1. State your intent to do a Basic Essence Test:

    I want to do a Basic Essence Test.

2. Place each box of essences, one at a time, in your lap. Ask:

    Do I need any Essences from this box? (Test.)

If you get a negative, none are needed.

If you test positive, place the box off to one side and test each bottle from that box individually by placing the bottle in your lap to determine which ones are needed. Ask:

    Do I need _____ Essence? (Test.)

3. Check your results by placing in your lap just the bottles that tested positive. Ask:

    Are these the only Essences I need? (Test.)

If the response is positive, go to step 4. If only one Essence is needed, skip step 4 and go to step 5.

If you get a negative, retest the other Essences. After retesting, ask the question once more:

    Are these the only Essences I need? (Test.)

If the response is still negative, keep testing the Essences to find what you missed and you get a positive response to the question. This will verify that you have all the needed Essences.

225

4. If you have more than one Essence, check them as a combination by placing all of them in your lap and asking:

> Is this the combination I need? (Test.)

If you get a negative but the Essences tested positive when tested individually, you may need to adjust the combination.

Place each of the combination bottles separately in your lap and ask:

> Do I remove this bottle from the combination? (Test.)

Whatever tests positive gets removed.

Put the remaining combination bottles in your lap and ask:

> Is this combination now correct? (Test.)

You should get a positive. If you don't, test the *original* combination again (the combination bottles before you removed anything), and keep working at it until they test positive as a unit.

5. Take these Essences orally, one drop each. Record the Essences.

Dosage: Number of Days

6. Hold in your lap all the bottles that tested positive as a unit. If only one bottle tested positive, hold that bottle in your lap.

7. Ask:

> Do I need the Essence(s) more than one time? (Test.)

If negative, you have already completed the dosage (in step 5) and you have completed the Basic Essence Test.

8. If you got a positive response in step 7, find out how many days you are to take the Essence(s). Do a sequential test. With all the needed Essence(s) still in your lap, ask:

> Do I need these one day? (Test.)
> Two days? (Test.)
> Three days? (Test.)

Do a count until you get a negative response.

9. Do another sequential test. (If you are testing a combination of Essences, treat them as a unit. Don't break up the combination and test each bottle separately.) While still holding the Essence combination in your lap, ask:

> Do I take the Essences once daily? (Test.)
>
> Two times daily? (Test.)
>
> Three times daily? (Test.)

Your last positive response tells you how many times per day the Essences are needed.

10. If you are to take these Essences once or twice daily, test to see if it is best to take them in the morning, afternoon or evening, or any combination of the three. Ask:

> Do I take these Essences in the morning? (Test.)
>
> In the afternoon? (Test.)
>
> In the evening? (Test.)

Whatever tests positive is when you should take your dosages.

Dosage and Follow-up Testing

● REMEMBER TO TAKE YOUR DOSAGES (one dropperful per dose) for the full period of time prescribed. It'll help you to remember if you set your solution bottle in an obvious place such as on your bedside table, in the kitchen or bathroom. Also record the end date for the solution on a calendar or computer so that you'll know when to do the follow-up testing.

● ADMINISTERING DOSAGES. Each time you take the Essence solution during the prescribed dosage period, prepare yourself first by activating the circuits the solution is addressing. Read aloud the intent written on the label.

> IMPORTANT: Once you make a solution bottle, the Essence drops have been diluted and are no longer concentrated. For each dosage, you will need to take ten to twelve drops (one dropperful) of each solution.

● COMPLETING A DOSAGE PERIOD. Once you complete a dosage period, do a new Basic Essence Test *within forty-eight hours* as a follow-up. Continue doing follow-up testing at the end of each dosage period until you test clear.

● AFTER TESTING CLEAR, do a new Basic Essence Test for the next three days. When you test clear for three days straight, you have completed the series of follow-up testing and no additional Essences are needed at that time.

● RETURNING AND NEW SYMPTOMS OR INJURIES. Should a Basic Essence Test and the follow-up tests not take care of all the symptoms or injuries, set up for a Basic Telegraph Test and list the persistent symptoms on the BTT checklist. Move the telegraph testing completely through all dosage periods and follow-up testing. Continue this until each listed symptom tests clear for seven days straight. ☉

MAKING A SOLUTION BOTTLE.

For full information, see chapter 6, pp. 63–64.

To make a solution bottle you will need:
- A clean, brown-glass, half-ounce dropper bottle
- Brandy or distilled white vinegar preservative
- A clean solution label
- Spring or untreated water (If this is unavailable, tap water will do.)

1. Add five drops of each Essence needed to the empty half-ounce dropper bottle.

Or, if you wish to economize on the number of drops you use, test for how many drops of each Essence are to be added to your half-ounce solution. Do a sequential test for each bottle, one at a time. Ask:

Do I need one drop of _____ Essence for this half-ounce solution? (Test.)
Two drops? (Test.)
Three drops? (Test.) And so on.

2. Then add one teaspoon of brandy or distilled white vinegar if you want to preserve the solution, and fill with water. You can also refrigerate the solution, thus eliminating the need for preserving. Label the bottle with the testing purpose/focus and dosage information.

3. Take one dropperful (ten to twelve drops) for each dosage.

1. Add nine drops of each needed Essence concentrate to four ounces of water.

2. Add three teaspoons of brandy or distilled white vinegar if you want to preserve this solution. Refrigerate it if no preservative is added.

3. Drink one good sip for each dosage needed.   ☉

DAILY ESSENCE TESTING

For full information, see chapter 6, pp. 56–57.

1. After completing steps 1–5 of the Basic Essence Test (pp. 225–226) and taking each Essence that tested positive, record the results, put the Essences away and get on with your day.

2. The next day, do another Basic Test, completing steps 1 through 5 (pp. 225–226). Take those Essences, record the results, put the Essences away and get on with your day. Repeat this process each day for as long as you would like.   ☉

BASIC TELEGRAPH TEST

For full information, see chapter 7, p. 69–91.

SUPPLIES:
- the five sets of Perelandra Essences
- pen, paper and calendar
- option: a blank Perelandra Essence Record Chart
- a blank Perelandra Essence Telegraph Test Checklist
- a watch or clock with a second hand
- a clean spoon
- clean solution bottles (one bottle for each symptom on the BTT checklist)
- brandy or distilled white vinegar preservative
- blank labels

NOTE: The Essences that test positive for the Basic Essence Test are not superceded by the Essences that test positive for the Basic Telegraph Test.

PREPARE FOR TESTING:
- Drink some water.
- Go to the bathroom, if needed.
- Find a quiet spot and sit comfortably.
- Place the boxes of Essences and the other supplies within easy reach.

1. State your intent:

> I want to set up for a Basic Telegraph Test.

2. Clear your electric system: Do a Basic Essence Test (steps 2–5, pp. 225–226). Take any needed Essences. Do not test for dosage.

3. Make a BTT checklist. (NOTE: You can also put the BTT checklist together anytime prior to beginning a Basic Telegraph Test.)

4. Focus on the first symptom or injury on your BTT checklist and ask:

> What Essences are needed for the circuits connected with
> [insert symptom/injury]? (Test.)

Keep your focus on the symptom or injury while following the Basic Essence Test, steps 2–5.

5. Take the needed Essences for this first symptom/injury. Record the Essences alongside the symptom listed on the BTT checklist.

6. Test for dosage (Basic Essence Test, steps 6–10, pp. 226–227).

If you are to take the Essences just one time, you don't need to do any further dosage testing and you can go on to BTT step 7.

If you are to take these Essences more than one time, complete the dosage testing now. On the BTT checklist next to the symptom, record the dosage information.

7. Repeat Telegraph Test, steps 4, 5 and 6 for every symptom or injury listed on the BTT checklist.

8. When you've finished testing every symptom/injury on your BTT checklist, complete the Telegraph Test for this issue by doing a Basic Essence Test for your full electric system. *Do not check for dosage. These Essences are to be taken one time only.*

9. Make any needed solution bottles. Label each bottle right after making the solution. Include the beginning and end date of the dosage and how many times a day you are to take it. Also include the times of day you are to take it (morning, afternoon, evening). ☺

● REMEMBER TO TAKE the needed dosages (one dropperful per dose) for the full period of time prescribed. Also, record the end date for each solution on a calendar or computer so that you'll know when to do the follow-up testing.

● ADMINISTERING DOSAGES. Each time you take an Essence solution during the prescribed dosage period, prepare yourself first by activating the circuits the solution is addressing. Read aloud the intent written on the label.

> IMPORTANT: Once you make a solution bottle, the Essence drops have been diluted and are no longer concentrated. For each dosage, you will need to take ten to twelve drops (one dropperful) of each solution.

● COMPLETING A DOSAGE PERIOD. Once you complete a dosage period for a symptom/injury, do a new Telegraph Test *within forty-eight hours* as a follow-up. Continue doing follow-up testing at the end of each dosage period until you test clear.

● AFTER TESTING CLEAR, do a new Telegraph Test for the symptom/injury for the next seven days. When you test clear for seven days straight, you have completed the series of follow-up testing for that particular symptom and no additional Essences are needed at that time. Cross the symptom/injury off your BTT checklist.

● RETURNING AND NEW SYMPTOMS OR INJURIES. Should a symptom or injury that tested clear return, just list it again on the BTT checklist and do a new Telegraph Test for this one symptom, starting with step 1 and testing through step 9. Move it completely through the dosage periods and follow-up testing. Continue this until it tests clear again for seven days straight.

If the returning symptom/injury exhibits any changes or anomalies that differentiate it from the old one in any way, consider this a new symptom/injury that needs to be added to the BTT checklist. Do a new surrogate Telegraph Test for that one symptom and move it completely through the dosage periods and follow-up testing.

TELEGRAPH TEST FOR FOCUS

For full information, see chapter 7, pp. 80–81.

1. Set up a Telegraph Test by doing a Basic Essence Test first. Take any needed Essences.

2. State:

> I want to test the circuits that are connected with and support my ability to focus. I need for these circuits to remain activated throughout the entire test, even if I am unable to properly hold the focus.

3. Test the Essences. Take any needed Essences and test for dosage. Wait twenty to twenty-five minutes before doing any other Essence testing.

Test your focus circuits whenever needed. And remember to do any needed follow-up testing once a dosage period ends. ☯

ADD "FOCUS AIDS" TO THE SYMPTOMS/INJURIES ON YOUR BTT CHECKLIST

For full information, see chapter 7, pp. 77–79.

● For most symptoms/injuries all you'll need to do is read the wording you used on the BTT checklist and keep that in mind as you test. Or look at the injury from time to time during the test.

● For a mystery item, just keep "Factor-X" in mind during the test.

● For the symptoms/injuries that may be difficult to see or feel, or even imagine, choose a visual symbol or code word that for you relates to the symptom/injury in some manner. Draw the symbol or write the code word next to that symptom/injury on your BTT checklist.

● Then "officially" link your symbol or code with the symptom/injury by stating out loud:

> I assign this [symbol/code] to [the name of the symptom/injury as described on the BTT checklist].

If it's a symbol, be sure to keep the symbol in your mind as you state the sentence aloud and name the symptom it represents. If it's a code word, insert the code and the symptom/injury as it's written on your BTT checklist as you read the sentence out loud.

When you are telegraph testing a symptom/injury with a code word or symbol, keep the word or symbol in mind as you do the testing *and* as you take the Essences.

THE HEALTH OVERHAUL SUGGESTION

For full information, see chapter 7, pp. 85–86.

Think about the areas in your health that need to be shored up and strengthened. Make a list. Then start with just one issue. Set up a Basic Telegraph Test with a BTT checklist and move that issue through the dosage periods and all the follow-up testing. Then take the next thing on the list and do the same. Work with your Health Overhaul list one issue at a time so you won't overwhelm yourself.

DAILY SYMPTOM SWEEP

For full information, see chapter 7, pp. 86–87.

Each evening sit down with your Essences and think about how you felt throughout the day. Make a written or mental list of the physical, emotional and mental "glitches."

● Do a Basic Essence Test to clear your electric system. Take any needed Essences *one time only.* No dosage test needed.

● Then do a Basic Telegraph Test for each symptom. Take the needed Essences before moving on to the next symptom. Don't test for dosage. The Essences are to be taken *one time only.*

● End with another Basic Essence Test to stabilize and balance your electric system as a unit after all the circuit repair. Take these Essences *one time only.*

● The next evening do it again. Think about how you felt that day and include any lingering symptoms from the previous day.

● If you have a symptom or issue that lingers for more than four days in a row, assume that it needs a Basic Telegraph Test including dosage and follow-up testing. Continue addressing it in the Daily Symptom Sweep until you have time to switch over and do a complete Basic Telegraph Test for this symptom. Once you begin the Basic Telegraph Test, discontinue including this symptom in the Daily Symptom Sweep.

For full information on using ETS Plus for the following situations, see chapter 8, pp. 99–104.

BASIC ETS PLUS DOSAGE

Within the first twenty minutes of experiencing a trauma, take three to four doses (ten to twelve drops), waiting five minutes between each dose.

TRAUMAS WITHIN TRAUMAS

You are recuperating from that injury or illness and you wake up one morning realizing that you have taken a step backward in your recuperation process and are feeling ill or in pain. Assume you have experienced another trauma that is impacting your healing process and take ETS Plus three or four times within the first twenty minutes of experiencing the new discomfort.

DAILY DOSES OF ETS PLUS

If you are regularly exposed to chemicals, pollution or a sick building, experiencing unusual stress or difficulty, or work in a high intensity job (EMT, police, hospital emergency room): take three to four doses (ten to twelve drops), throughout the day, including one dose at bedtime, for as long as you are in the situation or environment.

EXTENDED TRAUMA TIME FRAMES

For an Extended Trauma Time Frame take three to five doses of ETS Plus daily, including one dose at bedtime. Continue taking ETS Plus daily until you feel your changed or new life has settled in for you. If you've miscalculated and you realize you're not out of the Extended Trauma Time Frame yet, just go back to the three to five daily doses of ETS Plus.

ETS PLUS BATHS

For an ETS Plus bath, put ¼ cup (two ounces) ETS Plus in a full bath and soak for twenty minutes. Do not add any other bath ingredients such as bubble baths, salts, oils, etc. If you use PKTT, you can test for how many nights you would benefit from an ETS Plus bath.

If you hate sitting in a tub or don't have time for this but you know you could benefit from a full immersion, put undiluted ETS Plus in a spray bottle and spray the solution over your whole body. (You need to be naked for this!) Then air dry. It should take just a few minutes. (Pour any remaining ETS Plus back into its dropper bottle each time you have finished spraying.) ☉

TOPICAL APPLICATIONS

Take ETS Plus orally. Then place a drop(s) or spray ETS Plus directly on the injured area and let it air dry. ☉

USING ETS PLUS AND THE PERELANDRA ESSENCES

For full information, see chapter 8, pp. 104–106.

● INJURIES

    1. ETS Plus—Take three or four doses during the first twenty minutes.

    2. Do the Basic Telegraph Test.

● INJURIES NEEDING MEDICAL ATTENTION

    1. ETS Plus—Take three or four doses during the first twenty minutes.

    2. Call for help. Go to the hospital.

    3. If you are incapacitated, take ETS Plus daily until you are able to test.

    If you can do a little testing: do a daily Basic Essence Test (no dosage testing needed).

    4. Once you can resume testing: do the Basic Telegraph Test for the injuries.

235

- SERIOUS OR COMPLEX INJURIES

    1. ETS Plus—Take three or four doses during the first twenty minutes.

    2. Do the Basic Telegraph Test.

    If the injury includes seizures or attacks:
    1. ETS Plus—Take three or four doses as soon as you feel a seizure/attack coming on.

    2. ETS Plus—Take three or four doses right after a seizure/attack.

    3. Do the Basic Telegraph Test. Should an additional injury occur, add it to your BTT checklist and telegraph test this new injury right away and do all the follow-up testing. It is now a regular part of your BTT checklist.

- MISALIGNMENTS AND CHIROPRACTIC WORK. By "misalignment" I mean something like a vertebra that is not seated or anything in the rest of the skeletal system that has been knocked, pulled, banged or emoted out of its correct alignment.

    1. Take three or four doses of ETS Plus during the first twenty minutes when the problem occurs or when you first recognize the problem.

    2. Make a chiropractor appointment as soon as possible, if needed.

    Sometimes a misalignment will automatically adjust on its own if treated with ETS Plus and Essences right away. In this case a chiropractor appointment is not needed.

    3. While waiting for the appointment day to arrive, do a daily Basic Essence Test.

    4. Immediately after the appointment, take three or four doses of ETS Plus during the first twenty minutes.

    5. Post-appointment, do the Basic Telegraph Test for the misalignment.

- PHYSICAL THERAPY SESSIONS

    1. Use ETS Plus during the session whenever there is unusual difficulty, stress or pain. Take one dose only.

    2. Use ETS Plus immediately after the session. Take three or four doses during the first twenty minutes.

    3. Consider including the Perelandra Essences in your daily regimen for whatever is causing the need for physical therapy. Look at the Basic Essence Test, the Basic Telegraph Test and Telegraph Testing for Chronic Illness and decide which testing approach best suits your situation.

● COUNSELING SESSIONS

1. Use ETS Plus during the session whenever there is unusual emotional difficulty or pain. Take one dose only.

2. Use ETS Plus immediately after the session. Take three or four doses during the first twenty minutes.

3. Consider including the Perelandra Essences in your daily regimen for whatever is causing you to need counseling. Look at the Basic Essence Test and the Basic Telegraph Test and decide which testing approach best suits your situation.

● ANY SITUATION OR EVENT THAT MADE YOU GRAB YOUR ETS PLUS

1. ETS Plus — Take the three or four doses during the first twenty minutes.

2. As soon as possible *(within twenty-four hours)* and if needed, follow up with the appropriate Essence testing. A lot of times ETS Plus will take care of a problem and nothing more is needed. However, for the situations that go beyond the initial trauma and require more attention, decide which Essence testing is best for you to use. If you're not sure if a follow-up is needed, do a Basic Essence Test about an hour after taking the ETS Plus doses. If ETS Plus took care of it, the Basic Essence Test will test clear and no Essences are needed. If you did not test clear, take the Essences that tested positive. Then decide which Essence testing best addresses the situation and either switch to the Basic Telegraph Test or continue doing the Basic Essence Test (daily or with dosage testing) until you test clear.

ETS PLUS BIRTH-STABILIZING PROCESS

For full information, see chapter 8, pp. 107–108.

1. LABOR AND BIRTH. As soon as contractions begin, take two doses (ten to twelve drops per dose) of ETS Plus. Focus on yourself for the first dose and on the baby for the second dose. Should a problem arise or should you feel overly stressed or panicked during labor, take another dose of ETS Plus immediately for yourself and a second dose for the baby.

2. DAD (OR WHOEVER IS ASSISTING OR COACHING YOU) is to take a dose of ETS Plus once labor begins. Should he faint or become overwhelmed at any time during the process, he's to take another dose.

3. AS SOON AS POSSIBLE AFTER THE BIRTH

MOM: Take one dose of ETS Plus. If you received stitches or experienced any other problem during the birthing process and you work with the Perelandra Essences, plan to telegraph test using the surgery guidelines (see pp. 246–247) once you are up to testing the Essences again.

BABY: Place ten drops of ETS Plus on the baby's forehead and gently rub the drops into the skin. Let her forehead air dry.

DAD: Take one dose of ETS Plus.

EXTREME-TRAUMA REPAIR PROCESS

For full information, see chapter 8, pp. 108–113.

1. When you first arrive on a trauma scene, administer four doses of ETS Plus five minutes apart. If the person is unconscious or otherwise unable to open his mouth, put the drops on his lips, two or three drops at a time, until you've administered a total of ten drops. Repeat this three more times with five minutes between each round.

2. Once he has regained consciousness, have him take ETS Plus five times daily, including one dose at bedtime. If he is unable to handle the bottle and dropper, mix ETS Plus in a glass for him.

3. Mixing ETS Plus in a glass: Add twelve drops of ETS Plus to a half cup of water (four to six ounces) so that he can sip it throughout the day. Make sure someone stops by each day to mix the drops and water for him.

4. He is to continue taking ETS Plus daily until he feels he can cope with the situation well.

5. When he feels he's back on track and interested in life again, he can stop taking the daily ETS Plus doses. If he miscalculates and rushes the timing, he only needs to return to the five daily doses of ETS Plus.

After ETS Plus is no longer needed, you can surrogate Telegraph Test any remaining issues and symptoms. List them on the BTT checklist.

Old Extreme-Trauma Events

1. Take ETS Plus *five times daily,* including once at bedtime. Once you repair these trauma circuits, how you think about the event and how those memories impact you will change and you'll notice that the behavior that you know is not really you will be gone.

2. After ETS Plus is no longer needed, you can telegraph test any remaining issues and symptoms. List them on the BTT checklist.

3. Go on vacation to celebrate. ☺

Newborns and Infants

If the baby has been given ETS Plus when her mother went into labor and again right after birth, any damage to her trauma circuits will have been taken care of.

IF SHE HASN'T HAD THIS BENEFIT

1. Put ten drops of ETS Plus on her forehead, gently massage them in and then allow her forehead to air dry.

2. Repeat this routine *once daily* for the next four days.

3. Do whatever is necessary to make her environment baby-friendly. ☺

For Toddlers and Children Under Age Twelve

1. Administer two doses of ETS Plus daily, including once at bedtime.

2. Treat this as an Extended Trauma Time Frame and continue the daily ETS Plus doses until the damaged trauma-circuit symptoms are repaired. This may take a matter of days or a few weeks — or it can happen right away.

3. After ETS Plus is no longer needed, you can do a surrogate Basic Essence Test, including all the follow-up testing for addressing any residual electric system damage.

4. Straighten out the child's situation so that she doesn't have to experience trauma that causes her to function with damaged circuits. ☺

For Children and Young Adults Twelve to Eighteen

1. Have them take *four doses* of ETS Plus daily, including once at bedtime.

2. Treat this as an Extended Trauma Time Frame and continue the daily ETS Plus doses until the damaged trauma-circuit symptoms are repaired. This may take a matter of a few weeks or a few months.

3. After ETS Plus is no longer needed, you can do a Basic Essence Test, including all the follow-up testing for addressing any residual electric system damage.

4. This still applies: Straighten out the the child's situation so that she doesn't have to experience trauma that causes her to function with damaged circuits.

Coping with the Adolescence from Hell

● FOR THE ADOLESCENT. Take four doses of ETS Plus daily, including once at bedtime. Follow the guidelines for children and young adults twelve to eighteen.

● FOR THE PARENT(S). Take a dose of ETS Plus three times daily until you feel you can cope comfortably and nonviolently. Anytime the old urge to beat your head against a wall comes up again for you, resume the daily ETS Plus dosages.

For full information, see chapter 9, p. 121.

HEAD-START PROGRAM FOR CHRONIC ILLNESS

1. For your head-start, do a Basic Essence Test right away (pp. 225–228) and include dosage and follow-up testing while working on the CI checklist.

2. Once you have completed the chronic illness checklist, you may begin telegraph testing for chronic illness even if you are still taking an Essence dosage from the "Head-Start Basic Essence Test."

3. Continue taking that dosage and move through all the follow-up testing for the Head-Start Basic Essence Test until you test clear while simultaneously moving through the telegraph testing.

TELEGRAPH TESTING CHRONIC ILLNESS   *The Process Steps*

SUPPLIES:

For full information, see chapter 9, pp. 117–140.

- the five sets of Perelandra Essences
- pen, paper, calendar and the completed CI checklist
- option: a blank Perelandra Essence Record Chart
- a blank Perelandra Essences Telegraph Test Checklist
- a watch or clock with a second hand
- a clean spoon
- clean solution bottles (one bottle for each symptom on the CI checklist)
- brandy or distilled white vinegar preservative
- blank labels

PREPARE FOR TESTING:

- Be as alert and as well-rested as possible.
- Find a quiet spot.
- Drink water.
- Go to the bathroom.
- Be comfortable: sit in a comfortable chair or propped up in bed.

1. State your intent:

> I want to set up for a Telegraph Test for [name of chronic illness].

2. Clear your electric system: Do the Basic Essence Test (steps 2–5, pp. 225–226). Take any needed Essences. Do not test for dosage.

3. Place your completed symptoms CI checklist in front of you. (Also include the colored pages from the coloring book.)

4. Begin by telegraph testing your body's full electric system. Treat it as a symptom. Ask:

> What Essences are needed for my electric system as it relates to [insert name of illness]? (Test.)

> Keep your focus on your electric system while following the Basic Essence Test, steps 2–5. Test for dosage.

5. Telegraph test each symptom on the CI checklist, one by one, following the Basic Essence Test, steps 2–5.
   - Use an assigned code or symbol as a focus aid.

- Take the needed Essences after each test.

- Dosage: Test for dosage before moving on to the next symptom.

- On the CI checklist, record the Essences needed and the dosage for each symptom.

- If you are to take Essences just one time for a symptom, you don't need to do any further dosage testing and you can move on to the next symptom on the CI checklist.

If you need to make any solution bottles, wait until after all the telegraph testing is completed and make all the needed solution bottles at the same time.

6. When you've finished testing every symptom on your CI checklist, including the auxiliary symptoms, do a final Basic Essence Test for your full electric system. *Do not check for dosage. These Essences are to be taken one time only.*

7. The Telegraph Test for your chronic illness is completed. Make any needed solution bottles.

You are now free to get on with the rest of your day.

Dosage and Follow-up Testing

- REMEMBER TO TAKE ALL NEEDED DOSAGES (one dropperful per dose) for the full period of time prescribed. Also, record the end date for each solution on a calendar or computer so that you'll know when to do the follow-up testing.

- ADMINISTERING DOSAGES. Each time you take an Essence solution during the prescribed dosage period, prepare yourself first by activating the circuits the solution is addressing. Read aloud the intent written on the label.

> IMPORTANT: Once you make a solution bottle, the Essence drops have been diluted and are no longer concentrated. For each dosage, you will need to take ten to twelve drops (one dropperful) of each solution.

- COMPLETING A DOSAGE PERIOD. Once you complete a dosage period for a symptom/injury, do a new Telegraph Test *within forty-eight hours* as a follow up. Continue doing follow-up testing at the end of each dosage period until you test clear.

● AFTER TESTING CLEAR, do a new Telegraph Test for the symptom/injury for the next seven days. When you test clear for seven days straight, you have completed the work for that particular symptom and no additional Essences are needed at this time. Cross the symptom/injury off your CI checklist.

● RETURNING AND NEW SYMPTOMS OR INJURIES. Should a symptom or injury that tested clear return, just list it again on the CI checklist and do a new Telegraph Test for this one symptom, starting with step 1 and testing through step 9. Move it completely through the dosage periods and follow-up testing. Continue this until it tests clear again for seven days straight.

If the returning symptom/injury exhibits any changes or anomalies that differentiate it from the old one in any way, consider this a new symptom/injury that needs to be added to the CI checklist. Do a new Telegraph Test for that one symptom and move it completely through the dosage periods and follow-up testing. ☉

BEFORE SURGERY

For full information, see chapter 10, pp. 141–142.

The focus for using ETS Plus and the Perelandra Essences prior to surgery centers around the need to stabilize ourselves on the PEMS levels.

TRAUMA MOMENT #1 — When first told by the doctor that you need surgery:

- Stop him after he gives you the news, take a dose of ETS Plus,

- Then tell him to continue.

- Right after you leave his office, take three or four doses of ETS Plus, five minutes apart.

TRAUMA MOMENT #2 — You are told the date the surgery has been scheduled:

- Take ETS Plus again.

- If you are in the doctor's office or you are talking to him by phone, repeat the routine you did when he told you that you needed surgery. Stop him for a second, take a dose of ETS Plus, then tell him to continue.

- After the conversation, take ETS Plus three or four times, five minutes apart.

WAITING FOR THE DAY:

- During the waiting period, your focus is to achieve and maintain as deep a level of stability as possible.

- For this, do a daily Basic Essence Test (pp. 225–226) until you enter the hospital for the surgery.

- Add a Basic Telegraph Test (pp. 229–231) with just one focus to telegraph:
  My electric system and circuits in preparation for the [insert the surgical target name]. (Ex., gall bladder removal, valve replacement, appendectomy...)

- Take the needed Essences and do any follow-up testing until the day you leave for the hospital.

- At that point, consider the preparation period over and stop taking Essences.

- Leave your Essence sets at home but *take a couple of bottles of ETS Plus with you to the hospital.*

TRAUMA MOMENT #3 — The tests needed in preparation for surgery:

- Take one dose of ETS Plus immediately after every test is completed.

- Continue doing the basic testing each day throughout the entire period before surgery. Especially don't skip the days when you have appointments for tests.

TRAUMA MOMENT #4 — Maintaining balance while being stressed by your family, loved ones and friends:

- Any time you are not laughing and having a good time during a visit, take a dose of ETS Plus after they leave.

- This might be the right time for you to introduce ETS Plus to them and suggest they take it several times a day to calm their nerves! ☉

THE HOSPITAL

For full information, see chapter 10, p. 143.

1. Take a couple bottles of ETS Plus with you to the hospital. Once you enter the hospital, assume that you have entered an Extended Trauma Time Frame and take three to five doses of ETS Plus daily, including one dose at bedtime.

2. Take an additional dose anytime you feel "hit" by the experience as you wait for surgery.

3. After visits from your group of well-meaning but overly emotional family and friends, don't hesitate to take an additional dose of ETS Plus. (Or while they are still there, if they're making you crazy and they won't leave. This might be another opportunity for you to introduce ETS Plus to them and suggest they take it several times a day to calm their nerves!)

4. If you are close to the time you'll be going into surgery and you've been told you can't eat or drink anything, *don't take ETS Plus orally.* Instead, apply one drop topically to your forehead, lightly rub it in and then let it air dry.   ☺

Emergency Surgery

1. For the entire time you are dealing with this emergency up to the time of surgery, assume you are in an Extended Trauma Time Frame.

2. Take ETS Plus three to five times each day prior to surgery. If your emergency doesn't include that kind of time, take as many of the three to five doses as possible prior to going into surgery.

3. Once the surgery is over, follow the listed protocol starting with "Post-Surgery in the Hospital."   ☺

If your surgical emergency was caused by an accident that left you with multiple injuries, you'll need to telegraph test those injuries along with the surgery testing. Follow the steps as outlined for telegraph testing multiple injuries (pp. 79–80).   ☺

Post-Surgery in the Hospital

1. Take three to four doses of ETS Plus, five minutes apart, after surgery. Here's where a family member or friend can help by administering these doses to you.

2. While recovering in the hospital, you are still in the Extended Trauma Time Frame and need to take ETS Plus three to five times daily, including one dose at bedtime.

3. Should you experience sudden pain or discomfort, take an additional dose of ETS Plus immediately and buzz for the nurse.   ☺

For full information, see chapter 10, pp. 144–145.

If you don't have the strength to resume testing when you first get home, assume you are still in the Extended Trauma Time Frame and continue taking ETS Plus three to five times a day, including one dose at bedtime. ☉

The Extended Trauma Time Frame Has Ended and You Can Test Again

1. When you are able to test again, discontinue the daily doses of ETS Plus.

2. Set up two separate Basic Telegraph Tests (pp. 229–231) to be worked simultaneously. Each Basic Telegraph Test will have a different intent and focus:

(1) the surgical goal—the circuits in need of repair as a result of the original problem and the targeted work, and

(2) the surgical procedure—the circuits that were severed by the incision(s) or damaged during the overall surgical procedure.

● BASIC TELEGRAPH TEST #1.
State the intent:

Intent: Balance, stabilize and repair the electric system and circuits connected with and impacted by the original problem and the work done in the targeted surgical area.

The BTT checklist:
• Include both the areas/organs targeted by the surgery plus everything that is connected with the original diagnosis that led to surgery.

• Test the Perelandra Essence Telegraph Test Checklist to identify all the areas that need to be included on the BTT checklist for this first testing intent.

Proceed with the Basic Telegraph Test steps and do the needed follow-up testing *within forty-eight hours* after each dosage period ends. Continue doing this until you test clear for seven days straight for each item listed on your BTT checklist.

State the intent:

> Intent: Balance, stabilize and repair the electric system and circuits connected with and impacted by the incisions and surgical procedure.

The BTT checklist:

- Include the "external" incision and the deeper "internal" incision.

- If more than one external or internal incision was made, list each separately.

- Also include any injuries resulting from post-surgical treatment (sore or inflamed injection sites or where tubes were inserted, bruising, sore skin areas from bandages, etc.), areas of pain, difficulties in mobility…

- Test the Perelandra Essence Telegraph Test Checklist to identify additional areas that need to be included on the BTT checklist for this second testing intent.

Symptom Identification: If you have a symptom and you're not sure which BTT checklist you should list it on, test the symptom this way. Ask:

> Does [symptom in question] belong on the Basic Telegraph Test #1 checklist? (Test.)

> Does [symptom in question] belong on the Basic Telegraph Test #2 checklist? (Test.)

Include the symptom on the BTT checklist that tests positive. If both tested positive, this means the symptom needs to be included on both checklists.

Proceed with the Basic Telegraph Test steps and do the needed follow-up testing *within forty-eight hours* after each dosage period ends. Continue doing this until you test clear for seven days straight for each thing listed on your BTT checklist. ☉

ACTIVE SCARS

> For full information, see chapter 10, pp. 146–148.

Once you complete your full recovery and recuperation period after surgery, and you notice that your scar still looks raw, red or swollen, set up a Basic Telegraph Test right away.

Basic Telegraph Test for Active Scars

1. State the intent:

   Balance, stabilize and repair the electric system and circuits that are underlying and still causing this active scar.

2. THE ACTIVE SCAR CHECKLIST.

   - Include the active scar that you can see.

   - List the other incisions/scars (internal and external) that were included in the Basic Telegraph Test #2 checklist.

   - List any incisions that you needed to include on the #2 checklist the first time around but missed because you were not aware of them. Ask:

     Were there any incisions that I did not include on the original #2 checklist? (Test the question.)

   If the result is negative, you have all of the incision and scar locations on your BTT checklist and you are ready to telegraph test that list.

   However, if you get a positive response to the question, a mystery scar location needs to be included on the BTT checklist. Remember, had it been included on your original #2 checklist, you would have referred to it as an incision. Now it's no longer an incision. It's a scar.

   With your focus on the first mystery scar, state:
     I name this scar the "Factor-X scar."

   Write "Factor-X scar" on your BTT checklist for the active scar.

   You may have more than one mystery scar. Ask again:
     Is there another incision/scar that I haven't included on the BTT checklist? (Test the question.)

   If you get a positive response, state:
     I name this second scar the "Factor-Y scar."

   Include that on your BTT checklist.

   Continue asking the question and assigning names (just keep assigning letters) until you get a negative to the question and all the scars have been included in your new BTT checklist.

3. Proceed with the Basic Telegraph Test steps (pp. 229–231) and do the needed follow-up testing *within forty-eight hours* after each dosage period ends. Continue doing this until you test clear for seven days straight for each item listed on your BTT checklist.

4. Give the active scar five more weeks to finish its shift from active to healthy. If, after that time, it still looks raw, set up telegraph testing for an active scar again and do a new round of testing. This second round of active-scar testing will not be a frequent occurrence. ◐

AMPUTATION/PHANTOM LIMB SYNDROME

For full information, see chapter 10, pp. 149–154.

When faced with amputation, follow the surgery guidelines as written up to "The Extended Trauma Time Frame Has Ended and You Can Test Again" (pp. 243–246).

Once you can resume testing, you will discontinue the daily doses of ETS Plus and set up four Basic Telegraph Tests. Work with these four Telegraph Tests simultaneously.

BASIC TELEGRAPH TEST #1.

1. State the intent:

Intent: Balance, stabilize and repair the open circuits and severed circuit ends caused by the amputation and the removal of a significant portion of the electric system.

2. For BTT checklist #1, write:

Focus: All the open circuits and severed circuit ends caused by the amputation and the removal of a significant portion of the electric system.

3. Proceed with the Basic Telegraph Test steps (pp. 229–231) and do the needed follow-up testing *within forty-eight hours* after each dosage period ends. Continue doing this until you test clear for seven days straight. At that point, it's safe to assume you have completed your recovery and recuperation period, as far as the first test and intent are concerned.

BASIC TELEGRAPH TEST #2.

1. State the intent:

Intent: Establish alternate electric circuit connections and pathways to restore the balance, function and general health in areas of the body that were not amputated but suffered circuit damage resulting from the amputation.

The Process Steps

2. For BTT checklist #2, write:

Focus: Establish all needed alternate electric circuit connections and pathways to restore the balance, function and general health in areas of the body that were not amputated but suffered circuit damage resulting from the amputation.

3. Proceed with the Basic Telegraph Test steps (pp. 229–231) and do the needed follow-up testing *within forty-eight hours* after each dosage period ends. Continue doing this until you test clear for seven days straight.

BASIC TELEGRAPH TEST #3.

1. State the intent:

Intent: Shift the function of the remaining PEMS circuits that were part of the supportive foundation for the now-removed limb and are still active and connected with the body's remaining electric system, its nervous system and brain to reflect the overall new balance of the electric system as a unit.

2. For BTT checklist #3, write:

Focus: Shift the function of all the remaining PEMS circuits that were part of the supportive foundation for the now-removed limb and are still active and connected with the body's remaining electric system, its nervous system and brain to reflect the overall new balance of the electric system as a unit.

3. Proceed with the Basic Telegraph Test steps and do the needed follow-up testing *within forty-eight hours* after each dosage period ends. Continue doing this until you test clear for seven days straight.

BASIC TELEGRAPH TEST #4

1. State the intent:

Intent: Balance, stabilize and repair the remaining electric system as a unit with a new range of function, strength and balance.

2. For BTT checklist #4, write:

Focus: Balance, stabilize and repair the remaining electric system as a functioning unit with a new range of function, strength and balance.

3. Proceed with the Basic Telegraph Test steps and do the needed follow-up testing *within forty-eight hours* after each dosage period ends. Continue doing this until you test clear for seven days straight. At that point, it's safe to assume you have completed your recovery and recuperation period, as far as the fourth test and intent are concerned.

IMPORTANT: Anytime you experience pain or any other phantom-limb symptoms, take a dose of ETS Plus as soon as possible. If the symptom doesn't subside right away, take two to three more doses five minutes apart. These doses of ETS Plus are in addition to the Essences and ETS Plus you'll be taking as part of the treatment regimen.   ☉

A Recurrence of Phantom-Limb Problems

1. Set up a Basic Telegraph Test (pp. 229–231).

2. Now the checklist will look like a regular BTT checklist that includes all the symptoms you are feeling and experiencing.

3. Test each symptom and do all the needed follow-up until you test clear for seven days straight.   ☉

You Had the Surgery Some Time Ago

1. Set up the four post-surgery Basic Telegraph Tests.

Intent #1. Balance, stabilize and repair any remaining open circuits and severed circuit ends caused by the amputation and the removal of a significant portion of the electric system.

Intent #2. Establish alternate electric circuit connections and pathways to restore the balance, function and general health in areas of the body that were not amputated but suffered circuit damage resulting from the amputation.

Intent #3. Shift the function of the remaining PEMS circuits that were part of the supportive foundation for the now-removed limb but are still active and connected with the body's remaining electric system, its nervous system and brain to reflect the overall new balance of the electric system as a unit.

Intent #4. Balance, stabilize and repair the remaining electric system as a unit with a new range of function, strength and balance.

251

2. Proceed with the Basic Telegraph Test steps (pp. 229–231) and do the needed follow-up testing *within forty-eight hours* after each dosage period ends. Continue doing this until you test clear for seven days straight.

3. Should you experience any problems after completing these four Telegraph Tests:

- Set up a new Basic Telegraph Test.

- Now the BTT checklist will look like a regular BTT checklist that includes all the symptoms you are feeling and experiencing.

- Test each symptom and do all the needed follow-ups until you test clear for seven days straight.   ☉

SURROGATE BASIC ESSENCE TEST

For full information, see chapter 12, pp. 163–169.

SUPPLIES:
- the five sets of Perelandra Essences
- pen and paper
- option: a blank Perelandra Essence Record Chart
- one clean solution bottle
- brandy or distilled white vinegar preservative (his choice)
- a blank label
- a watch or clock with a second hand
- a clean spoon

BOTH OF YOU PREPARE FOR TESTING:

- Drink some water. Go to the bathroom, if needed. Find a quiet spot and sit comfortably. Place the boxes of Essences and the other supplies within easy reach for you.

- At the top of a clean sheet of paper or a new Perelandra Essence Record Chart, write the person's name and the date.

You are both ready to proceed with the surrogate Basic Essence Test.

1. Always clear your electric system with Essences just before testing another person. For this, the person cannot be touching you. State aloud or to yourself:
What Essences do I need to prepare for surrogate testing the Perelandra Essences? (Test the Essences.)

Then do a Basic Essence Test for yourself (steps 2–5, pp. 225–226) and take any needed Essences. You do not need to test for dosage.

2. Physically make contact with the person you are going to test and remain physically connected throughout all the surrogate testing, unless otherwise instructed. Have him place a hand on your knee or touch your foot with his foot or rest his hand lightly on your shoulder.

Focus on the person for five seconds. Both of you look at (focus on) where you are physically connected and hold that focus for five seconds.

Test your connection by asking (aloud):

> Are our two electric systems connected for this surrogate Essence testing? (Test the question.)

If negative,

- Spend a few more seconds focusing on the individual—and make sure you are physically touching.

- You both need to relax.

- If either of you is being distracted, move to a quieter room or quiet the environment you are in.

- Encourage him to keep his mind focused on the testing or on the hand (or foot) that is touching you.

- Test your connection again. This time you should get a positive result. If not, keep adjusting your physical connection (you may need to change how he is touching you) and applying a sharper focus until you get a positive response to the question.

3. State your intent:

> I want to do a surrogate Basic Essence Test for [person you are testing].

4. Place each box of Essences, one at a time, *in his hands or lap.* Ask:

Does he need any Essences from this box? (Test.)

If you get a negative, none are needed.

If you get a positive, move the box off to one side and test each bottle from that box individually by placing the bottle *in your lap* to determine which ones are needed. For each bottle, ask:

Does he need _____ Essence? (Test.)

5. Check your results by placing *in his hands or lap* just the bottles that tested positive. Ask:

> Are these the only Essences he needs? (Test.)

If the response is positive, that's a "yes." Go to step 6. If only one essence is needed, skip step 6 and go to step 7.

If you get a negative, retest the other Essences. A negative means you missed an Essence. After retesting, ask the question once more:

> Are these the only Essences he needs? (Test.)

If the response is still negative, keep testing the Essences until you get a positive response to the question. This will verify that you have identified all the needed Essences.

6. If you have more than one Essence, check them as a combination by placing all of them *in his hands or lap* and asking:

> Is this the combination he needs? (Test.)

If you get a negative even though the Essences tested positive when tested individually, you need to adjust the combination.

Just test each of the combination bottles separately by having *him hold each bottle* while you ask:

> Should this bottle be removed from the combination? (Test.)

Whatever tests positive gets removed. Then put the remaining combination bottles *in his hands or lap* and ask:

> Is this combination now correct? (Test.)

You should get a positive. If you don't, test the original combination again (the combination before you removed any bottles), and keep working at it until they test positive as a unit.

7. Administer these Essences to him orally, one drop each. You may put the Essence drops on a spoon for him to take or place each drop directly on his tongue. Record the Essences that tested positive.

Dosage: Number of Days

8. Have him hold *in his hands or lap* the bottle(s) that tested positive as a combination or unit.

9. Ask:

> Does he need the Essence(s) more than one time? (Test.)

If negative, that means he has already completed the dosage in the above step 7 and you have completed the surrogate Basic Essence Test.
To disconnect the two electric systems, just stop touching.

NOTE: If the person you are testing is addressing something like an illness or condition that you feel should logically require Essences for more than one day, yet you tested negative for step 9, he may need another test approach. To determine if this is so, PKTT test the options. Ask:

> Daily surrogate Basic Essence Tests?
> Surrogate telegraph testing?
> Surrogate telegraph testing for chronic illness?

Whatever tests positive is the next step for testing this person.

10. If positive, remain connected and find out how many days he should take them and how many times per day.

Do a sequential test. With the needed Essence(s) *in your lap,* ask:
> Does he need these one day? (Test.)
> Two days? (Test.) And so on.

Your last positive will tell you how many days he is to take the Essences. Record the number of days.

Dosage: Number of Times per Day

11. Using the same format with the bottle(s) still *in your lap,* ask:
> Should he take them one time daily? (Test.)
> Two times daily? (Test.) And so on.

Your last positive will tell you how many times per day they are needed. Record this dosage information.

12. Do another sequential test to see if it is best for him to take them in the morning, afternoon or evening, or any combination of the three. Ask:
> Should these Essences be taken in the morning? (Test.)
> In the afternoon? (Test.)
> In the evening? (Test.)

Whatever tests positive is when he should take each dosage.

Making a Solution Bottle

● Add five drops of each Essence needed to a clean half-ounce bottle.

● Then add one teaspoon of brandy or distilled white vinegar (his choice) if he needs to preserve the solution, and fill with spring or untreated water. If this is unavailable, tap water will do. He can refrigerate the solution, thus eliminating the need for preserving it.

● Label the bottle with the testing purpose/focus (surrogate Basic Essence Test) and dosage information. ☽

Solution in a Glass

● Add nine drops of each needed Essence concentrate to four ounces of water.

● Add three teaspoons of brandy or distilled white vinegar if he wants to preserve this solution. Refrigerate it if no preservative is added.

● Write down the dosage instructions to leave with him so that he'll know when to take his solution and what to focus on while taking it. ☽

Dosage and Follow-up Testing

● HELP HIM REMEMBER to take his dosages (one dropperful per dose) for the full period of time prescribed. It'll help him to remember if one of you sets his solution bottle in an obvious place such as on his bedside table, in the kitchen or bathroom. Also record the end date for the solution on a calendar or computer so that you'll know when to do the follow-up testing.

● ADMINISTERING DOSAGES. Each time he takes the Essence solution during the dosage period prescribed, he is to activate the circuits the solution is addressing. To do this he is to read the focus/intent that's written on the bottle label.

> IMPORTANT: Once you make a solution bottle, the Essence drops have been diluted and are no longer concentrated. For each dosage, he will need to take ten to twelve drops (one dropperful) of each solution.

● COMPLETING A DOSAGE PERIOD. Once he completes a dosage period, do a new Basic Essence Test *within forty-eight hours* as a follow up. Continue doing follow-up testing at the end of each dosage period until he tests clear.

● AFTER TESTING CLEAR, do a new surrogate Basic Essence Test for the next three days. When he tests clear for three days straight, you have completed the series of follow-up testing and no additional Essences are needed at that time.

● PERSISTENT SYMPTOMS OR INJURIES. Should a Basic Essence Test and the follow-ups not take care of all the symptoms or injuries, set up for a surrogate Basic Telegraph Test and list the remaining symptoms on his BTT checklist. Move the telegraph testing completely through all dosage periods and follow-up testing. Continue this until each listed symptom tests clear for seven days straight. ☉

SURROGATE BASIC TELEGRAPH TEST

> For full information, see chapter 13, pp. 171–175.

SUPPLIES:

- the five sets of Perelandra Essences
- pen, paper and calendar
- option: a blank Perelandra Essence Record Chart
- a blank Perelandra Essence Telegraph Test Checklist
- a watch or clock with a second hand
- a clean spoon
- clean solution bottles (one bottle for each symptom on the BTT checklist)
- brandy or distilled white vinegar preservative (his choice)
- blank labels

BOTH OF YOU PREPARE FOR TESTING:

- Drink some water. Go to the bathroom, if needed. Find a quiet spot and sit comfortably. Place the boxes of Essences and the other supplies within easy reach for you.

- At the top of a clean sheet of paper or a new Perelandra Essence Record Chart and a Perelandra Essence Telegraph Test Checklist, write the person's name and the date.

You're ready to proceed with the surrogate Telegraph Test steps.

1. *Always clear your electric system with Essences just before testing another person.* For this, the person cannot be touching you. State aloud or to yourself:

> I would like to prepare myself for surrogate testing the Perelandra Essences. What Essences do I need? (Test the Essences.)

Then do a Basic Essence Test (steps 2–5, pp. 225–226) and take any needed Essences. You do not need to test for dosage. These will be taken one time only.

2. Physically make contact with the person you are going to test and remain physically connected throughout all the surrogate testing, unless otherwise instructed. Have him place a hand on your knee or touch your foot with his foot or rest his hand lightly on your shoulder.

Focus on the person for five seconds. Both of you look at (focus on) where you are physically connected and hold that focus for five seconds. Test your connection by asking aloud:

> Are our two electric systems connected for the telegraph testing?
> (Test the question.)

If negative:

- Spend a few more seconds focusing on the individual—and make sure you are physically touching.

- You both need to relax.

- If either of you is being distracted, move to a quieter room or quiet the environment you are in.

- Encourage him to keep his mind focused on the testing or on the hand (or foot) that is touching you.

- Test your connection again. This time you should get a positive result.

- If not, keep adjusting your physical connection (you may need to change how he is touching you) and applying a sharper focus until you get a positive response to the question.

3. Before doing any of the surrogate telegraph testing, you must first clear *his* electric system. To do this, state aloud:

> I want to do a Basic Essence Test to clear [name of person] in preparation for telegraph testing for [state problem]. What Essences does he need? (Test.)

Do a surrogate Basic Essence Test (steps 4–7, pp. 253–254). Administer to him any needed Essences. He only takes these one time, so there's no need to test for dosage. NOTE: *With the statement in step 3, you also set the intent for the Telegraph Test.*

4. Together make a BTT checklist. (NOTE: You may put the BTT checklist together prior to beginning a surrogate Basic Telegraph Test.)

- List all the symptoms and/or injuries connected with the issue he is addressing.

- Include any symptoms or injuries that he is experiencing but eliminated from consideration because he felt they were not connected.

- Include any mystery symptoms/injuries and test the Perelandra Essence Telegraph Test Checklist. Then add whatever tested positive and isn't already included to the BTT checklist.

- Also, when dealing with an accident, separate the injuries according to their different locations.

- "Officially" assign a symbol or code for each out-of-sight or hard-to-discern symptom to facilitate focusing on those symptoms during testing. Record the symbol or code next to the symptom/injury, then state out loud:

   I assign this [symbol/code] to [the name of the symptom/injury as described on the BTT checklist].

5. Focus on the first symptom or injury on his BTT checklist and ask:
What Essences are needed for [insert symptom/injury]?
(Test the Essences.)

Instruct him to keep his focus on the symptom or injury while you do the surrogate Basic Essence Test, steps 4–7 (pp. 253–254).

6. Administer to him the needed Essences for this first symptom/injury.

- Record the Essences alongside the symptom listed on the BTT checklist or check the needed Essences on the Essence Record Chart.

- Remember to note on the Chart which Essences apply to which symptom.

7. Test for dosage (surrogate Basic Essence Test, steps 8–12, pp. 254–255): Find out how many days and how many times per day he is to take the Essences for this symptom/injury.

If he is to take the Essences just one time, you don't need to do any further dosage testing and you can move on to step 8.

If he is to take these Essences more than one time:

- Complete the dosage testing now.

- On the BTT checklist next to the symptom, record the dosage information: the beginning and end date of the dosage and how many times a day he is to take it.

- Also include the times of day he is to take it (morning, afternoon, evening).

> NOTE: If you need to make a solution bottle, wait until after all the telegraph testing is completed and make all the needed solution bottles at one time.

8. Repeat the surrogate Telegraph Test, steps 4, 5, 6 and 7 for every symptom or injury listed on the BTT checklist.

9. When you've finished testing every symptom/injury on his BTT checklist, complete the Telegraph Test for this issue by doing *a final Basic Essence Test for his full electric system.* Do not check for dosage. These Essences are to be taken one time only.

10. Make any needed solution bottles. Label each bottle right after making the solution. Include the solution's focus, the beginning and end date of the dosage and how many times a day he is to take it. Also include the times of day he is to take it.

You have completed the surrogate Telegraph Test. To disconnect the two electric systems, just stop touching. Do the follow-up testing as needed. ☊

Dosage and Follow-up Testing

● HELP HIM REMEMBER to take his dosages (one dropperful per dose) for the full period of time prescribed. It'll help him to remember if one of you sets his solution bottles in an obvious place, such as on his bedside table, in the kitchen or bathroom. Also record the end date for each solution on a calendar or computer so that you'll know when to do the follow-up testing.

● ADMINISTERING DOSAGES. Each time he takes a solution dosage, he is to activate the circuits the solution is addressing. To do this, he's to read what is written on the solution bottle label and keep it in mind while taking a dropperful (ten to twelve drops) of the Essence solution.

IMPORTANT: Once you make a solution bottle, the Essence drops have been diluted and are no longer concentrated. For each dosage, he will need to take ten to twelve drops (one dropperful) of the solution.

● COMPLETING A DOSAGE PERIOD AND FOLLOW-UP TESTING. Do all needed surrogate follow-up testing *within forty-eight hours* after a dosage period ends. For this, you need to be physically present and connected electrically, and you need to set up a surrogate Basic Essence Test (steps 1–12, pp. 252–255) as the follow-up. Continue doing follow-up testing at the end of each dosage period until he tests clear for seven days straight.

● RETURNING AND NEW SYMPTOMS. Should a symptom or injury that tested clear return, just list it again on his BTT checklist and do a new surrogate Telegraph Test for this one symptom, starting with step 1 and testing through step 12 (pp. 252–255). Move it completely through the dosage periods and follow-up testing. Continue this until it tests clear again for seven days straight.

If the returning symptom/injury exhibits any changes or anomalies that differentiate it from the old one in any way, consider this a new symptom/injury that needs to be added to the BTT checklist. Do a new surrogate Telegraph Test for that one symptom and move it completely through the dosage periods and follow-up testing. Continue this until it tests clear for seven days straight. If you used a code or symbol on the BTT checklist for the old symptom/injury, do not use that same one for the new symptom/injury. It will need its own code or symbol and you will need to "officially" assign the code/symbol. (See pp. 232–233.) ☉

THE SURROGATE HEAD-START PROGRAM FOR CHRONIC ILLNESS

For full information, see chapter 14, pp. 178–179.

1. Do a surrogate Basic Essence Test right away and include dosage and follow-up testing while working on the CI checklist.

2. Once the two of you have completed the CI checklist, you may begin surrogate telegraph testing even if he is still taking an Essence dosage from the Head-Start Basic Essence Test.

3. Continue taking that dosage and move through all the follow-up testing for the Head-Start Basic Essence Test until he tests clear while simultaneously moving through the telegraph testing for chronic illness. ☉

SURROGATE TELEGRAPH TESTING FOR CHRONIC ILLNESS

For full information, see chapter 14, pp. 177–183.

SUPPLIES:

- the five sets of Perelandra Essences
- pen, paper, calendar and the completed CI checklist
- option: a blank Perelandra Essence Record Chart
- a blank Perelandra Essence Telegraph Test Checklist
- a watch or clock with a second hand
- a clean spoon
- clean solution bottles (one bottle for each symptom on the CI checklist)
- brandy or distilled white vinegar preservative (his choice)
- blank labels

BOTH OF YOU PREPARE FOR TESTING:

- Drink some water. Go to the bathroom, if needed. Find a quiet spot and sit comfortably. Place the boxes of Essences and the other supplies within easy reach for you.

- At the top of a clean sheet of paper or a new Perelandra Essence Record Chart and a Perelandra Essence Telegraph Test Checklist, write the person's name and the date.

You're ready to proceed with the test steps.

1. *Always clear your electric system with Essences just before testing another person.* For this, the person cannot be touching you. State aloud or to yourself:

I would like to prepare myself for surrogate testing the Perelandra Essences. What Essences do I need? (Test the Essences.)

Do the Basic Essence Test (steps 2–5, pp. 225–226). Take any needed Essences. Do not test for dosage. These will be taken one time only.

2. Physically make contact with the person you are going to test and remain physically connected throughout all the testing, unless otherwise instructed.

Focus on the person for five seconds. Both of you look at (focus on) where you are physically connected and hold that focus for five seconds. Test your connection by asking (aloud or to yourself):

> Are our two electric systems connected for this Perelandra Essence testing? (Test the question.)

If negative:

- Spend a few more seconds focusing on the person—and make sure you are physically touching.

- You both need to relax.

- If either of you is being distracted, move to a quieter room or quiet the environment you are in.

- Encourage him to keep his mind focused on the testing or on the hand (or foot) that is touching you.

- Test your connection again. This time you should get a positive result.

- If not, keep adjusting your physical connection (you may need to change how he is touching you) and applying a sharper focus until you get a positive response to the question.

3. Before doing any of the surrogate telegraph testing, you must first clear *his* electric system. To do this, state aloud:

> I want to do a surrogate Basic Essence Test to clear [name of person] for telegraph testing for [name of the chronic illness]. What Essences does he need? (Test.)

- Do a surrogate Basic Essence Test (steps 4–7, pp. 253–254).

- Administer to him any needed Essences. He only takes these one time, so there's no need to test for dosage.

- Not needing Essences for clearing the electric system but needing them when telegraph testing the symptoms is not unusual. NOTE: *With the step 3 statement, you also set the intent for the Telegraph Test.*

Place one drop of each needed Essence on a spoon and have him take these Essences orally.

4. Place the completed CI checklist in front of you. (Also include any colored pages from the coloring book.)

5. Begin by telegraph testing his body's full electric system. Treat it as a symptom. Ask:

> What Essences are needed for [person's name] electric system as it relates to [name of illness]? (Test.)

> • Keep your focus on his electric system while following the surrogate Basic Essence Test, steps 4–7 (pp. 253–254).

> • Administer the needed Essences and find out how many times a day and how many days/weeks/months he is to take these Essences (surrogate Basic Essence Test: Dosage, steps 8–12, pp. 254–255).

6. Telegraph test each symptom on the CI checklist, one by one. Keep your focus on each symptom while following the surrogate Basic Essences Test, steps 4–7 (pp. 253–254).

> • Use the assigned code or symbol as a focus aid, if this has been set up.

> • Administer the needed Essences after each test.

> • Dosage: Find out how many times a day and how many days/weeks/months he is to take these Essences (surrogate Basic Essence Test: Dosage, steps 8–12, pp. 254–255) before moving on to the next symptom.

> • On the CI checklist (or Essence Record Chart), be sure to record the Essences needed and the dosage information for each symptom: the beginning and end date of the dosage and how many times a day he is to take it. Also include the times of day he is to take it (morning, afternoon, evening).

> • If he is to take the Essences just one time, you don't need to do any further dosage testing and you can move on to the next symptom on the CI checklist.

7. When you've finished testing every symptom/injury on the CI checklist, complete the Telegraph Test for this issue by doing a final Basic Essence Test for his full electric system. *Do not check for dosage. These Essences are to be taken one time only.*

8. The surrogate Telegraph Test for his chronic illness is completed. To disconnect the two electric systems, just stop touching.

9. Make any needed solution bottles. You may need to make one solution bottle for each symptom or issue listed on the CI checklist. Label each bottle right after making a solution. Include the solution's focus, the beginning and end date of the dosage and how many times a day he is to take it. Also include the times of day he is to take it.   ☺

Dosage and Follow-up Testing

● HELP HIM REMEMBER to take his dosages (one dropperful per dose) for the full period of time prescribed. It'll help him to remember if one of you sets his solution bottles in an obvious place such as on his bedside table, in the kitchen or bathroom. Also record the end date for each solution on a calendar or computer so that you'll know when to do the follow-up testing.

● ADMINISTERING DOSAGES. Each time he takes a solution dosage, he is to activate the circuits the solution is addressing. To do this, he's to read what is written on the solution bottle label and keep it in mind while taking a dropperful (ten to twelve drops) of the Essence solution.

> IMPORTANT: Once you make a solution bottle, the Essence drops have been diluted and are no longer concentrated. For each dosage, he will need to take ten to twelve drops (one dropperful) of the solution.

● COMPLETING A DOSAGE PERIOD AND FOLLOW-UP TESTING. Do all needed surrogate follow-up testing *within forty-eight hours* after a dosage period ends. For this, you need to be physically present and connected electrically, and you need to set up a surrogate Basic Essence Test (steps 1–12) as the follow-up (pp. 252–255). Continue doing follow-up testing at the end of each dosage period until he tests clear for seven days straight.

● RETURNING AND NEW SYMPTOMS. Should a symptom that tested clear return, just list it again on his CI checklist and do a new surrogate Telegraph Test for this one symptom, starting with step 1 and testing through step 12. Move it completely through the dosage periods and follow-up testing. Continue this until it tests clear again for seven days straight.

If the returning symptom exhibits any changes or anomalies that differentiate it from the old one in any way, consider this a new symptom that needs to be added to the CI checklist. Do a new surrogate Telegraph Test for that one symptom and move it completely through the dosage periods and follow-up testing. Continue this until it tests clear for seven days straight. If you used a code or symbol on the CI checklist for the old symptom, do not use that same one for the new symptom. It will need its own code or symbol and you will need to "officially" assign the code/symbol. (See pp. 232–233.)

SURROGATE TESTING CHILDREN: THE GUIDELINES

For full information, see chapter 15, pp. 187–188.

● INFANTS. Do not hold an infant while you are trying to test Essences.

● CRAWLERS, TODDLERS AND YOUNG CHILDREN. You may test them while they are asleep.

● MAINTAINING PROPER PHYSICAL CONTACT. If it's difficult to maintain physical contact with her (e.g., touching her hand, leg, arm or foot) because she's moving around too much or her crib is in your way, allow her to fall asleep on a blanket on the floor or couch that evening and then do the Essence testing. Sit next to her while testing and be sure to maintain physical contact with her while you test.

● CHILDREN AGE TWELVE OR OLDER should be tested using the regular surrogate procedure for adults. Mix the Essence solutions the same as you would for adults. Anyone age twelve or over should be awake and cooperative with the testing.

● IF A CHILD AGE TWELVE OR OLDER IS NOT COOPERATING with you, then you must consider if it is appropriate to be functioning as a surrogate tester for this young person.

● IF YOU ARE NOT THE CHILD'S PARENT. It is also not ethical to do surrogate Essence testing for anyone under age eighteen without the *verbal permission* of the child's parent(s) or legal guardian.

ADMINISTERING ESSENCES
TO CHILDREN

For full information, see chapter 15, pp. 188–191.

● UNDER NINE MONTHS OF AGE

Basic Essence Testing. If she is asleep when you test her, you can give her the first dose of needed Essences right then by stating, "For [baby's name]'s electric system," placing one drop at a time of each needed Essence on her forehead, and gently rubbing the solution in with your finger. Allow her forehead to air dry. You may also wait until she's awake the next day to give her the Essences orally or on her forehead and start her dosage then.

Telegraph Testing. When you are telegraph testing her, you'll need to give her the Essences for each symptom before moving on to the next symptom. Administer the Essence drops on her forehead. State (aloud) the symptom you are addressing—this sets up her circuits—then place one drop at a time of each needed Essence on her forehead, and gently rub the solution in with your finger. Allow her forehead to completely air dry before testing the next symptom.

You can wait until the next day to make any solution bottles she'll need. (Hope you took good notes during the testing.)

● IF THE CHILD IS OVER NINE MONTHS OF AGE, she will need to take all her Essences orally. If you need her to be asleep because she's so active, don't do a Telegraph Test. You're not going to be able to give her the Essences for each symptom as you do the testing. Instead use the surrogate Basic Essence Test and do all the needed follow-up until she tests clear. It may take longer to move her through an issue this way, but at least she'll have the benefit of the Essences.

● WHEN ADMINISTERING AN ESSENCE DOSAGE TO A CHILD. You don't need to physically connect with the child when administering an Essence dosage on the days following a test. Nor do you need to clear your electric system first. Just before you administer the dose, state aloud the reason for the solution. (Hint: It's written on the bottle label.)

  • For an infant, state the purpose of the solution aloud just before administering it. Hearing the sound of your voice will focus her attention on what's happening, and this will set up her circuits for the solution.

- For an older child you can trust to take the Essence dosages as prescribed, all you have to do is fix any needed solution bottles, label what each bottle is for and instruct the child to read the label aloud every time the solution is taken. She is to take one dropperful for each dose. If your child tends to be distracted or forgetful, the easiest thing is for you to hand her the bottle each time she needs to take a dose.

- BYPASSING THE BRANDY OR VINEGAR TASTE FOR A CHILD UNDER AGE THREE. Make a solution by adding one drop of each needed Essence to *four ounces* of water. Each time she needs to take a dosage, hand it to her for the necessary *three gulps* while saying out loud what it is for. Keep the remaining solution in the refrigerator for the next dosage.

If she doesn't mind the preservative taste, give her one drop of each needed Essence as prescribed in a spoon.

- YOU CANNOT OVERDOSE A CHILD WITH AN ESSENCE SOLUTION. So if you'd like to mix the four ounces in a sippy cup or baby bottle and let the child drink from it for half an hour or so, this is fine.

- BE SURE TO USE WATER and not juice or milk for Essence solutions.

- TELEGRAPH TESTING AND ADMINISTERING MULTIPLE ESSENCE SOLUTIONS. After telegraph testing her, you may end up with a solution for each of the symptoms/injuries that were tested. When administering multiple doses, do not mix all these different solutions together into one super solution. Keep each solution in its own bottle or glass and administer one dropperful of each one separately.

- ESTABLISHING FOCUS. Don't forget to state out loud what the solution is for when you give it to the child. (I'm repeating this several times because it is the easiest thing to forget, yet it is so important for administering the Essences correctly.)

- CHILDREN'S ESSENCE DOSAGES tend to be less complicated than the ones adults test for.

- DO FOLLOW-UP TESTING for her within forty-eight hours once the dosage for each solution is completed.

SURROGATE TESTING ADULTS AND CHILDREN WITH SPECIAL NEEDS: THE GUIDELINES

The Process Steps

For full information, see chapter 16, pp. 193–194.

● It is not ethical to impose a health regimen on someone eighteen years of age or over without verbal permission—and this includes someone with special needs. If she is capable of understanding a short description of the Perelandra Essences and able to answer for herself, give her that information and ask if she'd like you to test her. If she is unable to make an informed decision and give you permission directly, you will need to get verbal permission from her legal guardian.

● It is also not ethical to do Essence testing for anyone under age eighteen without verbal permission from the child's parent(s) or legal guardian.

● It is important that you be physically present with the person when you obtain her permission, do the testing, administer any multi-day Essence dosages, and do needed follow-up testing. If you are unable to be present for administering the multi-day dosages, instructing someone in the house to do this is fine. Just make sure they are clear about what they need to do each time they administer a dose. It might be helpful if you write down those instructions for them so they don't have to rely on memory.

● Do the appropriate surrogate testing and include the guidelines as outlined for children up to age twelve (pp. 266–268).

● If she cannot physically take an Essence dosage (e.g., she is unconscious), you may place one drop of each Essence concentrate on her lips. Allow fifteen seconds for the drops to mix with her saliva. This procedure takes a little patience on your part. If she needs a lot of Essences, you'll only be able to place one drop of two or three Essences at a time on her lips. Even if she is unconscious, talk to her and tell her what you are doing. Make sure your intent is to be gentle, not invasive. In this situation, use only the concentrate drops that are administered directly from the Essence bottles. ☽

POST-DEATH ETS PLUS PROCESS

For full information, see chapter 17, pp. 195–198.

YOU MUST DO THIS PROCESS WITHIN SEVENTY-TWO HOURS AFTER THE PERSON DIES.

1. To start, take one dose of ETS Plus to clear your electric system for the process.

2. State your intent:

> I wish to connect my electric system with _____'s electric system for administering ETS Plus.

3. Ask _____ (friend's name) to focus on you while you focus on him. *Hold the focus for ten seconds while the connection is completed.*

Test your connection by asking (aloud):

> Are our two electric systems connected for this Post-Death ETS Plus Process? (Test the question.)

If negative,

- spend a few more seconds focusing on the individual (think about him)—and relax.

- If you are being distracted, move to a quieter room or quiet the environment you are in.

- Remind him to keep his focus on you.

- Test your connection again. This time you should get a positive result.

4. Now, say hello and tell the person that you would like to offer ETS Plus. Give him an idea of what ETS Plus is and how it can help stabilize him now and assist in his healing process. Once you have explained ETS Plus, ask him if he understands what you are explaining. Use PKTT to discern his answer.

> NOTE: If at any time you feel that you could use more support, take another dose of ETS Plus, stating as you take it that the ETS Plus is for you.

5. Once the person understands, ask:

> Would you like me to administer ETS Plus to you? (Test the question.)

If he does not wish to receive the ETS Plus drops, move on to step 8.

6. Administering ETS Plus: With your two electric systems still connected, you will focus on this person and then take one dose of ETS Plus orally. Your focus will route the ETS Plus through your electric system and into his.

7. Wait one full minute. After the minute, PKTT test the person to make sure the ETS Plus shift occurred.

- If not, repeat steps 6 and 7.

- Once you get verification that the shift occurred, wait five minutes and test to see if he needs a second dose. Most of the time, just one dose will be needed.

- But if he needs another, focus on him, and repeat steps 6 and 7.

- Do this every five minutes until he tests that he doesn't need another dose of ETS Plus. Be sure to verify that each shift has occurred.

8. Once he tests clear:

- You may spend *up to a half hour* talking to him.

- Try not to press any feelings of grief and sorrow (or anger) you might have onto the person. This process and time is for the welfare of the person who has died.

- After the half hour is up, tell him you have to close down this process.

- Say goodbye and wish him well.

9. Close the process by stating aloud:

I request that our two electric systems be disconnected now.

The disconnect will occur immediately. It's the same as in surrogate testing when the two people stop touching.

10. If you experienced a lot of emotions during the process and after the disconnection, take another dose of ETS Plus. After about an hour or two, if you feel you still need support, do a Basic Essence Test for yourself.

SURROGATE TESTING ANIMALS

For full information, see chapter 18, pp. 199–200.

● First, every animal-friendly home and vet's office should have a bottle of ETS Plus for Animals.

● Immediately after an injury or if she shows signs of stress, give her two or three doses of ETS Plus for Animals.

● Should you observe any lingering symptoms, test the animal using the surrogate Basic Essence Test (pp. 252–255) or surrogate Basic Telegraph Test (pp. 257–261), whichever is more appropriate for the health situation.

● Set up the testing, go through the steps and administer the Essences orally as you would for a child over age twelve.

● Do all the follow-up testing. She only needs to test clear for *two days*. Then you'll know she has completed that Essence regimen.

● In general, to incorporate ETS Plus for Animals and the Perelandra Essences into an animal's health regimen, you can look to how both are used with humans for your guidelines. Be sure to include ETS Plus for Animals for vet visits, hospital stays and surgery, as well.

Administering Essences to a finicky animal

Work with them a bit to see if you can train them to lick the drops from your hand. If that fails:

- Try bribery. Put one drop of one needed Essence concentrate on a tiny bit of a treat. Repeat this for each Essence that's needed.

- Cats love butter. Place one drop of concentrate at a time on a little bit of butter (about $1/16$ teaspoon). Or try bits of tuna.

- Dilute the needed Essences by making a solution bottle using just water and no preservative. Be sure to refrigerate it.

- Get a dropper with a plastic pipette and administer one dropperful of a solution directly into the animal's mouth. (Don't store the plastic dropper in the solution bottle. Keep it alongside the bottle.)

ANIMAL DEATH PROCESS: PRE-DEATH AND POST-DEATH SUPPORT

The Process Steps

For full information, see chapter 18, pp. 200–207.

1. When the animal moves into the pre-death period, do a special surrogate Basic Telegraph Test (pp. 257–261), following the steps as outlined for children over age twelve (pp. 266–268). You will be testing one question as your "symptom":

    What Essences are needed to prepare [animal's name] for death? (Test.)

Include dosage testing to find out the number of days and times per day the Essences will be needed and do any follow-up testing. Also be sure you are taking *three to five doses of ETS Plus for humans daily* for personal support throughout the entire pre-death and post-death period.

2. As soon as possible after death, administer one dropperful (ten to twelve drops) of ETS Plus for Animals on the animal's chest area or the towel covering the chest area.

   • For a companion animal, the ETS Plus for Animals must be administered within three hours after death.

   • For wild or farm animals, it must be delivered within one hour after death.

3. If possible, wrap or lightly cover the body. Keep the body in a quiet spot for the required one to three hours.

4. Bury the body. Cover the body with a layer of lime (around one-half inch) before covering with dirt. The lime helps with the decomposition of the body and eliminates decomposition odor. It also helps keep curious animals from digging up the body. ☯

BASIC TELEGRAPH TEST FOR EMOTIONAL AND MENTAL ISSUES

For full information, see Appendix A, pp. 214–215.

If your emotions and/or thoughts are spinning and you can't move out of them, set up a Basic Telegraph Test with the emotion(s) and/or thoughts as the focus.

1. Set up a regular Basic Telegraph Test (pp. 229–231) that has the emotional and/or mental issues or problems as its focus.

2. The BTT checklist: List everything you are feeling or thinking about the issue. Include any Factor-X's on the BTT checklist as well.

3. Follow the Basic Telegraph Test steps for each thing you have listed.

4. Do all the dosage follow-up testing.

BASIC TELEGRAPH TEST FOR MIASMS

For full information, see Appendix A, pp. 215–216.

To treat an active miasm, you will be doing a Basic Telegraph Test (pp. 229–231). The main intent and focus for the Telegraph Test will be #1, the recurring physical health issue and all its symptoms. Divide the checklist into three different focuses:

1. List the recurring physical health issue and list all its symptoms.

2. List the emotions and thoughts you are experiencing because of this health problem and the difficulties you have had trying to deal with it.

3. List the active miasm.

Essence test the BTT checklist in order, starting with #1, the recurring physical health issue and all its symptoms, and continuing with #2 and #3.

For all three focuses, make solution bottles for each symptom/element requiring Essences that are to be taken more than one time. Let each dosage and follow-up testing run its full course. Do all the follow-up testing for each of the three focuses. Each item listed for the three focuses must test clear for seven days straight.